WILLIAMSBURG REPRODUCTIONS

Williamsburg®

REPRODUCTIONS

Interior Designs for Today's Living

Craft House

WILLIAMSBURG, VIRGINIA

Colonial Williamsburg · WILLIAMSBURG · VIRGINIA 23185

CONTENTS

Williamsburg
in the American Scene

FOR EIGHTY YEARS Williamsburg was the capital of Britain's largest colony in North America and a political and cultural center of influence far surpassing its size. Like Boston and Philadelphia, it was a hotbed of rebellion for more than a decade before the Revolution. Virginia's leaders in the drive for independence were familiar figures here, and they included George Washington, Thomas Jefferson, Patrick Henry and George Mason.

Williamsburg was always a small town. Its principal function was government, not commerce. Hence, it was crowded only when the House of Burgesses or the courts were in session. Yet its ties with England were perhaps closer than those of any other British colonial capital. The Virginia lands east of the Mississippi River covered an area three times the size of the British Isles. The capital of such a vast territory was the scene of numerous episodes in the struggle for power between royal governors and members of the colonial government. Neither side dominated, but the eighteenth century saw the habit of self-rule mature into a principle eventually claimed by Virginians as a basic right. This process went largely unrecognized by Great Britain until too late. One early governor, Alexander Spotswood, complained that Virginians were overfond of "the libertys which, by a long Custom, without any Lawfull foundation, they have been used to." These men, the

governor said, would submit to no authority except that "established by laws of their own making."

Williamsburg's years as Virginia's capital spanned five British reigns and the terms of almost a dozen governors. Despite its small size the city inevitably attracted men of affairs and ambition. Here lay the heart of the action. Petitioners and litigants, lawyers and land agents all sooner or later found their way to the town. Professional men likewise came here of necessity: For instance, Patrick Henry to sit for his law license; Washington for his license as surveyor and for his militia commissions. Williamsburg —containing all the elements of governmental administration—was thus a training ground for leadership. The challenges of creating and organizing were endless: the construction of a capitol, the maintenance of a militia, the registration of land grants, problems of taxation and cur-

Above: Bruton Parish Church, on the Palace Green, was built in 1715 and has been in continuous use ever since. In colonial Virginia, where church and state were united, the entire community—slave and artisan, planter and governor alike—worshipped here together.

Opposite page: On the east side of Palace Green stands the restored Brush-Everard House, which was built in 1717 by John Brush, gunsmith, armorer, and first keeper of the Magazine on Market Square. Later it came into the possession of Thomas Everard, clerk of York County Court, who in 1766 and again in 1771 was elected mayor of Williamsburg.

Opposite page, top: Virginia's General Assembly convened in this historic Capitol, now reconstructed, from 1704 to 1780. It was here that some of the nation's great men—George Washington, Patrick Henry, and Thomas Jefferson—laid the groundwork for American independence.

Opposite page, bottom: The Council Chamber was housed in the more elaborately furnished wing of the H-shaped Capitol. This is one of the most historically important rooms in Williamsburg and has been faithfully reconstructed.

Top: A horse-drawn carriage makes its way down the "most beautiful mile in American history" without stirring up the dust of 200 years ago.
Center: The Courthouse of 1770 has stood as a symbol of law and justice for nearly two centuries, serving Williamsburg and James City County until 1932. It is located on Market Square, the focal point of community activity. On this broad green, militia men were mustered, town fairs were held, and of course, the news of the day was exchanged.

Below: The informal side of Palace life took place in the upper middle room. Here the governor could relax with close friends or read a recent book sent from England.

rency, of the Anglican clergy and dissenters, of tobacco inspection, runaway slaves, and major crimes—and always the ominous vision of the mother country becoming provoked with her vigorous, self-willed colonies.

As an old man Jefferson enjoyed warm memories of this teeming scene of his youth, where he had gained training as a student, lawyer, politician, and sophisticate. "Williamsburg," he said, "was the finest school of manners and morals that ever existed in America."

Manners and style were always important in Williamsburg. With provincial adaptations, the city's social life, like its buildings and furnishings and clothing, reflected a conscious imitation of London fashion. Supported by a plantation economy based on the rich tobacco trade, Virginia's leading families became wealthy, and the capital reflected the grace and style of their lives. This did not occur by happenstance. Williamsburg was one of the first carefully designed cities in America, its streets, greens, and boundaries planned to accommodate public buildings, dwellings, taverns, and shops in considered relationship to the College of William and Mary and Bruton Parish Church, structures already in existence at the end of the seventeenth century. Though the new town was on the fringe of the wilderness, an enduring sense of order was imposed on its development by far-sighted governors, first Francis Nicholson, and then Alexander Spotswood, both competent city planners.

Duke of Gloucester Street was laid off to a width of ninety-nine feet. Greens were developed to lend a sense of openness. First came the Capitol, then the Governor's Palace, Magazine, and other public buildings. Like the houses themselves, large and small, the public buildings were of pleasing design, placed to conform to the town plan. Residences were built under restrictions specifying dimensions, setback, lot size, and fencing. As the city grew it was natural that standards represented by eighteenth century English architecture were also borrowed to some extent in Williamsburg, so that even the more modest dwellings bore ornamental details suggestive of prevailing English style and taste.

The influence of these buildings during the eighteenth century cannot be accurately traced, but it is known that Williamsburg architecture was copied in some of the large plantation houses of the day—the Palace, for example, probably inspired the design of the great York River mansion of the Page family, Rosewell. The city's architecture undoubtedly influenced building throughout Virginia.

English ships brought to Williamsburg the fine furniture, carriages, crystal, silver, brass, books, and clothing of the period, paid for in products of the colony—chiefly tobacco, lumber, wheat, and corn. Many imported goods were copied and adapted by local craftsmen, and artisans developed a thriving trade.

After 1780, when the capital was moved to Richmond, Williamsburg's importance declined. The modern town grew up slowly about the original buildings. The Palace was destroyed by fire, and, about fifty years later, the

9

former Capitol also burned. The Public Records Office became part of a private residence. The Magazine became successively a market, a church, a dancing school, and a stable. Numerous original buildings were altered or destroyed over the years. Nearby historic sites also declined. Seven miles away lay Jamestown, the first capital, its original buildings destroyed in the seventeenth century, except for the tower of its church. Twelve miles to the east of Williamsburg was Yorktown, where Lord Cornwallis had surrendered to Washington and his French allies, effectively ending the American Revolution.

In 1926, about 150 years after the movement of the capital, the restoration of Williamsburg commenced. John D. Rockefeller, Jr., set up a nonprofit foundation to save the historic original buildings of the city, to reconstruct the most important ones which had disappeared, and to preserve a large part of the colonial capital of Virginia as part of the heritage of the American people. Fortunately many historic buildings were among the surviving originals—the Courthouse of 1770, the Magazine, the Public Records Office, Bruton Parish Church, the Wren Building, President's House, and Brafferton Indian School of the College of William and Mary, Wetherburn's and Market Square Taverns, and a part of the Gaol. Many notable houses also stood: the homes of George Wythe, Peyton Randolph, Philip Ludwell, Robert Carter, St. George Tucker, James Geddy, John and Archibald Blair, and many others.

Today, eighty-eight of these original buildings survive in Williamsburg, several of them open to the public. In all there are thirty-eight residences, eight public buildings, thirty-six outbuildings (dairies, smokehouses and the like), two taverns, and four shops.

Mr. Rockefeller saw that of all the thirteen original colonial capitals, Williamsburg offered the best opportunity of restoring an eighteenth-century city to the appearance of earlier days, in a setting free from the presence of modern buildings. The restoration has continued for more than forty years.

Williamsburg was one of the first large-scale American preservation projects, but today it is only one of many in the nation. The Colonial Williamsburg Foundation has cooperated with and assisted other restorations, but it has retained its own unique characteristics. It maintains its original goals, and its entire organization is dedicated to the purpose "That the Future May Learn From the Past."

Mr. Rockefeller once expressed the significance of the project in these words:

"The restoration of Williamsburg . . . offered an opportunity to restore a complete area and free it entirely from alien or inharmonious surroundings as well as to preserve the beauty and charm of the old buildings and gardens of the city and its historic significance. Thus it made a unique and irresistible appeal.

"As the work has progressed, I have come to feel that perhaps an even greater value is the lesson that it teaches of the patriotism, high purpose, and unselfish devotion of our forefathers to the common good."

While the aristocracy of Virginia was tending to its Tidewater plantations, the "middling sort" set up shop in Williamsburg and supported the community through their specialized crafts. History is seen in the threads of the spinner and the muskets of the gunsmith (directly above).

Opposite page: The harnessmaker was responsible for treating leather and making tack for horses—the major mode of land transportation in colonial days. From the kitchen of Wetherburn's Tavern came meals to serve the hearty appetites of Washington and Jefferson. It was here these men and their political associates found themselves at home. Domestic tools such as rakes were turned out for outdoor and household use. During this period of fashion, when a wig was something of a badge of social rank, the wigmaker catered primarily to male customers, and was also well trained in shaving his clients and dressing their wigs. The man who put a roof over everybody's head in Williamsburg was the shinglemaker. Although there were square-butted and round-butted shingles, the latter were most popular. Not only were the round edges more attractive, but they had less tendency to curl at the ends. The local doctor operated in the Apothecary Shop (opposite page, far right), mixing "elixirs" and "ointments" or treating his patients in the back room.

The Historic Area Today

ITH THE RESTORATION of Williamsburg, the original town plan of 1699 took shape once more in most of its details, and the heart of the city returned to its eighteenth-century appearance. Broad Duke of Gloucester Street retains its mile-long unbroken view from the door of the Wren Building east to the Capitol. The Palace looks down a green vista between rows of catalpa trees to the main street, a perspective still remaining from the eighteenth century. In Market Square the Courthouse of 1770 and the Magazine and Guard House stand alone on the green.

Today, in fact, one can see from Market Square almost a score of the original buildings, including the George Wythe, St. George Tucker, Archibald Blair, Peyton Randolph, Allen-Byrd, and Tayloe Houses, the Tayloe Office with its unusual bell roof, the Archibald Blair kitchen and dairy, Market Square Tavern, and the Greenhow-Repiton Office.

The visitor who comes from modern America's congested urban areas immediately senses the wisdom of early planners who provided for spacious streets, harmonious building design, long vistas, and green open spaces. Much of Williamsburg's air of tranquility results from that initial conception.

The historian John W. Reps wrote in a recent history of colonial town planning:

"The plan of Virginia's second colonial capital deserves . . . recognition as the basic platform on which the third dimension of architecture could take form gracefully and with full visual effect. The approach to environmental design is a great lesson Williamsburg has to teach—that only where streets, open spaces, and building sites are conceived of, not as an abstract pattern but as part of a three-dimensional concept, can cities be beautiful as well as functional. It is not the exact architectural styles or details of the buildings or the precise form of the city plan that should be imitated, but this fundamental approach to the

This page: The supper room of the Governor's Palace saw many an evening of lavish official entertaining given by the royal representative. Lord Botetourt recorded in 1769, "Fifty-two dined with me yesterday, and I expect at least that number today."

Opposite page: The formal gardens of the Governor's Palace serve as silent reminders of colonial Williamsburg's strong ties to the mother country. The geometrical design, clipped boxwood hedges, topiary work, canal, and terraced gardens are English in every sense.

Opposite page, top: The George Wythe House on the west side of the Palace Green is often considered the most handsome of colonial houses in Williamsburg. The house, outbuildings, and gardens give the impression of a scaled-down plantation.

Opposite page, bottom: The peaceful and unpretentious gardens backing the frame house and brick office of John Greenhow, a Williamsburg merchant.

This page, top: Looking across the green is the Peyton Randolph House, noted particularly for having the best series of original paneled rooms in Williamsburg.

This page, above: Thought to be one of the earliest houses in Williamsburg, the Brush-Everard House was built in 1717 by John Brush, a gunsmith and the first keeper of the colony's Magazine. Years later, when owned by Thomas Everard, the house was enlarged and the interior embellished.

problem of creating urban spaces defined by buildings of pleasing size, materials, and proportions. The modern generation of urban designers wrestling with the problems of great cities might ponder the lesson of Williamsburg and find much to learn from this small town of the Virginia Tidewater."

The Historic Area has become known as a "living museum," of which the town plan is the foundation. The original homes, outbuildings, taverns, shops, and public buildings themselves are perhaps the most obvious appeal of Williamsburg. The city's architecture is not unique, but its old buildings comprise one of the largest groups of surviving buildings of their type in America. They are distinct in their own way, since the city plan required that the smallest dwelling on Duke of Gloucester Street be at least twenty by thirty feet. Those of larger size were built to carefully calculated dimensions and with an eye to scale. Typical designs called for houses in varying dimensions, some of them built to fit within cubes, (viz. 30 feet long, 30 feet wide, 30 feet from the ridge of the roof to the ground); some were twice as long as they were deep.

When the architecture of the times of William and Mary, Queen Anne, and the Georges was imported to the hot and humid climate of tidewater Virginia, original English and Dutch designs were adapted to the new conditions. Williamsburg's builders, like others in the coastal South, learned to build homes with central passages, high ceilings, and exterior chimneys, and to remove kitchens, storehouses, and other workaday rooms from the house—reflecting both the influence of climate and the precedent set by the placement of plantation service buildings. Such changes, of course, resulted in residences in new shapes and sizes. These houses, in particular, gave Williamsburg and tidewater Virginia architecture its distinction.

In the absence of stone, colonial Virginia's builders used brick and wood, for clay and timber—and labor—were plentiful and cheap. Though many Williamsburg buildings have solid brick walls, most were constructed of wood, which was thought more "wholesome" and was cheaper. The heart lumber used (especially pine) was an exceptionally durable material; hence, much of the original exterior wood finish of the buildings survives.

The more suggestively "English" of the houses are the two-story brick residences, solid Georgian structures of simple design that would have been at home in English settings—the George Wythe, Allen-Byrd, Ludwell-Paradise, and Palmer Houses are examples. The more typical Williamsburg house, of wood, is a story and a half high, usually with an A roof and from three to five dormer windows. A central passage runs through the center of the house from front to rear with a stairway to the upper floor.

The basic house plan allowed variations of roof lines and placement of chimneys, passages, stairs, and dormers. Restoration architects discovered early in their work that eighteenth-century householders frequently expanded their homes as families or fortunes increased, adding rooms or wings, usually achieving a pleasing effect.

15

Finishing details also received careful attention and were intended to enhance the overall design. Even a casual stroll through the city today reveals scores of these distinguishing exterior touches—weatherboards, shingles, moldings, shutters, windows and doors, picket fences and gates, finials on rooftops. This attention to detail is further notable in the interior finish, in the design of stairways, mantels, cornices and moldings, paneling and wainscoting. The designs are usually simple and appropriate and add to the spirit of the building and the town itself. In brief, these are houses built during an era of good taste by men who devoted much time and skill to their work. These artisans left their mark even in the lesser details of the humble outbuildings. Owner, builder-designer, craftsman, and laborer worked together under the restrictions of the city plan to erect buildings whose usefulness and appeal have endured for two centuries.

The restoration begun by Mr. Rockefeller in 1926 continues actively today. In recent years more original buildings have been opened to the public, the Peyton Randolph and James Geddy houses and Wetherburn's Tavern being added in 1968.

The Historic Area covers the heart of the old town, more than a mile in length and about half a mile in width. Most of the buildings in this area are occupied by employees of Colonial Williamsburg, who lead normal social and professional lives in close proximity to the public exhibition buildings that attract some 850,000 visitors annually. Others are occupied by life tenants from whom the foundation has acquired the properties.

Visitors are attracted to Williamsburg for many reasons. Architecture and the effective town plan draw much of their appeal from other aspects of the city, any one of which bears its individual historical distinction: the re-created gardens and greens, the extensive crafts program, the broad and comprehensive programs of preservation research, the year-round interpretation of the historical heritage of colonial Virginia, and the fine collections of seventeenth-, eighteenth-, and nineteenth-century furnishings.

The gardens emphasize eighteenth-century horticultural practices, and plant material is chosen carefully from both native flora and from plants known to have been introduced here during the eighteenth century. There are gardens both formal and informal, including some wild areas. There are kitchen and herb gardens, and pastures and orchards, and peripheral areas planted to such field crops as cotton, corn, and tobacco.

The handcraft program, designed to preserve and demonstrate rapidly disappearing skills, involves thirty-five domestic and skilled crafts and more than one hundred artisans. The activities range from gunsmithing, blacksmithing, and harness-making to music teaching and paper marbling. Visitors may see experts pour molten brass or pewter, or see fibers spun, woven, and dyed to make cloth; they may see paper made, books bound, candles molded, soap produced, silver bowls hammered into perfect shapes,

Perfect relationship between jutting dormers and slanting roof surmounted by a brick chimney, this one matched by a second at the other end of the house.

This hip-roofed dormer is on an A-shaped roof. Note the angle of the dormer roof is that of the main roof, and the side boards, too, pick up the same slant —precision in all details.

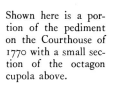

Shown here is a portion of the pediment on the Courthouse of 1770 with a small section of the octagon cupola above.

The eighteenth-century bricklayer often achieved a varied effect, using different sizes and shapes of brick. His creativity is seen in the pattern of this brick wall.

The gates and fences of Williamsburg deserve individual study: Wide, narrow, flat, pointed, arched or scooped. Decorative—but always functional. A gate such as this is kept tightly closed by a ball-and-chain device on the back side.

The many doors of Williamsburg were fastened tight by a variety of handsome locks —often made of brass. Hardware collectors today would envy a heart-shaped iron lock such as the one pictured here.

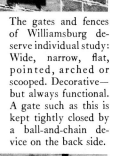

Opposite page: John Holt opened his "new store" about 1745, stocking it with all kinds of merchandise: dry goods, china, and groceries. The sign of the three sugar loaves hanging above the entrance is the traditional insignia of grocers. Hunter's Store was built on the adjoining property sometime after 1772.

16

Brick paths everywhere, leading from one garden to another, contribute to a harmonious symmetry so characteristic of the colonial capital.

The pretty picket gate of the Elkanah Deane House opens into a formal garden with tree-box in topiary forms and small-leaved lindens.

A unique balustrade on an interior stairway of the Coke-Garrett House.

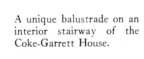

Ladies and gentlemen alike broke bread at the tables of the Raleigh Tavern (opposite page, top) which was a center of social activity in eighteenth-century Williamsburg. Only gentlemen were welcome to spend the night. The various bedrooms of Wetherburn's Tavern (a typical one is shown on opposite page, bottom) could accommodate up to 38 persons, counting two to a bed which was necessary during crowded Publick Times.

hats decorated, wigs dressed, or shingles rived out of cypress logs.

Supporting the Historic Area as it is seen by visitors is a broad program of preservation research that has matured, and often pioneered, over the years. A historian with a Ph.D. in the field of eighteenth-century social life will work with a specialist in early prints and maps to guide the curator in planning to furnish a small, unpretentious room. Before the work of documenting details is done, historians will have consulted wills, deeds, early maps, insurance policies, letters, diaries, inventories of estates, and court records.

When the work of these specialists is complete, interpreters begin the task of distilling from voluminous reports the narratives of colonial life presented to visitors in the furnished buildings. Hostesses and escorts are trained in a specialized curriculum covering all phases of the eighteenth century in Virginia—an intensive and continuing course of training. The publications program has produced some fifty volumes, ranging from scholarly treatises to books for children, all concerned with eighteenth-century Virginia. The audio-visual program produces films for theatre and television presentation and circulates them to all parts of the country. Slides and film strips are also distributed to schools, clubs, and special interest groups. Much of this interpretive activity focuses in the Information Centers, where films, lectures, books, tour planning, and accommodations services are designed both to initiate and to supplement the visitor's experience.

With the opening of the first exhibition building in the early 1930s, Colonial Williamsburg began to assemble its collections of seventeenth-, eighteenth-, and nineteenth-century furniture and furnishings. As the programs of documentary and archaeological research grew, the collections expanded. Today they are recognized as among the most notable of their kind. From them each exhibition building is furnished and each becomes, in effect, a small museum gallery in itself.

The furnishings range from handsome examples of ornate furniture to the crudest of kitchen utensils. The collections are rich in furniture, glass, porcelain, pottery, fabrics, silver, pewter, brass and ironware, lighting fixtures, weapons, prints, wine bottles, and tableware. The rooms of the exhibition buildings, including kitchens, dairies, smokehouses, and other working areas, reflect the range and depth of the collections. It is from this abundance and variety that Colonial Williamsburg's Reproductions Program grew.

The Reproductions Program

Facsimile of Certificate of Authenticity that accompanies each hallmarked reproduction

THE EIGHTEENTH CENTURY in Europe was a brilliant period in the history of domestic furnishing, a time when skilled craftsmen designed and produced objects in styles admired to this day—furniture and silver, brass and pewter, fabrics and wall coverings, looking glasses, chandeliers, glassware, porcelain, and earthenware. Colonial commerce and communication with England brought to Virginia many fine products from this flourishing era of design and craftsmanship, and stimulated their production in this country. When examples of these furnishings were installed in the exhibition buildings in the mid-1930s, the response of visitors was immediate: how can we obtain accurate reproductions of such pieces?

Obviously, original pieces, both rare and fragile, could not meet the demand. Colonial Williamsburg then carefully considered its rapidly expanding collections of period furnishings and selected a number of them based on the criteria of beauty, soundness of design, and appropriateness for daily use in modern American homes. Subsequently, Colonial Williamsburg turned to a few manufacturers, with both the resources and the desire to produce fine replicas, and licensed them to turn out reproductions bearing the Colonial Williamsburg hallmark. In 1937 Craft House was opened to serve as the public display and sales area for the Reproductions Program.

But it was not merely to enter the merchandising field that Colonial Williamsburg inaugurated this effort. From the start, the handsome, durable, and useful items have been regarded as interpretive objects, part and parcel of

the Colonial Williamsburg Foundation's educational activity. A sturdy wing chair purchased in 1937, for example, has not only served its household in a utilitarian sense; its beauty of design also has been a constant reminder of eighteenth-century craftsmanship. In fact, the program has been credited with elevating public taste. Thus, these items fulfill an educational purpose and, as they have been produced largely by handcraftsmen and as the older pieces will soon be forty years old, it may be said that they are in truth becoming heirlooms in their own right.

The building of the program was cautious and slow. Manufacturers realized that their artisans had to meet the rigid standards of quality and design mutually developed with Colonial Williamsburg. The painstaking process of selection and the specifications controlling acceptable reproduction have been continued since the outset of the program.

The Director of Merchandising selects an article to be reproduced or adapted (with changes in design for modern use). The original is temporarily removed from exhibition and the manufacturer copies it in detail—though small variations in handcrafted work are inevitable now, as they were characteristic of their period.

The reproduced article then goes before the Craft Advisory Committee, a team of experts from many divisions of the foundation, including the director of research, the curator, master silversmith, interior design consultant, director of archaeology, and architectural historian. After thorough critical analysis, the item is approved, suggestions made for resubmission, or disapproved. Following approval the manufacturer is then consulted, and if there is agreement production begins.

The reproductions are strikingly similar to the originals. For years, in fact, one of Colonial Williamsburg's most popular displays has consisted of two pieces of furniture, the antique and the copy—so nearly identical that the layman's eye can hardly detect a difference.

This program has been so successful that at least a dozen of the original manufacturers still participate in the program some thirty-five years later. Today, twenty-five manufacturers produce a total of 1,500 items.

There are exceptions to this process of selection. The department of archaeology, for example, unearths fragments of earthenware of porcelain, from which reproductions or adaptations are made. This provides the program with unique items and strengthens its ties with the eighteenth century.

In recent years the Adaptations Program has grown rapidly in importance and influence. In this phase of furniture manufacture, the foundation and its licensed furniture manufacturers have followed a process commonplace in every century and in every period of design: originals have been modified to meet changed use requirements. This frequently means that the adaptations, though handcrafted with the same meticulous care given to reproductions, are redesigned to smaller, simpler scale, so that they are at home in the smaller homes and apartments of overcrowded modern America.

Of course no one can say with assurance precisely how every room in eighteenth-century Williamsburg was furnished—but the collections, the basis of our Reproductions Program, have become more complete and authoritative each year. Behind thousands of items is a mass of data, documentary and archaeological, to lend the authority of authenticity to the original pieces and thus to the reproductions.

Fortunately for this endeavor, men of many stations in life who died in early Williamsburg left inventories of their estates—governors, blacksmiths, tavern-keepers, and merchants alike. Armed with these, and with an array of wills, deeds, letters, diaries, shipping invoices, contemporary newspaper advertisements, and other evidence, Colonial Williamsburg's curators have assembled one of the largest and most distinguished collections of seventeenth-, eighteenth-, and nineteenth-century English and American furnishings.

Though these collections are constantly expanding, the purpose of the growth is to reflect faithfully the life of tidewater Virginia and Williamsburg in colonial days. The most important guideposts in the acquisitions program are those set by the foundation's specialists in documentary history, colonial social life, architecture, and archaeology. They now work from an enormous body of cumulative data and insure the continuing validity of the Reproductions Program, which has become an important by-product of Colonial Williamsburg's efforts in this field.

Williamsburg and the Hallmark

"Williamsburg" and the hallmark, both registered trademarks owned by the foundation, may be used only on reproductions and adaptations made by licensed manufacturers. The Williamsburg hallmark, which appears below, was designed from old and new symbols. The letters "C.W.," for Colonial Williamsburg, have been joined to the central symbol, an elongated "4" ending in what appears to be a double "X." This symbol was used by English shippers of the seventeenth and eighteenth centuries and was sometimes combined with the initials of merchant and consignee.

Origins of the merchants' and makers' mark are obscure and possibly ancient. One legend has it that the mark traces back to the Greek god Hermes, patron of commerce and trade, in whose honor the symbol "4" was worshipped. The double "X," according to one theory, symbolized man looking up to a benevolent god. Yet another theory is that the symbol "4" is of runic origin—that its past is buried in the unwritten and little-known history of early European alphabets. Some scholars suggest that it might have been intended as a sign of the cross. Whatever its origin, this central symbol has appeared on merchandise of quality for centuries and continues today in the Colonial Williamsburg hallmark.

Many products in the Colonial Williamsburg program are displayed and sold in fine stores throughout the United States, as well as at Craft House.

Selections may be purchased at Craft House or ordered from this catalogue for prompt delivery. Careful attention is given to mail orders, instructions for which may be found on page 229.

The Significance of Small Things

HAND-CRAFTED
HARDWARE
FOR
WILLIAMSBURG
REPRODUCTIONS

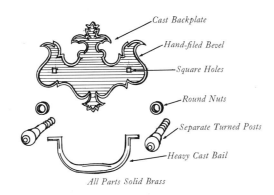

Cast Backplate
Hand-filed Bevel
Square Holes
Round Nuts
Separate Turned Posts
Heavy Cast Bail
All Parts Solid Brass

MACHINE-MADE
COMMERCIAL
HARDWARE

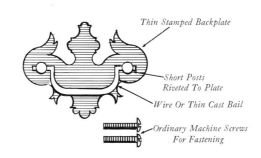

Thin Stamped Backplate
Short Posts
Riveted To Plate
Wire Or Thin Cast Bail
Ordinary Machine Screws
For Fastening

Construction Features

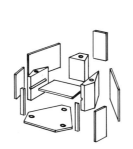 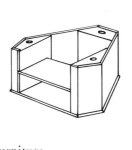

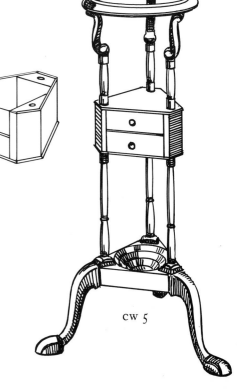

Skilled craftsmanship is apparent in every detail of *Williamsburg* Furniture Reproductions. Some of the most interesting points of construction, which add greatly to their value and authenticity, are not visible. These costly hidden details cannot be duplicated by modern machines. They can only be reproduced by skilled hands in the same manner as the originals were made.

The top rim of this basin stand is hand-turned from a solid piece of mahogany. The legs are hand-dovetailed into the pedestal base, and individually mitered mouldings are around the bottoms of each turned column. The drawer unit is built of twelve separate pieces of wood including mahogany facings and three corner blocks of yellow pine—a most unusual construction.

cw 5

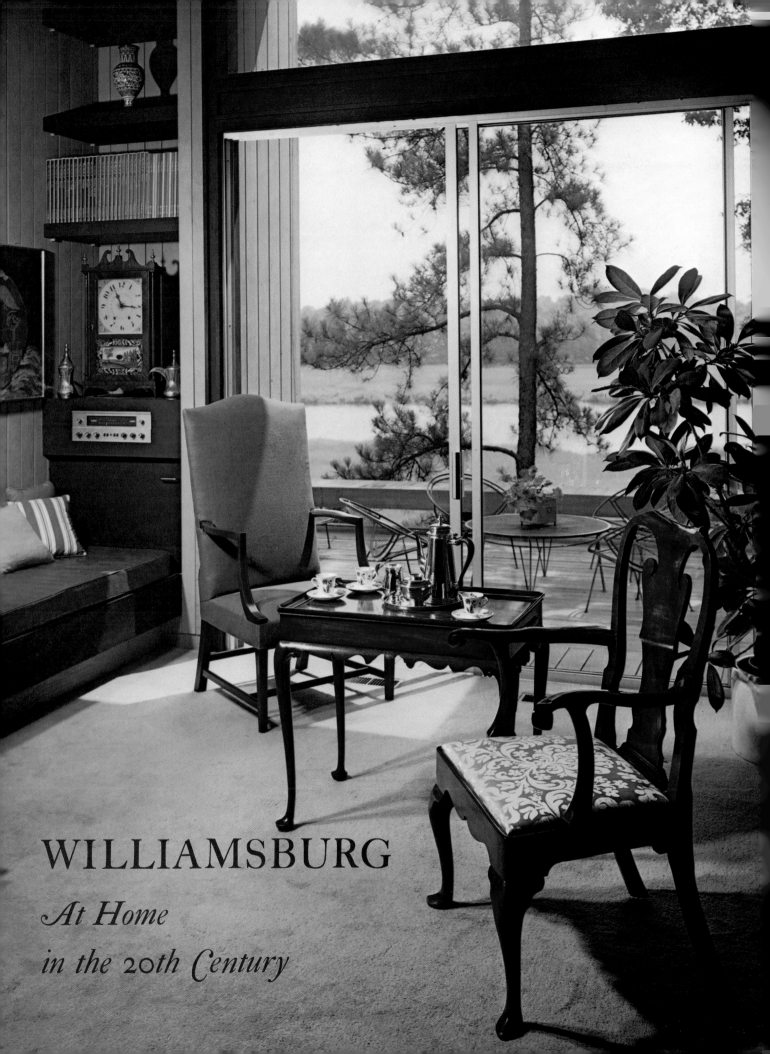

WILLIAMSBURG

At Home

in the 20th Century

BEST OF BOTH WORLDS

Colonial Williamsburg

in

20th-Century Homes

by Sarah Tomerlin Lee

COLONIAL WILLIAMSBURG chandeliers, chests, chairs, mirrors, damasks, linens and silver are manufactured from designs born at the very zenith of creative excellence in the late 17th and 18th centuries. Adding them to today's homes—cooled, heated, plumbed, and cooked in by electrical "servants"—is not only adding undeniable grace and beauty but also the implication of stability, authority, and roots-to-living in this topsy-turvy age.

Because of its role in the history of the decorative arts, Williamsburg's charm moves easily through the time zones of period and century, and across international borders.

In this fourteen-page portfolio we have tried to show how Williamsburg furnishings take the chill off chrome-and-transparent, and nonobjective art, decor by adding grace, comfort, and reality. This transmits the assurance of real lead crystal, real silk, linen and cotton, real leather, real mahogany—with the hand of man upon it. What a "Grand Alliance" it makes with French, Oriental, Italian, or Scandinavian design. Few other periods in the history of design have such remarkable qualities of compatibility and urbanity and timelessness. Each trivet and flowering bowl, hinge, lock, and rat-tail silver spoon is faithful to the spirit of an ancestor which has already stood time's test. Each is the best that can be made today.

And for us all there is an extra, though perhaps subliminal, dimension, since it evokes memories. (There are no memories in foam or plastic.) These are the desks and cupboards, the draft-proof wing chairs, the expanding dining tables that furnished the homes our Founding Fathers planned and built and fiercely defended. It is glorious decor . . . and considerably more.

On the preceding page:
"Williamsburg at home in the 20th century."
Against the dramatic impact of the great sliding glass wall, sound system, red-wood, et al., note the comfort and charm of the high-backed HIS LORDSHIPS CHAIR, CW 13, facing the elegant Queen Anne's OPEN ARM CHAIR, CW 151 and adjacent to the lovely tea table. Made today as a Massachusetts cabinetmaker made the original in the 1700s, of mahogany with pine candle-slides, it is CW 8.

Williamsburg

Partners' Desk for a chief's office

Reigning over an executive skyline office is Williamsburg's massive double-faced mahogany desk, enhanced by polished brass escutcheons and handles. It is cw 168. Other Williamsburg harmonies in this contemporary international setting (Finnish wall hanging. Swedish-design couch, Oriental carpet) are a shapely mahogany box once for precious tea, AP 102, and a particularly handsome open-arm leather chair, cw 152.

25

Williamsburg
Grand International Alliances

with France and Portugal

In a New York East River apartment an old French bergère
chair and a modern Oushak-patterned Portuguese rug live
in splendid rapport with Williamsburg's curving high-armed
love seat, WA 1055; and with a Hepplewhite
mahogany table which lifts its sides to a 39″ diameter,
WA 1006.

with India

In the tiled hall of a modern Virginia country house a long
sideboard detailed exactly as its 1740 ancestor, with
cross-banded mahogany paneling and unusual brasses
(CW 148), couldn't have a more congenial partner than the
modern Indian batik panel over it.

with Scandinavia

Its slender legs deep in a Nordic shag rug, its polished mahogany top reflecting a Swedish peasant wall hanging, ready to serve a Danish leather-and-chrome swivel chair, Williamsburg's Pembroke table is a distinguished international triumph. cw 27.

with the Orient

Counterpoint to the Oriental perfections in this contemporary American house—the interior pool, planting and lovely Japanese screen—is the design point of Chippendale, circa 1790, an open arm leather chair that is all simple grace, cw 171.

Colonial Williamsburg

Dines

Elegantly

Across 200 Years

Presiding over a contemporary redwood dining room is Williamsburg's DROP LEAF TABLE, WA 1026. In finest mahogany like its antique Hepplewhite counterpart. SIDEBOARD CW 87 adds grace and elegance with its tapering legs, scoop center, its heavy rounded brasses. Like lovely jewels that span the generations, Williamsburg dining accessories: HURRICANE CANDLESTICKS, CW 16–80, tall squared DECANTER, CW 13 and sloping DECANTER, CW 42S. On the table: rimmed and footed PEWTER BOWL, CW 7 and an endearing 18th-century pitcher, CW 38P.

No generation gap here
between this crystal and metal dining table and the charming SIDE CHAIRS, CW 128 although they stem directly from a library chair of 1740. Also circa 1740 is the handsome BACHELOR'S CHEST, CW 68, adding stability and character to this contemporary room. The timeless SIDEBOARD, CW 87, is Sheraton. The COFFEE POT, RT 29; CREAMER, RT 18; SUGAR BOWL AND COVER, RT 15 and 16, are sterling and originally made by three famous silversmiths of early America: Charles Le Roux of New York, John Allen and John Burt of Boston whose classic designs have never been surpassed.

Ready to spread its sides
and become a graceful oval the better to serve the 20th century and beyond, is this beautiful GATE LEG TABLE CW 117. Of selected mahogany, hand-carved with a shell motif on the cabriole legs, it is an unusually handsome table open or closed. The QUEEN ANNE SIDE CHAIRS, CW 142, are identical twins to the six antiques at the Governor's Palace, graceful tall backs and scroll carving flanking the knees.

When Space Is at a Premium
Williamsburg!

The very word Williamsburg implies living in the colonial period on a scale of dignity and beauty. High 4-posters reaching toward a high ceiling, long generous tables, perfectly proportioned to fit easily in today's scaled-down rooms. They don't waste space, they use it. Many have multiple uses. On these four pages see how Williamsburg can save you space without seeming to.

Table with three lives.
FLAP TOP, CW 141. Top open, as shown, this fine reproduction of an English antique is a perfect writing, telephone, or double-solitaire table. With half its hinged top flat up against the wall, its legs folded in, it becomes a console. Its top folded over itself it is a serving table of the right height.

A most elegant "storage wall."
Take two cw 164 BOOKCASES, intermediate in size
(79½" high, 15¾" deep, 46¾" wide) with adjustable shelves and
locking doors. Store books, objets d'art, china, silver.
Below in big drawers keep linens, blankets, papers. Use the curving end
of DINING TABLE, cw 33 and 34, as a side or writing table.
Joining twin ends it becomes a round dining table for four.
With its drop leaf center (not shown) it becomes a full
formal dinner table. The QUEEN ANNE SIDE CHAIR, cw 146, with
"cone and heart" piercing adds true style to the house or apartment.

When Space
Is at a Premium

(continued)

A four-poster in that room?

The cw 58½ is less than five feet tall, notwithstanding its soaring appearance. The actual measurements are generous: height, 58½"; width 44⅜", and length, 81⅜".

A copy of a New England 18th-century bed where space was then a problem too. Like the original it is of mahogany with maple sides. BRASS SPOOL LAMP, L 4, with china silk shade is 24" high for good reading.

Use the corner.
QUEEN ANNE CORNER TABLE, CW 2, is only 18″ deep closed, as here. Filling what is sometimes lost space, it measures 25″ x 25″ open. QUEEN ANNE SIDE CHAIR, CW 67, is welcome in a hall, at a desk or dinner table.

Small but mighty desk.
Nine drawers! Two that lock. Ample writing surface. Correspondence storage sections. When the slant-top DESK, WA 1037, is closed, this compact adaptation of an English Chippendale piece is only 26½″ wide and 21″ deep but its charm and capability are enormous. Pewter CHAMBERSTICK LAMP is L 14. QUEEN ANNE SIDE CHAIR is WA 1018.

Perfect Foil for the Rugged Setting of a Reconstructed Barn... The Elegance of Williamsburg

Chippendale at the wide window-wall.
Gentleman's WING CHAIR, CW 12. An 18th-century craftsman in Rhode Island first shaped the wings and scrolled arms of this particularly comfortable chair; fluted the straight legs à la Chippendale. The same influence gave this classic SOFA, CW 23, its serpentine back. Even the galleried COFFEE TABLE, WA 1042, combines a Chippendale style tray with a base designed to echo its graceful shape.

The grace and polish of Williamsburg furnishings are shown here in exciting contrast to the massive rough-hewn beams, wide plank floors, the unmistakably rustic flavor of a house-made-from-a-barn so popular today.

At home with the big beams
is BACHELOR'S CHEST, CW 68. Reproduction of a mid-18th-century English piece done by a master craftsman. Graduated drawers, top slide, splendid brass locks and handles. The side CHAIR, CW 142, because of the integrity of its design, defies improvement either in comfort or beauty.

In the ell of the barn
in a sitting-dining room, is Williamsburg's GATELEG TABLE, CW 117. Oval and drop-leaf, it is one of the most important of all the Williamsburg tables. Its graceful carving becomes even more striking when contrasted with this unpolished setting.

The Golden Touch of Williamsburg

The gleam and sparkle of polished brass that caught the light of fire and candle in 18th-century homes . . . fireplace fenders, andirons, candlesticks and candelabra, locks and keys and hinges and trivets . . . more than fifty objects have been duplicated by Williamsburg master craftsmen in heavy brass to give that same sparkling magic to homes today. See appropriate catalogue sections for descriptions of these items.

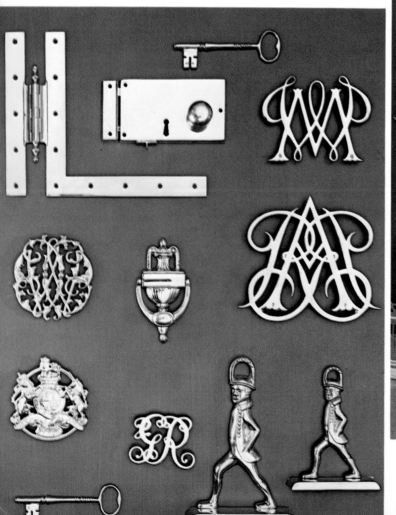

Colonial Williamsburg Furniture
Reproductions and Adaptations

ABOUT the time Williamsburg was founded in 1699, most people were sitting on stools and benches, not chairs. The furnishings of our first colonists were crude and few. But a change was stirring, and the 1700s witnessed a revolution in demand for home furnishings. For the first time that demand came not just from the limited upper classes. It also came from a rising and numerous middle class who were newly experiencing the benefits of comfortable homes. This was true in England and it was certainly true of the American colonies. In Virginia the tobacco planters had grown wealthy; it was they who initiated the steady consumption of fine articles. Prosperous townsfolk were not slow in following their example.

The "furniture revolution" began in England with the return of Charles II and his more open Court, influenced by the manners and arts of Versailles. Plain Cromwellian chairs gave way to spiral turnings and elaborate carvings. William and Mary brought in Dutch craftsmen and European baroque design. But the greatest period was to begin in the short reign of Queen Anne and to run through Georgian times to the early nineteenth century.

American colonists, tied to England by blood and trade, bought this furniture, copied it in their own workshops and made it their own. Today a Queen Anne chair of the period, made in America, is as authentic (and expensive) as one made in London.

Virginia's tidewater planters bought furniture in London and had it delivered to their doorsteps by the tobacco ships. The citizens of Williamsburg furnished their homes, taverns, and public buildings with imports, but soon were buying American pieces from New England, Philadelphia, and later from Baltimore. Such treasures constitute the present furnishings and collections of Colonial Williamsburg. They provide the pattern and examples for *Williamsburg* Furniture Reproductions and Adaptations.

Colonial tastes followed, at a little distance, the growing sophistication of the imports. At first, articles of the previous century were still in vogue: a chair of Charles II with a cane back; or a William and Mary dressing table. Often a style would long outlive the monarch for whom it is named. Typical are the Queen Anne side chairs, now in the Governor's Palace, which were made in England about 1740, 26 years after the Queen's demise, and the Philadelphia version of the same type in the Brush-Everard House; both are reproduced in the Colonial Williamsburg program.

Gradually, without displacing the old, new styles appeared. Soon after the middle of the century the products of Mr. Chippendale were all the rage, and his publication *The Gentleman and Cabinet Maker's Director* became a bible for some English and colonial cabinetmakers. This was the peak of the highly decorated, rococo style: natural objects like shells and foliage were carved in wood, along with motifs from the Gothic and Chinese. Thomas Chippendale's name has been applied to furniture of every description: the comfortable (and draft-proof) wing chairs, the elaborate breakfronts, the elegant sofas. He was the inspiration for a New England-built tall post bed, a Philadelphia lowboy and a New Jersey highboy. All these Chippendale pieces are represented in the Williamsburg collections; they, in turn, are faithfully reproduced or adapted to serve in traditional and modern decors alike—for "modern" is always relative.

In the last quarter of the eighteenth century a change of taste developed as the classical revival swept Europe and the North American colonies. It was the architectural era of the "southern mansion" with its pillared portico; George Washington's Mount Vernon and Thomas Jefferson's Monticello. In furniture, Chippendale's successors, the brothers Adam, George Hepplewhite and Thomas Sheraton designed exquisite examples of the furnituremakers' art, abundantly represented in the collections of Colonial Williamsburg. These masters introduced a lighter style of design with slender and tapering supports. Decoration with carved foliage, drapery, fans, and urns was fanciful and elaborate.

Throughout these periods of change the American workmen followed their English compatriots' lead and also developed their own modifications. A tall post bed made in New England in the late eighteenth century and now a Williamsburg Reproduction is nevertheless immediately recognizable as Hepplewhite in style with its slender tapering posts finished off with delicate finial urns.

In mid century the beautiful and durable American mahogany achieved pre-eminence in English furniture making; it was shipped to England in vast amounts and mahogany became the touchstone of fine furniture. Sometimes mahogany veneer was used when especially decorative and matching wood effects were sought. The mahogany tradition is integral to the Colonial Williamsburg Reproductions and Adaptations Program. The combination of fine woods, hand workmanship and eighteenth-century design produced products that were eagerly sought after; their use for two centuries is witness to their essential durability.

Adaptation of these pieces to modern living is a matter of taste and subtlety. It may take two forms: first, a scaling down to meet the space and ceiling dimensions of the modern apartment. Yet oddly enough, while some adaptations have been scaled down, others had to be scaled up. We have actually "grown" since the eighteenth century and for real comfort our dining tables are now made an inch higher than theirs.

Also modern homes call for such items as coffee tables, unknown to Chippendale and Hepplewhite. An eighteenth-century butler's tray is the inspiration for a sturdy and adequate coffee table in the Chippendale tradition. In another adaptation, the bench section of a Queen Anne day bed made in Rhode Island in 1740 provides an ample low table for use in a drink-and-conversation setting.

Truly eighteenth-century taste has found an echo in the twentieth century's demand for elegant, decorative, and eminently practical articles of furniture.

Periods and Styles of Furniture

English furniture styles take their name either from the reigning monarch—Charles II, Queen Anne, George II, etc., or from the great designers who appeared as a veritable galaxy in the last half of the eighteenth century—Thomas Chippendale, the brothers Adam, George Hepplewhite, and Thomas Sheraton, whose names are immortalized in their furniture designs. These styles were taken up, sometimes promptly, sometimes with a time lag, by American craftsmen. Partly this was due to transportation delays, partly to a hesitation to switch to "new models" before the public taste was ready to accept them.

As far as England was concerned, the eighteenth century was characteristically "Georgian" and the successive periods closely match the reigns of the four Georges. In America, the dominant styles were (in modern terminology): "William and Mary," "Queen Anne," "Chippendale," "Hepplewhite," and "Sheraton." The Williamsburg Reproductions Catalogue carefully attempts to convey as much information as possible as to the date and style of a given piece of furniture, and its origin, whether from England or from a center in the original colonies.

The chart below shows the reigning periods of the monarchs and the approximate times when a given style enjoyed its peak of popularity, both in England and in the colonies.

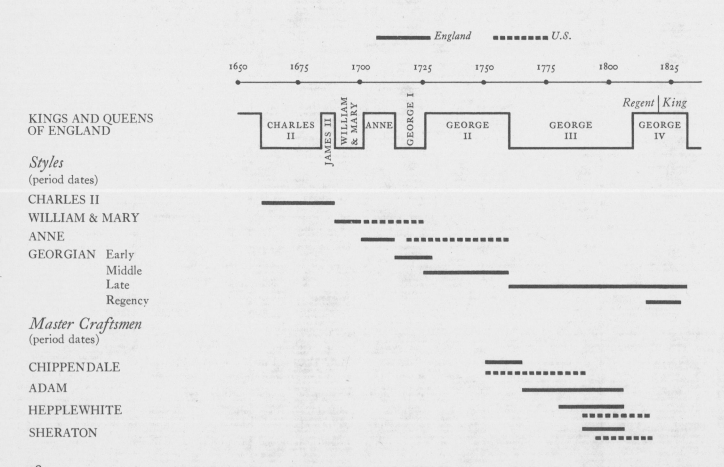

38

Charles II

When Charles II was called to the throne in 1660, England joyfully shed the spartan austerity of the Cromwell period. Returning from exile on the Continent, the court brought with it an air of luxury and elaborate manners. The rectilinear lines of Cromwellian furniture were replaced with elaborate designs from the Continent. Deep carving (1) and spiral turning on legs and stretchers (2) appeared. Oak was gradually supplanted by walnut. Flemish scroll feet were used on chairs, tables, and bed terminals (3); cane chairs made their first appearance (4). Rich and bold, the style and forms developed during this period reached a peak of refinement in the following decades.

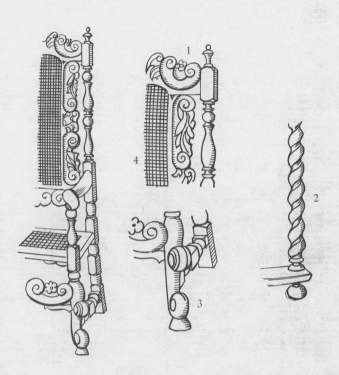

William & Mary

In 1688 Mary, daughter of James II, and her husband, Prince William of Orange, accepted the throne of England, bringing with them from Holland numerous craftsmen and quantities of baroque furniture. During their reign a style of furnishings emerged which was to be a transition between the elaborate forms of the Stuart period and the grace of the Queen Anne style.

Pieces distinctive of the period were china cabinets, round and oval gate-leg tables, banister-back chairs with crestings, higher bedsteads (some reached 16 feet), small tables for gaming, and the newly developed chest-on-frame (highboy) and dressing table (lowboy). Walnut was the most popular wood during this era.

Prominent characteristics of William and Mary furniture include turnings in the shape of the inverted cup (1), trumpet (2), gadrooning (3), perpendicular legs, the bun foot (4), the straight bracket foot (5), and the Spanish foot (6), with shaped stretchers often set crosswise between the legs (7).

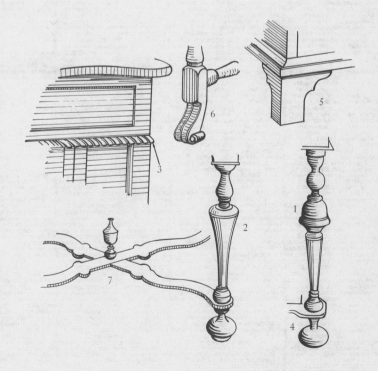

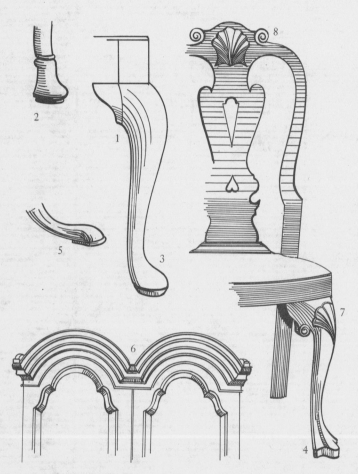

Queen Anne

Queen Anne, second daughter of James II, ruled England from 1702 until 1714. The furniture style that bears her name, however, covers a period of forty years and includes the reign of George I and part of the reign of George II.

The style developed during this age of flourishing craftsmanship is considered one of the most graceful of the century. Its most distinctive feature is an undulating line based on the "S" or cyma curve—an unbroken line with a convex and concave curve. William Hogarth, the celebrated eighteenth-century English painter and engraver, called this curve the "line of beauty."

The most fashionable wood was walnut, but mahogany was introduced about 1720. With the use of this wood furniture became lighter and more graceful; and elaborate carving, to which mahogany was especially suited, began to appear.

The Queen Anne chair is perhaps the most familiar design of the period. It has an extremely comfortable splat often shaped to fit the back. Card tables with turnover hinged tops, small tables, and lower chests of drawers were popular.

Characteristics of the Queen Anne style as interpreted in America were cabriole legs (1) with numerous forms of the foot: hoof (2), pad (3), trifid (4), and slipper (5). The claw-and-ball foot was also used during this time.

Other characteristics of this style are scroll tops on chests (6), and scalloped shells on knees of legs (7) and on crests of chairs (8).

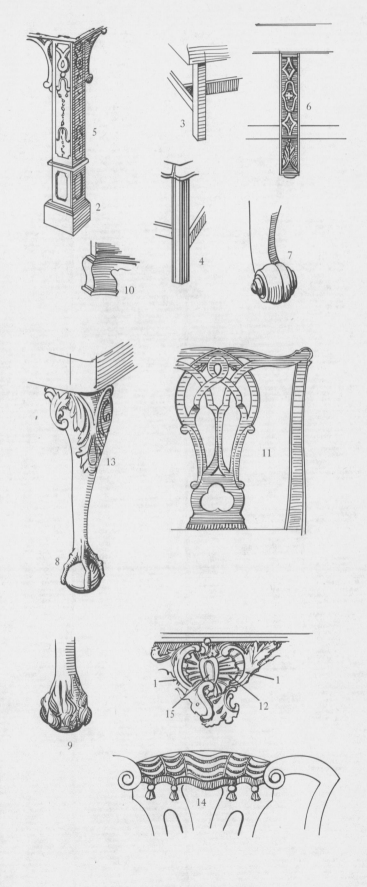

Chippendale

Thomas Chippendale, the best-known and best-advertised figure in the history of furniture-making, was born about 1705 and died in 1779. The first cabinetmaker to have his name associated with a furniture style, Chippendale was paradoxically a master of the derivative. Rarely inventive, he borrowed elements from Gothic, Chinese, and French designs and translated them into a new style.

Walnut and fruit woods, as well as mahogany, were widely used in America at this time, while English cabinetmakers preferred mahogany, an excellent wood for the crisp carving associated with Chippendale. Other popular Chippendale motifs included rococo or asymmetrical designs, simulated Chinese bamboo, the "C" scroll (1), and extensive use of fretwork.

The Chippendale straight leg, often terminating in a distinct Marlborough foot (2), was plain (3), fluted (4), carved (5), or decorated with applied frets (6). His cabriole leg was supported by the following types of feet: scroll or French toe (7), claw-and-ball (8), and hairy paw (9). The ogee bracket foot (10) was often used on case pieces. Characteristic carved forms were the pierced or interlaced splat (11), tattered shell (12), acanthus leaf (13), drapery (14), and cabochon (15).

Many of his contemporaries were his equal as designer and craftsman; but in 1754 he published *The Gentleman and Cabinet-Maker's Director*, and this established him in the public mind as one of the foremost furniture designers of the period. Two later editions of the treatise were published, the last in 1762.

These publications are known to have reached America, and the style they delineated was adapted by American cabinetmakers to suit colonial tastes. For this reason many American-made pieces have wide variations from the original designs. For example, while the highboy or chest-on-frame went out of style in most parts of England in the mid-eighteenth century, it continued in America and was developed in the American Chippendale style to include the elegant Philadelphia chest-on-chest, the Boston bombé type chest-on-chest, and the handsome Newport block front form. When we refer to "Chippendale" in this text, then, we are using the term in the American sense.

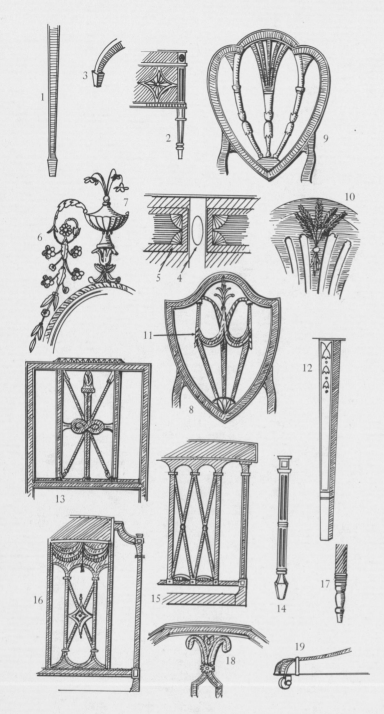

The Classical Revival

During the latter part of the eighteenth century Europe was swept by a wave of "classicism," inspired by renewed interest in Greek and Roman art and architecture.

In English furniture the classical revival meant the end of the elaborate, rococo Chippendale style and the introduction of the light, classical lines of Adam, Hepplewhite, and Sheraton.

Robert Adam, the best-known of three brothers, was among the first to popularize the new style in England.

Furniture in the Adam style was generally made of mahogany or satinwood, and cane-back pieces were popular. Slim tapered legs, often fluted (1,2), were distinguishing features of the style. The legs were square or round and usually supported by block or spade (3) feet.

Classical motifs in inlay or low relief carving were widely used; ornamental discs and ovals, spandrel fans, floral swags and pendants (4,5,6), and most importantly the classic urn (7).

George Hepplewhite was one of the many skilled craftsmen associated with the making of furniture to Adam's design. He was also important on his own as an interpreter of the classical in eighteenth-century English furniture.

Some distinguishing features of his designs include shield-shaped chair backs (8), heart-shaped backs (9), sheaves of wheat (10), carved drapery (11), bell flowers (12), prolific use of inlay, and painted designs decorating whole sets of furniture. Mahogany and satinwood were the popular woods.

American furniture of the late-eighteenth century was tremendously influenced by the design books of Thomas Sheraton, and his furniture enjoyed great popularity during an affluent period in America. The celebrated Duncan Phyfe was one of many American cabinetmakers who were influenced by the Sheraton style.

Sheraton used rectangular chair backs (13), rounded and tapered legs with reeding or fluting (14), diamond and lattice designs in chair backs (15), decorative motifs of swags, flowers, and drapery (16), spiral turnings (17), Prince of Wales feathers (18), and applied brass terminals (19).

Furniture Terms

Apron
A narrow strip of wood, adjoining the base of a cabinet carcase and extending between the tops of the legs or feet brackets. (As best represented by cw 1, 19, 148; wa 1017, 1020).

Bail Handle
A metal or wood handle curved upward at the ends (depending) from the sockets. (Represented by cw 1, 68; wa 1031).

Baluster
A small, slender turned column, usually swelled outward at some point between the base and the top. (Represented by cw 70, 49; wa 1009).

Baroque
An architectural style of Italian origin, characterized by conspicuous curves, scrolls, and highly ornate decoration.

Block Foot
A square, vertical-sided foot at the base of a straight, untapered leg. (Represented by cw 170).

Bombé
Outward swelling, curving or bulging. (Represented by cw 176).

Bracket Foot
A protruding straight or ogee support. (Represented by cw 68; wa 1008).

Bun Foot
A flattened globe, or bun-shaped foot, with slender ankle above. (Represented by cw 157).

Burl
A swirled grain within wood which has been cut from a crotch or the stump of a tree. (Represented by cwLG 5).

Cabriole
A springing curve. Term applied to legs that swell outward at the upper part, or knee, and inward at the lower part. (Represented by cw 19, 8, 146; wa 1020).

"C" Scroll
A carving in the shape of the letter "C". (Represented by cw 67-142)

Carcase or Carcass
A body of joinery, or cabinet work. (Represented by cw 1, 68; 18).

Cartouche
An ornamental form of irregular shape enclosing a plain central surface, often used as a field for painted devices or inscriptions.

Chamfer
A beveled cutting away of a corner angle. (Represented by cw 3, 57, 33; wa 1004).

Compo
(short for composition) A mixture of resin and other materials for the fabrication or molding of relief for application (billiard balls are made of a mixture called compo). (Represented by cwLG 3, 6).

Cresting
Ornamental topping, usually a chairback (Represented by cw 146).

Cross Banded
Wood which has been banded (cut) across the grain for molding or decorative purposes. (Represented by cw 68, 148; cwLG 9).

Cyma Curve
A wave curve; a double or compound curve. (Represented by cw 151).

Dentil
A form of molding ornamentation made by a set of oblong blocks set at equal distance from each other. (Represented by cw 169).

Dovetail
Double fan, butterfly, or dovetail key block, fitted into conforming cuts in the surface of boards or planks to make a tightly fitted joint. (Represented by cw 1, 153, 87, 19; wa 1024, 1027).

Dowel
A wooden pin fastening two pieces of cabinet work together.

Escutcheon
Keyhole cover of brass, silver, ivory, etc. (Represented by cw 68, 87, 143; wa 1037).

Finial
A decorative finishing device for corners or projecting uprights. (Represented by cw 92, 58).

Fluted
A series of grooves used to decorate columns or legs. (Represented by cw 12).

Fret
Interlaced ornamental work, sometimes applied to solid background and sometimes perforated. (Represented by cw 37, 3, 23; wa 1004).

Gadroon
A carved or curved, fluted or ruffled, ornament for edges. (Represented by cw 3).

Gallery
A raised rim of fretwork, or metal bar, surrounding tops of furniture. (Represented by cw 57).

Greek Key
A border design of angular broken lines, repeated continuously. (Represented by cw 158, 308).

Hoof Foot
Resembling a hoof. (Represented by cw 179)

Inlay
Where one wood is set into the body of another for decorative effect. (Represented by cw 27, 13, 172; wa 1050).

Japanning
In earlier parlance, synonymous with lacquering. (Represented by cwLG 7).

Knee
The uppermost curve of a cabriole leg.

43

Masque
A full face, human, animal, or grotesque, used without the rest of the body, as a form of ornament.

Mortise and Tenon
A method of joinery whereby one piece (tenon) is cut to precisely fit into another (mortise). Sometimes the tenon is further locked by means of a peg inserted through it.

Ogee
A form made by two opposite cyma curves, with their convex sides meeting in a point. (Represented by cw 176).

Pediment
An architectural cresting for large cabinet work, either triangular or scrolled. (Represented by cw 158, 169).

Pendant
A hanging ornament.

Rococo
An elaborate form of ornamentation full of curves, shells, and other rustic details conventionalized. (Represented by cwlg 6).

Skirt
See Apron

Slipper Foot
Usual on tripod legs and sometimes called snake foot. (Represented by cw 5, 149, 182; wa 1009).

Spiral Turning
A twisted form of turning frequently seen on legs and bed posts. (Represented by cw 69).

Splat
The central member of a chair back. (Represented by cw 142).

Stretcher
The bracing between legs. (Represented by cw 136).

Trifid (or Drake) Foot
Usual on cabriole leg (like pad foot) which has been carved. (Represented by cw 146).

Wainscot
Boards used for panel work. Panel work itself. (Represented by wa 1050).

Williamsburg Furniture Reproductions
and *Adaptations* BY KITTINGER

Williamsburg Furniture Reproductions are approved copies of eighteenth-century antiques used in furnishing the exhibition buildings of Colonial Williamsburg. The Furniture Adaptations are pieces inspired by similar antique prototypes. Both series are manufactured for Craft House, under license, by the Kittinger Company of Buffalo, New York.

Williamsburg furniture is made of mahogany, and each piece, whether it be a Reproduction or Adaptation, is individually constructed and finished.

The Reproduction is a close replica of an original antique using careful selections of fine woods. Solid white brass is hand-filed to the same weight of the colonial mounts. Details of construction and decoration are hand-copied by Kittinger's master craftsmen following the traditions of the skilled artisans of the past.

The Adaptation aims at a different ideal. It attempts to modify an original piece to conform to modern necessities of size, function, comfort, or all three, while adhering to the basic principles of eighteenth-century design. These demanding requirements are rigorously supervised by the Craft Advisory Committee experts. Falling into this category are adaptations to smaller apartment proportions by a general scaling down of the generous originals; adaptations to modern functions as in the devising of coffee tables or the partitioning of a storage cabinet; adaptations

to comfort as in the height of a table or chair, or the modification of springs and upholstery.

Indeed, an Adaptation may be an exact replica of the original piece with the exception of details of internal construction which conform more closely to the finest up-to-date methods.

Reproduction and Adaptation pieces are available in a variety of finishes and, in the case of upholstered chairs and sofas, in many different fabrics. The Price List gives information about fabric yardage, down cushions, leather upholstery, and the like. The muslin prices of upholstered pieces include the cost of applying fabric provided by the purchaser.

Williamsburg at home! Exhibiting the grace and charm of the eighteenth century in today's world, this comfortable conversational grouping bespeaks agelessness. A Chippendale sofa, scaled for modern living, faces two chairs that are quite different in their visual appeal, yet complement each other beautifully. Smaller details from lamps and candlesticks to delftware and prints are refreshing ornaments that personalize this dignified, restful room. Among notable items, clockwise: wa 1005 Sofa, l 1 Pulpit Finial Lamp, cw 16-33 Candlesticks, c 4 Posy Holders, cw 100-2 Andirons, cw102-1 Fender, cw 103-1c Fire Tools, wa 1047 Wing Chair, wa 1010 Table, cw 49 Cup, cw 16-34e Candlestick (electrified), various pieces of delftware, p 22 and p 23 Maps, cw 8-7 Bookend, wa 1031 Bachelor's Chest, wa 1025 Open Arm Chair, and ap 102 Tea Caddy.

CW 33 *and*
CW 34
Dining Room Table

CW 34

This three-part dining room table illustrates the simplicity of line typical of the late Chippendale style. Diverse in its appearance and function, the table may be used in a variety of ways. The drop-leaf section alone is an excellent dining table for small parties. Two end sections locked together make a graceful round table or used separately they become console tables. When these three pieces are joined, a handsome long table is formed, accommodating 12 persons. The over-all length of the completed table is adjusted by dropping one or both leaves of the center section.

CW 33 Center Section. Height 29¼″; width 48″; length 22″ closed, 67″ open.

CW 34 End Section. Height 29¼″; width 48″; depth 23½″.

At top, two end sections and one center section with top open are joined. Total length 114″, seating capacity 12. *At right*, two end sections joined, form a round table 47″ in diameter. *Below*, the drop-leaf center section will accommodate six persons with top open, 67″ long.

CW 33

An example of versatility, CW 33 is ready to serve as a buffet table in today's limited space. This party setting is handsomely accented with CW 55 Tankards. The CW 54 Strawberry Dish makes a pleasant container for party treats as well as fresh fruits. Hurricane Shades (CW 9) placed over candlesticks (CW 30) add a colorful note for festive occasions. The arm chair in front of the table is WA 1119. All of these time-tested pieces blend happily with the modern wall sculpture.

WA 1035
Drop-Leaf Coffee Table

This 20th-century coffee table—a form unknown in the 18th century—has been adapted from a small drop-leaf table in the Williamsburg collection. The dimensions of the antique have been reduced in proper proportions to form a table of delightful simplicity.

Height 18¾″; width 35″ open, 20⅛″ closed; length 42″.

*American
Circa 1770
Chippendale*

cw 65 *and* cw 66 *Dining Room Table*

The original pedestal table, made in England about 1770, is now in the Allen-Byrd House. The center and end sections used together, or in combination with 24″ leaves, create a good-sized table for a separate dining room. In limited space, two end sections (cw 66) may be joined to make a charming dining table in a small contemporary room; or an end section alone is a handsome console table. All sections are made with tilt tops for additional use in a corner or against a wall.

cw 65 Center Section
Height 28½″; length 32½″;
width 48″.

cw 66 End Section
Height 28½″; length 33¼″;
width 48″.

*English
Circa 1770
Chippendale
(George III)*

At left are two end sections with one 24″ leaf, making a total length of 90½″. Also available with additional 24″ leaf and support.

Shown at right are two end sections, one center section, and two 24″ leaves, totaling 147″ in length.

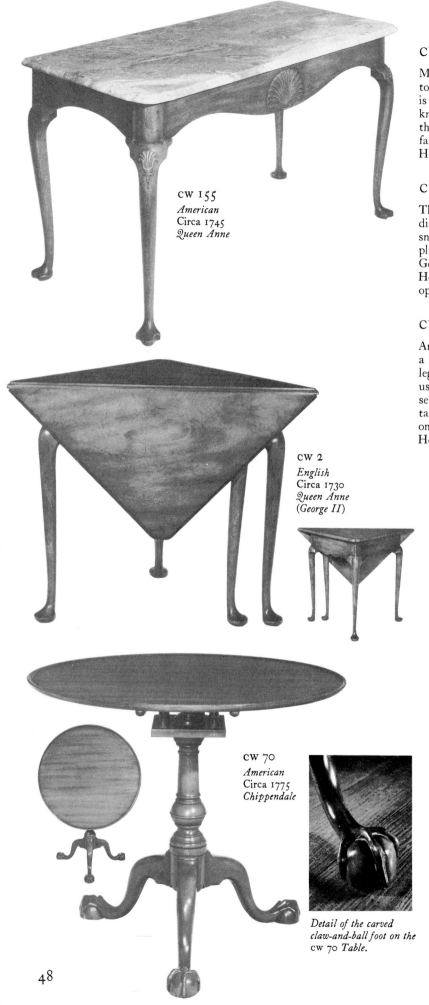

cw 155
American
Circa 1745
Queen Anne

cw 2
English
Circa 1730
Queen Anne
(George II)

cw 70
American
Circa 1775
Chippendale

*Detail of the carved
claw-and-ball foot on the
cw 70 Table.*

cw 3
American
Circa 1770
Chippendale

cw 155 *Serving Table*

Made in the Queen Anne style, about 1745, this marble-topped table is supported by cabriole legs on trifid feet and is graced by delicate shell carvings on the apron and front knees. It is an exact copy of an American antique now in the Governor's Palace in Williamsburg. The marble surface makes it useful as a serving table and easy to maintain. Height 27½"; length 52⅛"; depth 24".

cw 2 *Corner Table*

The pad feet and graceful scalloped apron are particularly distinctive features of this Queen Anne table. Closed it fits snugly into small spaces, opened it provides a two-foot-plus square surface. The original is in the study of the George Wythe House.
Height 26¾"; diagonal width 35"; depth closed 18"; open 25" x 25".

cw 70 *Tilt-Top Table*

An unusual example of Chippendale design, this table has a bird-cage construction and claw-and-ball feet on curved legs. With a revolving tilt-top such pieces were frequently used as tea tables in the colonial period. Today it may serve a similar function or it could even be used as a small table for dining. The original Philadelphia antique is now on display in the Wythe House study.
Height 28¾"; diameter 34¾".

cw 3 *Card Table*

A Rhode Island cabinetmaker is believed to have made the original of this card table, which is now in the parlor of the Brush-Everard House. The thumb-print molding on the flap-top edge and cavetto molding lighten the appearance of a double top. Throughout the entire piece, graceful Chippendale lines are faithfully copied in the reproduction.
Height 28¾"; length 30¼"; depth 15¾" closed, 31½" open.

48

The rough texture of brick and bold brush strokes of the contemporary painting provide a striking backdrop for the Queen Anne table (cw 117) and side chairs (cw 146 and 142). The tall candlestand (cw 49) on the side gives the setting an unexpected dimension.

CW 117 *Gate-Leg Table*

An elegant feature of this oval gate-leg table is the delicate shell and pendant design carved on the knee of each cabriole leg (see detail). When completely open the table provides comfortable places for as many as eight persons. With both leaves down the table becomes a narrow 24″—perfectly suited for today's smaller apartments. The original is in the supper room of the Governor's Palace in Williamsburg. Height 29″; width 58″; length 24″ closed, 70″ open.

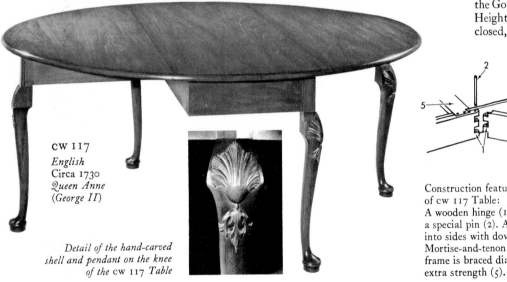

CW 117
*English
Circa 1730
Queen Anne
(George II)*

Detail of the hand-carved shell and pendant on the knee of the cw 117 *Table*

Construction features of cw 117 Table:
A wooden hinge (1) is held in place by a special pin (2). Apron rails are locked into sides with dovetail tenons (3). Mortise-and-tenon joint (4). Apron frame is braced diagonally for extra strength (5).

WA 1022 *Drop-Leaf Table*

A handsome small dining table, this Queen Anne adaptation was inspired by an antique made in Virginia and now in Christiana Campbell's Tavern. As useful as it is handsome, this table is only 16½″ wide when closed and fits conveniently against a wall. With the leaves open it provides a comfortable setting for three to four.
Height 29½″; length 42¾″; width 43″ open, 16½″ closed.

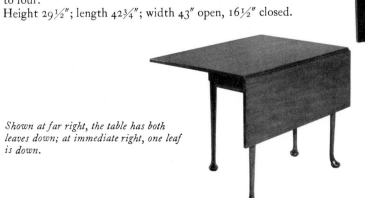

Shown at far right, the table has both leaves down; at immediate right, one leaf is down.

WA 1022
*American
Mid-18th Century
Queen Anne*

49

An inviting window area accentuates this harmonious study in shape. The table's (WA 1020) graceful cabriole legs complement the simple Chippendale lines of the CW 12 Wing Chair. Three CW 40 Wine Bottles brighten the window sill while a CW 60 Porringer and CW 10-11 Trivet adorn the table top.

American
Circa 1730–1740
Queen Anne

WA 1020 *Drop-Leaf Table*

The Queen Anne styling of this elegant single drop-leaf table is seen in its graceful lines, cabriole legs, and pad feet. The original, made by a Massachusetts craftsman, is in the Colonial Williamsburg collection, and the adaptation differs from it only in unseen interior construction details.
Height 25¾"; length 31"; width 23½" open, 13½" closed.

The WA 1020 Table with its leaf down.

American
Late 18th Century
Hepplewhite

WA 1029 *Table*

This graceful Hepplewhite table was inspired by an American antique now among the furnishings of a Williamsburg guest cottage. The slightly tapered legs and appealing proportions are exactly like those of the original. Useful as an occasional or end table, it also provides a good surface for a lamp or vase of flowers. The drawer is handy for small objects.
Height 29½"; width 25¼"; depth 18¾".

50

American
Circa 1735–1750
Queen Anne

cw 8 *Tea Table*

A Massachusetts cabinetmaker designed the original of this elegant tea table which is now used in the Peyton Randolph House. This table, like the antique, is made of carefully selected mahogany with pine candle slides. Note the graceful scallops of the apron and the delicate hand carving of the cabriole legs in this fine Queen Anne reproduction.
Height 26¼″; length 29¾″; depth 18½″.

cw 27 *Pembroke Table*

According to tradition, tables of this type were named for the Earl of Pembroke. This Hepplewhite version found great favor in the American colonies and is distinguished by the holly inlay on the legs and drawers, the shape and thickness of the oval top, and the size and taper of the legs.
Height 28¼″; width 22″ closed, 46¾″ open; depth 33″.

American
Late 18th Century
Hepplewhite

American
Circa 1760
Queen Anne

cw 57 *Table*

This small table is a fine reproduction of an English antique in the Governor's Palace. Notable Chippendale features are the scalloped gallery with pierced hand-holes, delicate leg brackets, and paneled doors. It is frequently used as a bedside table but serves equally well next to a chair.
Height 31″; width 21″; depth 19¼″.

wa 1010 *Table*

Today, as in the 18th century, circular tables are popular as small occasional or end tables. This Queen Anne adaptation is derived from the original piece seen in the parlor of the Wythe House.
Height 26¾″; top diameter 20¼″.

English
Mid-18th Century
Chippendale
(George III)

51

English
Circa 1760–1775
Chippendale
(George III)

English
Circa 1760–1775
Chippendale
(George III)

American
Third Quarter
18th Century
Hepplewhite

WA 1009 *Table*

This tripod table has been simplified in its adaptation from the original to create a sturdy occasional table. The original is featured in the Brush-Everard House.
Height 27¼"; top 25" x 25".

WA 1066 *Table*

This useful tripod table is an adaptation of the original now in the Brush-Everard House. Also available with a square top (WA 1009.)
Height 27¼"; Diameter 26½".

CW 20 *Tilt-Top Table*

The snake feet on the tripod base and the serpentine top of this small table are especially distinctive. When the top is tilted it forms a diamond and can easily fit into any corner. The original of this New England table is now in The Raleigh Tavern of Williamsburg.
Height 27½"; top 19½" x 19½".

American
Late 18th Century
Hepplewhite

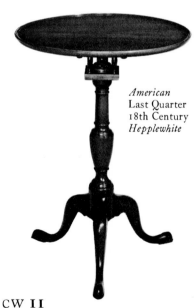

American
Last Quarter
18th Century
Hepplewhite

English
Circa 1760
Chippendale
(George III)

CW 135 *Oval Tilt-Top Table*

Characteristic of late 18th-century furniture, this oval table's tripod legs terminate in spade feet.
Height 27½"; length 26"; width 17¾".

CW 11 *Revolving Tilt-Top Table*

This intermediate-size table is a reproduction of a New England antique now in the parlor of the Allen-Byrd House. An intricate bird-cage construction connects the revolving tilt-top to the base.
Height 27"; diameter 21½".

CW 69 *Square Tilt-Top Table*

Distinguished by a delicate tripod base and finely proportioned carved stem, this table is graceful yet unusually sturdy. As in all *Williamsburg* furniture each part is carefully hand-joined. The original of this tilt-top table was made in England about 1760 and is now in the dining room of the George Wythe House.
Height 26¾"; top 25⅝" x 25⅝".

52

CW 141 *Flap-Top Table*

This reproduction of an English antique (now in the Williamsburg collection) changes appearance as it does function: suitable as a serving table (above), a writing table, or a console (left). The rectangular folding top is supported on slender columnar legs terminating in turned feet. A delicate candle slide pulls out on either side; and two gates support the top when it is open. Height 28½"; length 35¾"; depth 12" closed, 24" open.

English
Circa 1720
Queen Anne
(George I)

The versatile CW 141 Table is shown above with the CW 33 Candlestick, delft brick C 26, and the Catesby print *The Chatterer* (P10-6).

WA 1058 *Table*

The English provincial original of this adaptation table is now in the Great Room of Wetherburn's Tavern. The practical size and single drawer permit a variety of uses for this mahogany table with its gracefully turned legs and feet. Height 26⅜"; width 24"; depth 17".

English
First Quarter 18th Century
William and Mary

53

CW 134 *Drop-Leaf Table*

A copy of a New England piece, this reproduction, with its oval shape and graceful legs, has retained the clean lines and crisp hand carving of the antique. The original of this drop-leaf table is used in the library of the Brush-Everard House.
Height 26¾″; width 13¾″ closed, 40½″ open; depth 33½″.

CW 156 *Card Table*

The original of this circa 1735 card table is among the furnishings of the Peyton Randolph House. This reproduction details the antique's elaborate design of scroll shoulders and shell with pendant leaf. The claw-and-ball foot and the half-round design are attractive characteristics.
Height 28¾″; width 32¾″; depth 32¼″ open, 16⅛″ closed.

CW 167 *Drop-Leaf Table*

This six-sided gaming table, a copy of an English antique, has three gracefully indented corners on each leaf and tapered legs with capped knees and pad feet. With leaves extended, it seats four comfortably. The original may be seen in the Palace Northwest bedroom.
Height 28″; width 38¾″; length 14½″ closed, 45″ open.

CW 150 *Card Table*

This table is a faithful reproduction of a Queen Anne piece on display in the Allen-Byrd House. It may be used closed (below center), with its flap top against a wall (below), or with its top open and supported by a leg that swings from the back (not shown).
Height 30½″; length 31″; depth 15″ closed, 30″ open.

CW 134
American
Circa 1750
Chippendale

Detail of claw-and-ball foot on CW 134 *Table*

CW 156
English
Circa 1735
Chippendale
(George I)

CW 167
English
Circa 1740
Queen Anne
(George II)

CW 150
English
Mid-18th Century
Queen Anne
(George III)

The many faces of eighteenth-century furniture create a rich decor for dining in this spacious room. The Sheraton table (WA 1044) is accompanied by Chippendale dining chairs (CW 17 and 17½), and is accented by two Hepplewhite WA 1047 Wing Chairs on either side of the fireplace. The chairs are covered in Tulip fabric (page 127). A delicate Queen Anne occasional table (WA 1010) in the background is balanced by the massive Chippendale double chest (CWA 1050) on the side. From the ceiling hangs the K 12596 Capitol Chandelier. Small but important appointments, such as the cathedral candlesticks (CW 16-34) on the table and the Furber print over the chest, contribute to the overall harmony.

WA 1043 *and* WA 1044
Pedestal Dining Room Table

Inspired by an American antique in the furnishings of Colonial Williamsburg, this three-part dining room table is 108″ in length. Two end sections (WA 1044) may be joined together for more compact dining; used separately an end section provides a pleasant console or serving table. Eighteen-inch leaves are available if the length needs to be further increased.

The dimensions of the antique have been reduced in the adaptation, and the angle of the legs changed for increased comfort and stability. Also, the drop leaves of the original end sections have been altered to the popular console form.

WA 1043 Center Section
Height 29½″; width 46″; length 36″.

WA 1044 End Section
Height 29½″; width 46″; length 36″.

*American
Circa 1810–1820
Sheraton*

Two end sections joined together for a total length of 72″.

Two end sections and one center section making a total length of 108″. This three-section table seats 12 persons.

55

American
Circa 1770
Chippendale

cw 160 *Table*

This copy of an antique drop-leaf "breakfast table" in the Williamsburg collection could serve for intimate dining in a small apartment or double as an end or card table. The openwork stretchers of this mahogany table are illustrated in Chippendale's *Director* of 1754.
Height 28½"; depth 30¼"; width closed 20¼", 40¾" open.

English
Circa 1735
Queen Anne
(George II)

cw 179 *Tea Table*

The original English antique is in Wetherburn's Tavern. Mahogany throughout, the cabriole legs are distinctive with their molded edges and hoof-shaped feet. These charming tables can be used in hallways or vestibules.
Height 25½"; width 25"; depth 16¾".

wa 1039 *Tea Table*

The original is in a Palace bedroom, painted black with an elegant Chinese lacquered tray top. The stretchers have the mark of Chippendale's style and insure sturdiness. It is very effective as an occasional table in mahogany or any authentic Williamsburg color.
Height 27½"; width 26"; depth 20⅜".

English
Circa 1750
Chippendale
(George II)

cw 161
Revolving Book Table

Eminently useful in library, den, or office and a conversation piece too, this perfect reproduction keeps volumes close at hand. The hexagonal top in swirl-figured mahogany holds a lamp and knicknacks. The original is now in the Peyton Randolph House.
Height 29½"; top 25½" across flat sides.

English
Circa 1760
Chippendale
(George III)

American
Third Quarter
18th Century
Queen Anne

wa 1057 *Porringer Table*

This handsome and useful table is adapted from an antique in Wetherburn's Tavern. Originally a tea or gaming table, it is typical of those made in New England. Candlesticks were placed on porringer-shaped corners.
Height 26¾"; width 34"; depth 24".

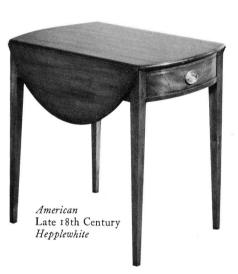

American
Late 18th Century
Hepplewhite

wa 1006 *Pembroke Table*

Classic Hepplewhite design has been given a fresh look in this *Williamsburg* adaptation by the use of molding instead of inlay around the drawer and leaves. The original table is now used in the furnishings of Colonial Williamsburg.
Height 28"; width 39" open, 20¾" closed; depth 29¾".

56

American
Mid-18th Century
Queen Anne

CW 145 *Dressing Table*

The original of this mahogany dressing table is a mid-18th-century Philadelphia piece now in the Williamsburg collection. Both the hardware and the details of carving on the cabriole legs are very elegant (see insets below). Height 28¼"; length 35"; depth 19½".

Detail of shell and leaf carving on the knee of the CW 145 *Table.*

Detail of fluted stocking and web foot of the CW 145 *Table.*

American
Circa 1750
Queen Anne

English
Circa 1720
Queen Anne
(George II)

WA 1059 *Table*

The antique from which this versatile mahogany table was adapted was probably made in tidewater Virginia. Note the pattern caused by the joined top and the distinctive scribed outline of the drawer.
Height 27½"; width 28¾"; depth 18¼".

WA 1042
Coffee Table

An antique butler's tray was copied for the top of this table. It is fitted to a specially designed base shaped to the contour of the tray. Useful as a coffee or magazine table.
Height 21½"; width 27¾"; depth 21¾".

English
Late 18th Century
Chippendale
(George III)

CW 172 *Corner Table*

This unusual Queen Anne corner table is reproduced from an antique made in England about 1720. It has a triangular top with a serpentine front edge and a skirt which conforms to the shape of the top. There are holes in the sides of the table so that it can be secured to adjacent walls. The single cabriole leg terminates in a pad foot. The knee is outlined with carved "C" scrolls and is decorated with a carved shell and pendant bellflowers.
Height 30"; width 22¼"; depth 16" at center.

American
Circa 1810
Sheraton

CW 177 and CW 178 *Dining Table*

This three-part dining table is copied from a Boston example of about 1810. The deep leaves of the sections are each supported by two gates with tapered columnar posts and splayed legs ending in brass paw feet with casters. Extensive use of reeding appears in the edge of the top, the lower edge of the apron, the columnar supports, and the upper face of the legs.

CW 177 and CW 178 Dining Table. Each section: Height 28¼″; width 56¼″; length 14¾″ closed, 60⅝″ open. Three section open, length 182″.

CW 177 Drop-leaf center section, four square corners (not shown).

CW 177-RC Drop-leaf center section, four round corners. Shown at right with top closed; above with top open.

CW 178 Drop-leaf end section, two square and two round corners (not shown).

WA 1033 *Coffee Table*

Based on the design of an antique day bed made in Rhode Island and now displayed in the library of the Brush Everard House, this adaptation has Queen Anne cabriole legs and finely turned stretchers. The table proportions are ample enough for use as a coffee table and for the display of objects.
Height 17¾″; length 46″; width 22½″.

American
Circa 1730–1740
Queen Anne

English
Circa 1760
Chippendale
(George III)

WA 1014 *Table*

The straightforward simplicity of the antique is matched in this fine Chippendale table. Unlike the original, the adaptation is finished on the back so that it may be used as a free-standing table. The original is in the Wigmaker's Shop of Williamsburg.
Height 28″; width 28¾″; depth 16″.

WA 1004 *Table*

Modeled on a Virginia Chippendale antique now in the Wigmaker's Shop, this adaptation may be used as a dressing table, small desk, side or serving table.
Height 29½″; width 42″; depth 21″.

American
Circa 1750–1775
Chippendale

American
Late 18th Century
Hepplewhite

WA 1024 *Serving Table*

The original Hepplewhite antique is found in the King's Arms Tavern. The adaptation has been scaled down to make it particularly useful for a small dining room. One of the drawers has a sliding, removable silver tray.
Height 34¼″; length 47¾″; depth 20½″.

English
Circa 1790
Hepplewhite
(George III)

WA 1026 *Drop-Leaf Table*

This type of table became popular in the colonies. The original, which inspired this piece, was owned by Lucy Ludwell Paradise. Its dimensions have been slightly adjusted in the adaptation and two legs added for strength and stability. Extra table space is obtained by the addition of two WA 1049 Console Ends at either end of the large table.
Height 29½″; width 48″; length 76″ open, 28″ closed.
WA 1026 Drop-Leaf Table and two WA 1049 Console Ends, a total length of 124″.

WA 1049 *Console End*

This piece can be used by itself as a handsome wall or hall table. It acts as an extension when fitted to either end of WA 1026 Drop-Leaf Table.
Height 29½″; width 48″; depth 24″.

WA 1040 *Lady's Chair*

This handsome Chippendale chair, shown here covered in Liverpool Birds, was adapted from an antique now in the George Wythe House. In the adaptation the back has been given more pitch and the seat more depth for added comfort.
Height 41″; width 27½″; over-all depth 21½″; arm height 24¾″.

American
Circa 1760
Chippendale

cw 136 *Corner Chair*

The original of this chair was constructed in Philadelphia about 1750–1775. It is an occasional, corner or desk chair, often called a "roundabout chair" and demonstrates the woodcarver's art.
Height 31¼″; width 26″; over-all depth 26″; arm height 29¾″.

American
Circa 1750–1775
Chippendale

Just right for reading as well as for casual conversation, this cw 44 Wing Chair (covered in Country Linen, page 124), offers not only the beauty of the eighteenth century, but its solid comfort as well. The scene is handsomely completed with the L 13 Lamp on a revolving book table (cw 161). Wall treatment: framed Williamsburg Military Prints (P 20).

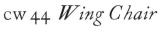

cw 44 *Wing Chair*

The original of this graceful and comfortable chair dates from about 1750 and is in the Williamsburg collection. The reproduction, in mahogany, is a true copy. Particularly noteworthy are the cabriole legs with beautifully turned stretchers. These chairs fit into formal or informal settings alike. The fabric depicted here is Floral Bough.

American
Circa 1750
Queen Anne

61

cw 12 *Wing Chair*

Made by a Rhode Island craftsman, the original of this chair is now in the Williamsburg collection. The otherwise severe legs are stop-fluted and the chair has a sturdy appearance that makes it a natural for a study, den, or club.
Height 45½″; width 31″; over-all depth 28″; arm height 25½″.

American
Third Quarter 18th Century
Chippendale

cw 13 *His Lordship's Chair*

This high-backed Hepplewhite-style chair, sometimes called the Martha Washington type, is an approved reproduction of an antique in the Williamsburg collection. The delicate inlay, tapering legs, and slender open arms are frequently seen in cabinet-maker's work of the late eighteenth century. The fabric is Raleigh Tavern Resist.
Height 48″; width 26″;
over-all depth 26½″;
arm height 28″.

American
Circa 1790
Hepplewhite

English
Circa 1760
Chippendale
(George II)

cw 14 *Arm Chair*

Like the original, this reproduction is made of mahogany. Thomas Chippendale's style is apparent in the straight legs with delicate brackets, the graceful arms and the comfortably sloping back. The fabric is Multi-Stripe.
Height 38¾″; width 28¼″; over-all depth 29″; arm height 27″.

Construction features of cw 13 Chair:
Most Williamsburg upholstered pieces are constructed with webbing (1), springs (2), burlap (3), curled hair (4), cotton (5), muslin (6) and finally the cover (7). The seat rails are mortised and tenoned into the legs (8).

cw 16 *Chair*

There are two originals of this mahogany Chippendale straight chair in Williamsburg, one in the Governor's Palace and the other in the Wythe House. Of simple design, except for the pierced or interlaced back splat, this chair is sturdy and comfortable.

Height 37¼"; width 22"; over-all depth 21½".

*English
Circa 1765
Chippendale
(George III)*

*American
Late 18th Century
Chippendale*

cw 17

cw 17½

cw 43
*English
Circa 1760
Chippendale
(George III)*

cw 17 *Chair*

Made in Philadelphia, the original of this chair is an example of Chippendale simplicity. This reproduction is covered in Spotswood Fabric.
Height 37½"; width 22½"; over-all depth 23¾".

cw 17½ *Arm Chair*

This armchair version of cw 17 can be used as a pair at either end of a dining table along with other cw 17 chairs on the sides. It is solid mahogany and upholstered in Spotswood in this example.
Height 37½"; width 25"; over-all depth 24½"; arm height 26¾".

cw 43 *Smoking Chair*

The padded back and arm of this chair provide extra comfort for smoking or for sitting at a desk. The original is in the little middle room of the Governor's Palace.
Height 34"; width 29"; over-all depth 24¼"; arm height 29½".

63

CW 47 *Arm Chair and*
CW 47½ *Side Chair*

Meticulously copied from the originals, these chairs can be used in combination at a dining table or singly at a desk. The back splats are elegantly interlaced. The examples shown are covered in Multi-Stripe.

English
Circa 1765
Chippendale
(George III)

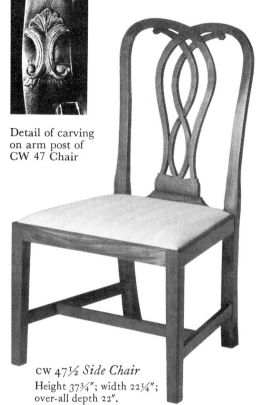

Detail of carving on arm post of CW 47 Chair

CW 47 *Arm Chair*
Height 37¾"; width 26"; over-all depth 22½"; arm height 27".

CW 47½ *Side Chair*
Height 37¾"; width 22¼"; over-all depth 22".

CW 67 *Side Chair*

This chair is an elegant copy of an original George I side chair in the hallway of the Peyton Randolph House. The cabriole legs in front are decorated with a scalloped shell and bellflower motif finished in antique gold leaf.
Height 41½"; width 22¼"; over-all depth 24¼".

English
Circa 1725
Queen Anne
(George I)

Detail of hand-carved leg on
CW 104 Chair, showing acanthus leaves
and ball-and-claw foot.

CW 104 *Wing Chair*

Sturdiness, comfort and elegance were often distinguishing marks of Chippendale, and this approved reproduction captures these qualities. The original English piece is now in the furnishings of Colonial Williamsburg. It is shown here with Gloucester Damask fabric.
Height 44"; width 33"; over-all depth 31½"; arm height 26".

English
Circa 1745
Chippendale
(George II)

64

*English
Circa 1740
Queen Anne
(George II)*

CW 128 *Side Chair*

Reproduced in mahogany like the original in the Brush-Everard House library, this chair shows Georgian grace and dignity. The cabriole legs and pad feet are most attractive.
Height 38½″; width 23¼″; over-all depth 23″.

A rare antique Japanese screen sets the mood for this striking room; the wing chair (cw 104) and table (cw 134) enhance this lavish setting. On the cabinet is the Wythe House Clock and in the foreground, the cw 78 Pewter Inkstand. Here is an example of how eighteenth-century furnishings can be combined comfortably in our own time.

CW 142 *Side Chair*

The original of this chair is one of a set of six in use at the Governor's Palace. For comfortable dining, the back splat was contoured. Particularly noteworthy is the graceful scroll carving flanking the knees.
Height 40½″; width 21¼″; overall depth 20½″.

CW 142

*English
Circa 1740
Queen Anne
(George II)*

CW 142½

Detail of the hand-carved scroll on the knee of cw 142 Side Chair and cw 142½ Arm Chair.

CW 142½ *Arm Chair*

Graced by the same fine features as cw 142, this has the addition of arms and handsomely heads a table surrounded by the side chairs.
Height 40½″; width 24″; over-all depth 22¾;
arm height 27½″.

65

English
Circa 1740
Queen Anne
(George II)

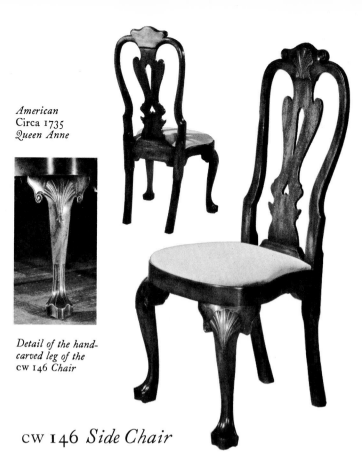

American
Circa 1735
Queen Anne

Detail of the hand-carved leg of the
cw 146 *Chair*

cw 146 *Side Chair*

The original of this Queen Anne chair was made in Philadelphia and is now in the Brush-Everard House. It is fairly elaborate in design and details, with "cone and heart" piercing in the splat, a serpentine crest rail with scallop shell and additional carving on the knee and leg—particularly appropriate as a dining room chair.

Height 43¼"; width 20¼"; over-all depth 20".

cw 151 *Open Arm Chair*

A hand-carved and hand-finished copy of an English antique now in the Allen-Byrd House, this chair has a solid, contoured back splat, cabriole legs and scroll arms—elegant and distinctive.
Height 39¾"; width 28"; over-all depth 23½"; arm height 27¼".

cw 163 *Wing Chair*

This timeless piece enters into any setting with magnificent effect. The front legs are cabriole with disc feet and the rear ones S-shaped. The example is upholstered in Bruton Damask.
Height 49"; width 32½"; over-all depth 32¼"; arm height 26¼".

English
Circa 1720
Queen Anne
(George I)

CW 166 *Barrel Chair*

The original of this chair is in a bedroom of the Peyton Randolph House, but the reproduction is at home in any room: cozy, comfortable and pleasing. Its cabriole front legs end in high pad feet and the flaring rear legs are square.
Height 40″; width 28″; over-all depth 29½″; arm height 26″.

*English
Circa 1750
Queen Anne
(George II)*

CW 152 *Open Arm Chair*

Copied in precise detail from an antique in the Williamsburg collection, this unusual chair has been reproduced for use in homes and offices. It has square legs, rectangular stretchers, and simple curved arms.
Height 38½″; width 27″; over-all depth 27″; arm height 27½″.

*English
Circa 1765
Chippendale
(George III)*

CW 171 *Open Arm Chair*

The original chair, a fine American interpretation of Chippendale design, is now in the Peyton Randolph House. This handsome reproduction, finished here in leather, is ideal for study or den.
Height 38″; width 24¼″; over-all depth 25¼″; arm height 26½″.

*American
Circa 1790
Chippendale*

*English
Circa 1725
Queen Anne
(George I)*

CW 180 *Side Chair*

This Queen Anne side chair is copied from one of a pair of English antiques in the Williamsburg collection. The curves in the serpentine cresting rail are repeated in the shaped stiles that flank the broad, vase-shaped splat. A slip seat is supported on cabriole legs. The front legs terminate in claw-and-ball feet with curved hocks while the rear ones terminate in pads.
Height 38″; width 21⅞″; over-all depth 22¼″.

WA 1011 *Open Arm Chair*

This small open arm chair was inspired by an American antique now in the George Wythe House. It subtly modifies the original Chippendale lines by extra height and additional pitch to the back for enhanced comfort. It is shown here in Raleigh Tavern Resist.
Height 39″; width 24″; over-all depth 27¼″; arm height 25¾″.

WA 1018 *Side Chair and*
WA 1118 *Arm Chair*

This adaptation of a Chippendale side chair made in Virginia between 1760 and 1780 borrowed the antique's sturdy construction and simple pierced back splat. Arms for the arm chair were designed from another Chippendale model of the same period. They have slip seats and are also available with upholstered seats (WA 1048 and WA 1148).

WA 1118 Arm Chair with slip seat
Height 37½″; width 25″; over-all depth 21¼″; arm height 27¼″.

WA 1148 Arm Chair with upholstered seat
Height 37½″; width 25″; over-all depth 21¼″;
arm height 27¼″.

WA 1011

*American
Circa 1765–1770
Chippendale*

WA 1018 Side Chair with slip seat
Height 37½″; width 21″; over-all depth 20″.

WA 1048 Side Chair with upholstered seat
Height 37½″; width 21″; over-all depth 20″.

WA 1148

WA 1048

*American
Circa 1770
Chippendale*

WA 1018

WA 1118

This conversational setting is a study in compatibility. The crisply modern feeling of the WA 1011 Open Arm Chair (upholstered in Lateral Stripe, page 128) is an appropriate partner for the WA 1012 Wing Chair and its richly traditional Spotswood covering, page 123. Also featured: a Queen Anne tilt-top table (cw 20), the K 13162 Sconce, and Stencil Square wallpaper.

WA 1012 *Wing Chair*

Modeled after a rare wing chair in the Brush-Everard House, this adaptation has the same fine bow in the upper wing and a thicker cushion for extra comfort. The fabric shown here is Plantation Calico.

Height 45"; width 32"; over-all depth 32"; arm height 24".

American
Circa 1775–1780
Chippendale

69

*American
Circa 1770
Chippendale*

WA 1046 *Side Chair and*
WA 1056 *Open Arm Chair*

The original of these fine mahogany chairs was from a New England workshop, and is now in the Brush-Everard House in Williamsburg. Both adaptations retain the interesting crest rail and excellent proportions of the original.

WA 1046 Side Chair
Height 37¾"; width 22¾"; over-all depth 23½".

WA 1056 Open Arm Chair
Height 37¾"; width 24¾"; over-all depth 25½".

*American
Circa 1770
Chippendale*

Simple and contemporary in feeling is this combination of side chair and table—particularly appropriate in a hallway or entry area. The WA 1046 Side Chair (fabric, Liverpool Birds, page 129) is paired with the CW 160 Table which provides the right surface for the AP 101 Tea Caddy and the delft brick and mahogany lamp (L 2). On the wall is a hand-colored copy of the Nova Virginia Tabular (P 22). Simplicity and understatement often are keys to tasteful decorating.

English
Second Quarter 18th Century
Queen Anne
(George II)

WA 1019 *Side Chair and*
WA 1119 *Arm Chair*

These two stylishly simple Queen Anne chairs were copied from antiques in the Williamsburg collection. For greater comfort the adaptations have upholstered rather than slip seats. Those pictured here are covered in a cheerful woven fabric, Apples.

WA 1019 Side Chair
Height 38″; width 21¼″;
over-all depth 21½″.

WA 1119 Arm Chair
Height 38″; width 26″;
over-all depth 23½″;
arm height 28¼″.

WA 1025 *Open Arm Chair*

Based on an American antique now in the George Wythe House study, this fine Chippendale chair covered in leather and studded with brass nailheads is often used in a study, den, or office. The adaptation has a deeper seat and boldly raked back for solid comfort. It is also available upholstered in fabric (without nailheads). Height 43½″; width 27¾″; over-all depth 27¼″; arm height 27¼″.

American
Circa 1770
Chippendale

WA 1047 *Wing Chair*

Elegance and comfort are combined in this adaptation of an English antique in the Williamsburg collection. The wings and beautifully proportioned rolled arms are carefully copied. The front legs are somewhat more tapered for greater lightness in feeling and the chair has been lowered slightly. Pictured is a cover in Wythe House Border Resist.
Height 45″; over-all width 29″; over-all depth 28″; arm height 27½″.

Accents of orange enrich this room which features *Williamsburg* Furniture Adaptations. A WA 1047 Chair, upholstered in Wythe House Border Resist (page 121), a chair (WA 1011) covered in Country Linen (page 124), and a Pembroke table (WA 1006) are the center of great interest. Four handsome *Williamsburg* brass candlesticks are grouped on the mantle.

English
Circa 1790
Hepplewhite
(George III)

English
Circa 1740
Queen Anne
(George II)

English
Circa 1760
Chippendale
(George III)

CW 147 *Bench*

The perfect occasional seat, now as in the 18th century: the original, made in England about 1740, is in the ballroom of the Governor's Palace. It has been perfectly reproduced in solid mahogany.
Height 17″; length 17″; width 21½″.

WA 1016 *Bench*

A copy of an English antique in the Williamsburg collection, made about 1760. Practical as an extra seat or as a dressing table bench.
Height 16¾″; width 19¾″; depth 15¾″.

*English
Circa 1740
Queen Anne
(George II)*

cw 148 *Sideboard*

A reproduction of an English antique of about 1740, this low sideboard is equally at home in a hallway or dining room. Note the carved apron, paneled sides, cross-banded mahogany encircling the drawers, and the unusual brasswork.
Height 33¾″; length 77½″; depth 21¼″.

Construction features of cw 148 Sideboard:
Custom-made oval brass knobs with nickel silver insert through center (1). Cross-banded border of mahogany (2).
Dovetail tenons (3).

cw 87 *Sideboard*

Reproduced from an antique now in use in Christiana Campbell's Tavern, this compact sideboard has four finely tapered square legs in front and two in the rear. Octagonal key escutcheons and heavy round brass knobs add distinctiveness to a simple and classic design.
Height 40½″; length 57″; depth 20¼″.

*American
Late 18th Century or
early 19th Century
Hepplewhite*

WA 1017-1 *Sideboard*

A low cupboard in the Chippendale style now in the Williamsburg collection inspired this unusual sideboard of fine mahogany fitted with brass escutcheons and H-hinges. For modern living the original has been scaled down and fitted inside with two silver storage drawers and six adjustable shelves. The middle compartment opens for additional storage space.
Height 36"; length 66"; depth 20¾".

WA 1041 *Sideboard*

An elegant accessory for the small dining room, this Hepplewhite sideboard was copied from an American antique now in Christiana Campbell's Tavern in Williamsburg. The two cabinets may be locked and the top drawer is partitioned and lined for silver flatware. The drawers have traditional brass fittings.
Height 39¾"; length 56½"; depth 24".

cw 169 *Secretary Bookcase*

The original of this piece is believed to have been made in Virginia during the last quarter of the eighteenth century. While the antique is of walnut, this secretary has been reproduced in the finest solid mahogany, and mahogany veneer. Behind the glass doors on the upper section there are three shelves, two of which are adjustable. The slant-top desk folds out for a writing surface, and there are four graduated drawers below for storage space. All doors and drawers have locks.

Height 99⅝"; width 44¼"; depth 23".

cw 169½ *Slant-Top Desk*

This desk is the same as the one used for the cw 169 Secretary, but it does not have the bookcase on top. Where space is limited, this piece of furniture stands well on its own and still provides a useful writing area and storage space.

Height 42⅞"; width 44¼"; depth 23".

American
Late 18th Century
Chippendale

English
Circa 1740
Chippendale
(George II)

cw 164 *Bookcase*

Handsome and versatile, this mahogany piece is reproduced from the antique now located in the Peyton Randolph office. Shelves are adjustable to display objets d'art and fine books, and it has a capacious full-width drawer in the base. Its intermediate size would recommend it as a useful and tasteful addition to library, study, office, or executive suite. It has full locks on cabinet and drawer.

Height 79½"; width 46¾"; depth 15¾".

English
Circa 1750
Chippendale
(George II)

CW 158 *Breakfront Bookcase*

This stunning reproduction in solid mahogany and selected mahogany veneer matches in every detail its antique prototype in the Governor's Palace. It is also related to bookcases illustrated in Chippendale's *Gentleman and Cabinet-Makers' Director*. Like the original, it is made in sections—cornice, cabinet and base—for greater ease in moving. Three drawers are "hidden" in the Greek key design atop the base section. Striking brasswork, adjustable shelves, and locking cabinets and drawers complete this beautiful display piece.
Height 95⅞″; width 71½″; depth 18¾″.

Detail of
hand-carved leg
on cw 23 *Sofa*

cw 23 *Sofa*

Oriental motifs were popular in the late 18th century, and the front legs of this Chippendale sofa, following its original, have a Chinese fretwork design. Not as long as the typical sofa of the period, this piece achieves distinction in its classic flowing lines in back and arms. Here it is shown upholstered in Spotswood.
Height 35½"; over-all length 73"; over-all depth 31½"; arm height 30".

cw 118 *Sofa*

The 18th-century original of this handsome English piece is in the King's Arms Tavern. For an unusually large private or public room, this reproduction faithfully copies the unusual length and sweeping back of the antique.
Height 35¾"; over-all length 91"; over-all depth 30"; arm height 28¾".

English
Circa 1770–1790
Chippendale
(George III)

English
Circa 1760
Chippendale
(George III)

CW **174** *Sofa*

This sofa with serpentine cresting and front seat rail, horizontally rolled arms, and four cabriole front legs with claw-and-ball feet is copied from an English antique dating to the 1760s. The original piece was owned by a person in Newburyport, Massachusetts during the eighteenth century. This history is of importance, for it further documents the use of high-styled English furniture in American homes from an early date.

Height 35⅞"; length 88½"; over-all depth 33¼"; arm height 31".

CW **154** *Settee*

An elegant Queen Anne settee in mahogany from an original, made in England about 1725 and now in the Williamsburg collection. Its basically simple construction is complemented by skillful details in the woodwork; the cabriole legs have scroll-like wings and pad feet, while the outcurving arms terminate in graceful volutes.

The fabric shown here is Spotswood.
Height 36¾"; length 53¾";
over-all depth 29¼"; arm height 25¾".

English
Circa 1725
Queen Anne
(George I)

This sofa is a major statement, perhaps *the* piece for a handsomely appointed room. Rich yet simple in lines, it combines harmoniously with the cw 37 Hanging Shelf and the cw 57 Table. The high luster of the pewter humidor (cw 94) and porringer (cw 16) contrast dramatically with the lamp (L 1). Note how the character of the sofa changes with different kinds of upholstery: Spotswood, above; Pomegranate Resist, below. (See pages 123 and 124)

CW 129 *Sofa*

This beautiful mahogany sofa, copied from an English antique in the Allen-Byrd House, is distinguished by its flowing lines and ample proportions. Comfortable and practical, it seats three persons with ease.

Height 36″; length 79″; over-all depth 30½″; arm height 30¾″.

English
Circa 1760–1775
Chippendale
(George III)

79

American
Circa 1770
Chippendale

WA 1005 *Sofa*

The unmistakable lines of the original
Chippendale antique are matched in this
adaptation. This is the humpbacked sil-
houette, with lines flowing into the graceful
arms. The sofa provides comfortable seating for three persons. The fabric shown
here is Bellflower.
Height 36¼″; over-all length 84″;
over-all depth 32½″; arm height 30½″.

This dramatic room is proof that traditional
and contemporary design can be exciting
partners. The WA 1005 Sofa upholstered in
Spotswood is a graceful foil for the soaring
window and Chinese rug. With the sofa are a
CW 128 Chair and a WA 1033 Table.

American
Circa 1770
Chippendale

WA 1055 *Love Seat*

A smaller version of the WA 1005 Sofa,
this upholstered mahogany love seat would
go in a conversation nook, entrance hall, or
bedroom, or could serve as an additional
piece in a fair-sized living room. It is here
illustrated in Ludwell Adaptation fabric.
Height 36¼″; over-all length 61″; over-all
depth 32½″; arm height 30½″.

cw 18 *Chest*

The original of this piece is an antique mahogany chest of drawers now used in the George Wythe House. This meticulous reproduction has graduated drawers, bracket feet, reeded quarter-round columns, and striking brass lock fixtures and drawer pulls.
Height 35½″; width 38¼″; depth 19½″.

Construction features of cw 18 Chest:
Drawer runners (or dust panels) are tenoned into ends (1). Drawers are dovetailed front (2) and back (not shown). Cock bead is around each drawer (3). Custom hardware is used (4). Fluted quarter-round column pilasters cover complex joinery of chest frame (5).

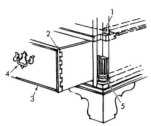

American
Circa 1770
Chippendale

cw 19 *Lowboy*

Solid elegance marks this lowboy of Chippendale design. It is based on an antique in the Governor's Palace attributed to a Philadelphia cabinetmaker about 1760. The reproduction faithfully duplicates the fluted columns, carved cabriole legs, and fine brass hardware of the original and is a superb hallway or study piece.
Height 32″; length 38½″; depth 20″.

American
Circa 1760
Chippendale

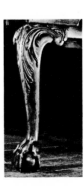

Detail of carved leg and foot of cw 19 Lowboy, with acanthus leaf and claw-and-ball.

81

cw 68 *Bachelor's Chest*

An English antique of the mid-eighteenth century, in a hold-over of the Queen Anne style, is the model for this exact reproduction. The drawers are finely graduated, and an intriguing detail is a top slide which turns the piece into a dressing stand. It was called a "bachelor's chest" because of its somewhat smaller size which detracts not at all from its superb design.
Height 29¾"; width 30"; depth 17½".

English
Circa 1740
Queen Anne
(George II)

wa 1030 *Commode*

The original English antique is in the Brush-Everard House and is here adapted as a handsome and practical side table for books and magazines. The deep storage drawer is a useful addition.
Height 31½"; width 23¼"; depth 19".

English
Circa 1750
Chippendale
(George II)

WA 1060 *Chest*

The paneled ends, simple brass drawer pulls, and joined top gives this handsome mahogany chest an air of quiet distinction. It would be equally at home in a bedroom, living room or hallway. There are locks in four drawers. Height 31⅞″; length 52½″; depth 20⅞″.

American
Circa 1740–90
Chippendale

CW 162 *Cellarette*

This handsome cellarette is an exact copy of the American antique now in the Williamsburg collection. The top compartment provides ample storage space for bottles and the lower section has a convenient drawer for necessary bar equipment and a handy sliding shelf for service. Both sections may be locked. Height 40¾″; width 25¼″; depth 15½″.
Inside cellarette compartment: Height 11¾″; width 22″; depth 12⅞″.

American
Circa 1790
Hepplewhite

83

This piece has the authority to make a major statement in any room. As functional as it is beautiful, the Chippendale cw 153 Highboy can hold table linen in a dining room, or can be used to store a man's accessories in his bedroom. The accompanying chair (cw 104) is upholstered in Wythe House Stripe (page 127), and Stencil Square (page 138) is the pattern of the wallpaper.

cw 153 *Highboy*

The original of which this is a copy is believed to have been made in New Jersey about 1760, and now stands in the upstairs hall of the George Wythe House. Beautifully proportioned, the highboy stands on four cabriole legs and has a boldly carved and scalloped skirt. It is an elegant and impressive piece for hallway or bedroom.

Height 69¾"; width 42¾"; depth 22⅞".

American
Circa 1760
Chippendale

Impressive alone and even more of a visual treat used in pairs, this chest of drawers (WA 1002), can grace a hall, living room, or bedroom. Its medium size makes it a desirable piece for today's apartments. Also seen are the side chair (CW 47½), the CW 16-80 Hurricane Candleholder, and the AP 101 Tea Caddy which is serving here as a flower container.

WA 1002 *Chest of Drawers*

A Virginia antique, circa 1775, was adapted to make this medium-sized Chippendale chest of drawers. Like the original, the adaptation has clean lines and simple but effective brasswork.

Height 35¼"; width 37½"; depth 21¾".

American
Circa 1775
Chippendale

WA 1008 *Chest of Drawers*

A Virginia-made antique was the inspiration for this Chippendale chest. It follows a colonial tradition of simplicity combined with gracious proportions: a bracket base, with subtly graduated drawer size, and simple but effective brasswork. The original is now in Williamsburg's Market Square Tavern. Height 46¼"; width 40"; depth 20".

American
Circa 1770
Chippendale

CW 176 *Chest*

The design and details of this mahogany chest make it a most attractive reproduction. The top surface conforms to the serpentine shape of the front, and the hand-carved fretwork embellishes the chamfered corners. Graduated drawers are generous in size, and each one has a lock. The original Pennsylvania chest is now in the Peyton Randolph House.
Height 33½"; width 44¼"; depth 23".

American
Circa 1770
Chippendale

WA1050 *Double Chest*

An important and substantial piece for any room, this handsome chest is marked by its elegance of detail. In mahogany, it has quarter-round turned columns at the corners, paneled ends, and ogee base brackets. The nine drawers are outlined by boxwood inlays and have a highly decorative pattern of simple brass escutcheons and drawer pulls. There are locks on the top three drawers.
Height 34″; length 61½″; depth 22½″.

WA1031 *Bachelor's Chest*

This adaptation of an English Chippendale chest reflects the fine, masculine lines of the original. It is beautifully made of grained mahogany, and embellished on both front and sides with fine brasses. Practical in a dressing or bedroom with its pull-out shelf, it can also serve as a small desk in a study. The antique is now housed in the Raleigh Tavern.
Height 30½″; length 31¼″; depth 18″.

cw 1½ *Desk*

This slant-top desk opens to disclose nine small drawers and four letter pockets. With a bookcase unit on top, it becomes the cw 1 Secretary Desk, which may be seen on page 90 with additional information.
Height 40″; width 41½″; depth 20½″.

American
Circa 1770
Chippendale

Detail of the shell carving in the apron of the cw 1 Secretary Desk and cw 1½ Desk.

cw 181 *Sideboard*

Classical in style, the high spade feet of this sideboard show the Robert Adam influence on this reproduction of a late eighteenth-century English antique. A center serpentine drawer is bordered by two drawers on the left and a cupboard (double drawer effect) on the right. This sideboard is made of mahogany and mahogany veneer with a banded border around the top edge.
Height 36″; length 72″; depth 27″.

English
Late 18th Century
Hepplewhite
(George III)

English
Circa 1770
Chippendale
(George III)

wa 1037 *Desk*

This desk was copied from an English Chippendale piece made about 1770, and both desk and frame match the lines and spirit of the antique. In the adaptation, the leather writing surface is replaced by mahogany. The lid and the two lower drawers have fine brasses.
Height 38″; width 26½″; depth 21″; height of writing surface 29″.

An impressive piece, the cw 168 Partner's Desk lends great dignity to a professional man's office. In a home, this desk distinguishes a library or study, and its double drawer space (front and back), allows husband and wife to have separate storage areas. The open arm chair (cw 171) is in the foreground, and the cw 164 Bookcase and cw 12 Wing Chair are in the background.

cw 168 *Partner's Desk*

This is a double desk, copied from an antique in the Colonial Williamsburg collection, with nine drawers identically placed front and back. It is also sectional, with the two pedestals separate from the top. The ormolu handles are of cast brass. Modesty panel optional. Available in two lengths.

cw 168 Height 32¼"; length 58¾"; width 40¼".

cw 168-68 Height 32¼"; length 68¾"; width 40¼".

English
Circa 1765
Chippendale
(George III)

89

CW 1 *Secretary Desk*

This slant-top secretary is a fine reproduction of an historic antique made in New England about 1770. Elegant and serviceable, there are several drawers and pockets on the desk level, and a bookcase unit on top. (Without the bookcase, the desk is CW 1½ which is illustrated on page 88.) The four large lower drawers and the lid are furnished with highly decorative brasses. The apron, too, is quite elaborate on both front and sides, and carries a shell carving (see detail on page 85). Altogether a piece of the finest inspiration. The original may be seen in the Williamsburg Information Center.

Height 61″; width 41½″; depth 20½″.

American
Circa 1770
Chippendale

Construction feature of the
CW 1 *Secretary Desk:*
Six dovetail tenons (1)
hold upper case (2) secure by
locking top to ends at pediment (3)

Shown here in a modern setting, this classic desk can be the focal point of many rooms. Also illustrated is its perfect complement, the CW 43 Chair. *"Williamsburg in a Contemporary Setting," designed by William E. Katzenbach, AID.*

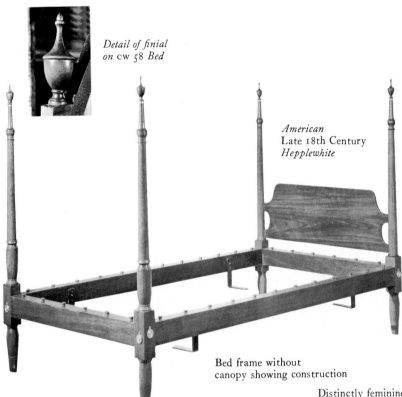

*Detail of finial
on cw 58 Bed*

*American
Late 18th Century
Hepplewhite*

Bed frame without
canopy showing construction

cw 58 *Double Bed*

This bed, with mahogany frame and maple side rails, is reproduced from a late eighteenth-century New England antique. Definitely a lighter construction than those made earlier in the century, the finely turned posts are small and the canopy frame light and arched. The bed can be used without a canopy, thus exposing the delicate finials; it is available either way. Particularly effective in, and complementing, a bedroom with feminine decor.
Height 58½″ (with canopy 77⅛″); width 59⅜″; length 81⅜″.

cw 58½ *Single Bed*

The bed described above is also available as a charming single bed.
Height 58½″ (with canopy 77⅛″; width 44⅜″; length 81⅜″.
Both beds use standard springs and mattresses.

Distinctly feminine, perhaps for the young lady growing up, this cw 58½ Single Bed has great charm. The ruffled canopy and bedskirt are Shir-O-Shakkar (page 128). The draperies are made of the delightful cotton fabric, Horse and Fox (page 129). The cw 68 Bachelor's Chest (left) and the cw 57 Table (right) are placed on either side of the bed. The canopy bed is a focal point, suitable to a small room.

American
Circa 1760–1775
Chippendale

*Detail of
claw-and-ball
foot on
cw 139 Bed*

Where space allows a gracious bedroom setting, a pair of cw 139½ twin beds gives great warmth and stateliness. Note the curved design in the canopy, a striking contrast to the bold multi-stripe fabric (page 127). Other *Williamsburg* items used to complete this room are the WA 1012 Wing Chair in the foreground, the cw 57 Table (between the beds) with a Wythe House Clock, the cw 2 Corner Table, and the cw 19 Lowboy on the far wall.

CW 139 *Double Bed*

The original of this four-poster canopy Chippendale bedstead was made in New England in the second half of the eighteenth century and is now in the Brush-Everard House in Williamsburg. Reproduced in solid mahogany, it has a flat canopy and tapered head posts united by an arched headboard. The foot posts are fluted and end in cabriole legs with bold claw-and-ball feet. Height 87¾"; width 61½"; length 82¼".

CW 139½ *Single Bed*

The handsome bedstead described above is also available as a single bed. Height 87¾"; width 46½"; length 82¼". Both beds use standard springs and mattresses

Bed frame showing construction

92

American
Circa 1780
Chippendale

Bed frame
showing construction

cw 170 and cw 170½ *Bed*

The original from which this bed has been copied is in the corner bedroom of the Peyton Randolph House. A Newport cabinetmaker fashioned it of mahogany about 1780. The elaboration of the front posts above the rails is unusual.

cw 170 Double Bed. Height 95¼"; length 82¾"; width 61⅜".

cw 170½ Single Bed. Height 95¼"; length 82¾"; width 46⅜".

American
Last Half
18th Century.

Bed frame showing construction

In this setting the WA 1003 bed has a coverlet of the fabric Pleasures of the Farm (page 128) with color related bed hangings of Country Linen (page 124).
The WA 1031 Bachelor's Chest is ideal at bedside with the Wythe House Clock and the L 19 Carolina Tobacco Jar Lamp.

WA 1003 *and* WA 1003½ *Half-Canopy Bed*
WA 1063 *and* WA 1063½ *Full-Canopy Bed*

These beds are adapted from an original made in New England and now on exhibit in the Raleigh Tavern. Beds of this type were produced in all the colonies in the eighteenth century and remained popular over a long period of time. The classic simplicity is ideal for today's living, as the bed fits in perfectly with both formal and informal furnishings of antique or modern design. Available as either a half-canopy or full-canopy bed.

WA 1003 Half-Canopy Bed (Double)
WA 1063 Full-Canopy Bed (Double) Height 79½"; width 56½"; length 79½".
WA 1003½ Half-Canopy Bed (Single)
WA 1063½ Full-Canopy Bed (Single) Height 79½"; width 41½"; length 79½".
WA 1003–60 Half-Canopy Bed (Queen Size)
WA 1063–60 Full-Canopy Bed (Queen Size) Height 79½"; width 63½"; length 85½".
Standard side rails for the WA 1003 and the WA 1003½ beds are 75". They are available, however, in 78" and 81" lengths at no additional cost.

WA 1034 *and* WA 1034½ *Low-Post Bed*

An antique bed made in Newport, Rhode Island, and now used in the Brush-Everard House, provided the precedent for this adaptation. The curved headboard and deep fluting on the posts are taken from the original.

WA 1034 Double Bed
Height 40¼"; length 79½"; width 56½".

WA 1034½ Single Bed
Height 40¼"; length 79½"; width 41½".

Both beds use standard springs and mattresses. Standard side rails for the WA 1034 and WA 1034½ beds are 75". They are available, however, in 78" and 81" lengths at no additional charge.

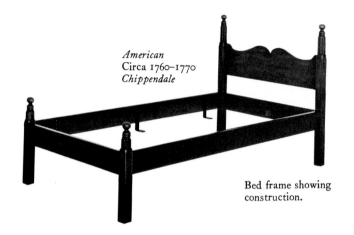

*American
Circa 1760–1770
Chippendale*

Bed frame showing
construction.

As important for the use of fabric—and its treatment—as for furnishings, this picture shows how a harmonious grouping can be achieved. The bedspread on the low-post bed (WA 1034½) and the window jabots are made of the attractive Potpourri fabric (page 130). The WA 1014 Table with the Chippendale mirror (AP 104) and companion wall bracket (AP 109) demonstrate the importance of form and shape. Also shown: L 3 Lamp, CW 7 Finger Bowl, C 40 Round Brick and Rolandson Prints (P 2 and P 3).

95

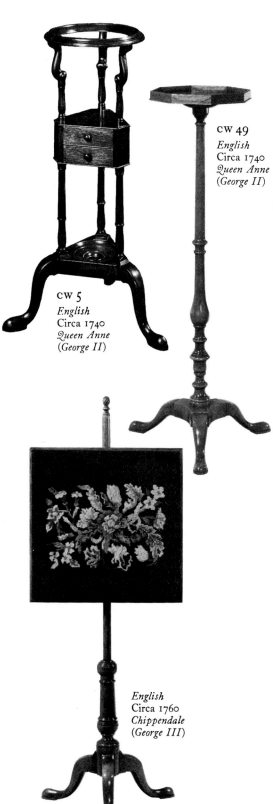

CW 49
English
Circa 1740
Queen Anne
(George II)

CW 149
English
Circa 1725–1730
Queen Anne
(George I)

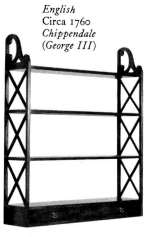

CW 182
English
Circa 1750
Queen Anne
(George II)

CW 5
English
Circa 1740
Queen Anne
(George II)

CW 182 *Kettle Stand*

The top of this small kettle stand was designed to hold a cup and saucer in front of a tea urn. The columnar pedestal has ring turnings at the top and an urn surmounted by a spiral twist below. It is supported on three cabriole legs terminating in pad feet. It was copied from an English antique made about 1750 that is on exhibit at the Peyton Randolph House.
Height 22¾"; top: large 12" diameter, small 4⅞" diameter.

CW 5 *Basin Stand*

This mahogany basin stand reproduces an antique now in the Governor's Palace in Williamsburg. Doubling nowadays as a charming indoor planter, the CW 9 Pewter Bowl fits into the rim of the stand.
Height 32"; diameter 11¾".

CW 49 *Candlestand*

This mahogany candlestand was copied from an English provincial antique in the Governor's Palace. It matches in detail the octagonal top, with gallery, the turned stem, and the tripod base of the original piece. Handsome with a trailing plant.
Height 38½"; top 10½" x 10½".

CW 149 *Kettle Stand*

This mahogany kettle stand with a spun copper top exactly copies an antique displayed in the dining room of the Brush-Everard House. Practical as a small moveable table or for a pot of hot-house flowers.
Height 21"; diameter 10".

English
Circa 1760
Chippendale
(George III)

English
Circa 1760
Chippendale
(George III)

English
Circa 1760
Chippendale
(George III)

CW 92 *Fire Screen*

An approved *Williamsburg* reproduction of an antique English fire screen now in the George Wythe House, the stand, frame, and finial are of mahogany. A charming and decorative period piece.
Height 47½"; panel 17¼" x 17¾".

CW 37 *Hanging Shelf*

This mahogany hanging shelf, a typical Thomas Chippendale design, is a reproduction of an old stand of bookshelves now used in the Governor's Palace. The four shelves and two convenient drawers are united by upright ends of delicate fretwork.
Height 39"; width 36"; depth 7".

WA 1038 *Shelf*

A fine mahogany adaptation of a typical Chippendale piece. Four shelves and a drawer are supported by openwork ends which terminate in fine scroll crestings. Available also in painted finish.
Height 34"; width 30"; depth 7".

WA 1038-24

Same as above, but 24" wide.

Williamsburg Furniture Reproductions and Adaptations

Furniture Reproductions

Finish samples available upon request.

		Standard Finish	Heirloom Finish	Ancient Heirloom Finish				Standard Finish	Heirloom Finish	Ancient Heirloom Finish
CW1	Secretary Desk......	$2,415	$2,550	$2,685		CW117	Gate-leg Table.......	$1,120	$1,175	$1,230
CW1½	Desk...............	1,900	2,000	2,100		CW134	Drop-leaf Table......	680	710	740
CW2	Corner Table.......	485	510	535		CW135	Oval Tilt-top Table...	300	315	330
CW3	Card Table.........	550	575	600		CW139	Double Bed..........	1,330	1,390	1,450
CW5	Basin Stand........	455	475	495		CW139½	Single Bed..........	1,310	1,370	1,430
CW8	Tea Table...........	540	570	600		CW141	Flap-top Table.......	595	620	645
CW11	Revolving Tilt-Top Table.............	380	400	420		CW145	Dressing Table.......	935	990	1,045
CW18	Chest..............	1,025	1,080	1,135		CW148	Sideboard...........	1,320	1,400	1,480
CW19	Lowboy.............	1,560	1,650	1,740		CW149	Kettle Stand........	215	225	235
CW20	Tilt-top Table.......	260	270	280		CW150	Card Table..........	625	665	705
CW27	Pembroke Table......	630	660	690		CW153	Highboy............	2,000	2,110	2,220
CW33	Dining Room Table, Center Section.....	905	950	995		CW155	Serving Table........	935	980	1,025
CW34	Dining Room Table, End Section.......	430	450	470		CW156	Card Table..........	1,055	1,095	1,135
	(1 CW33 and 2 CW34)	1,765	1,850	1,935		CW158	Breakfront Bookcase (add $280 for electrification).....	5,500	5,700	5,900
CW37	Hanging Shelf........	595	625	655		CW160	Table...............	615	650	685
CW49	Candlestand.........	245	255	265		CW161	Revolving Table.....	735	775	815
CW57	Table...............	620	650	680		CW162	Cellarette...........	700	735	770
CW58	Double Bed..........	810	850	890		CW164	Bookcase............	2,275	2,390	2,510
CW58½	Single Bed...........	795	830	865		CW167	Table...............	655	690	725
	Canopy Frame.....	125	—	—		CW168	Partners' Desk.......	3,100	3,200	3,300
CW65	Dining Table, Center Section, 48".......	810	850	890		CW168–68	Partners' Desk L. 68¾"	3,500	3,625	3,750
CW66	Dining Table, End Section, 48"........	690	725	760		CW169	Secretary Bookcase...	4,540	4,750	4,960
	(1 Center, 2 Ends & 2 leaves, 48")......	2,450	2,580	2,710		CW169½	Slant Front Desk.....	2,510	2,650	2,790
	(2 Ends & 1 Leaf, 48")	1,510	1,590	1,670		CW170	Double Bed..........	1,215	1,275	1,335
	(2 Ends & 2 Leaves with support, 48")..	1,690	1,780	1,870		CW170½	Single Bed...........	1,195	1,255	1,315
CW68	Bachelor's Chest.....	820	860	900		CW172	Corner Table........	450	470	490
CW69	Square Tilt-top Table.	385	400	415		CW176	Chest...............	1,485	1,550	1,615
CW70	Tilt-Top Table.......	655	690	725		CW177	Dining Table, Drop-Leaf Center Section four square corners.	1,480	1,550	1,620
CW87	Sideboard...........	990	1,035	1,080		CW177–RC	Dining Table, Drop-Leaf, four round corners.......	1,480	1,550	1,620
CW92	Firescreen (one-half yard fabric required)	295	310	325		CW178	Dining Table, Drop-Leaf End Section, two square and two round corners......	1,480	1,550	1,620
						CW179	Tea Table...........	480	510	540
						CW181	Sideboard...........	1,885	1,975	2,065
						CW182	Kettle Stand........	285	295	305

All prices include shipping charges within the Continental United States and are subject to change without notice.

Upholstered Furniture Reproductions

Muslin prices of upholstered pieces include the cost of applying fabric provided by the purchaser. Yardage requirements of plain or small over-all patterns are listed below. Also listed below are prices of these particular pieces upholstered in top grain leather. Samples of leather and upholstery fabrics available upon request.

		Fabric Required 50"	Muslin Price	Upholstered in Top Grain Leather— Standard Finish	Extra Charge Heirloom Finish	Extra Charge Ancient Heirloom Finish
*CW12	Wing Chair	5	$ 595	$ 961	$15	$30
CW13	His Lordship's Chair	3	525	716	15	30
CW14	Arm Chair	2½	580	779	15	30
CW16	Chair	⅔	550	589	20	40
CW17	Chair	¾	495	538	20	40
CW17½	Arm Chair	¾	625	672	25	50
*CW23	Sofa	8½	1,160	1,686	20	40
CW43	Smoking Chair	1¾	625	745	20	40
*CW44	Wing Chair	5½	730	1,122	15	30
CW47	Arm Chair	† ¾	585	615	25	50
CW47½	Side Chair	† ¾	435	465	20	40
CW67	Side Chair	1¾	570	713	15	30
*CW104	Wing Chair	5½	760	1,152	15	30
*CW118	Sofa	10½	1,150	1,904	20	40
CW128	Side Chair	1½	495	621	15	30
CW129	Sofa	6¾	1,095	1,621	15	30
CW136	Corner Chair	¾	490	524	25	50
CW142	Side Chair	† ¾	600	630	20	40
CW142½	Arm Chair	† ¾	695	734	25	50
CW146	Side Chair	† ⅔	700	730	25	50
CW147	Bench	¾	290	338	15	30
CW151	Open Arm Chair	¾	750	780	25	50
CW152	Open Arm Chair	2½	540	697	20	40
CW154	Settee	5	1,030	1,354	25	50
*CW163	Wing Chair	7	740	1,216	15	30
*CW166	Barrell Chair	5	610	975	5	10
CW171	Open Arm Chair	2½	420	561	15	30
CW174	Sofa	11½	2,050	—	25	50
CW180	Side Chair	† ¾	850	880	25	50

*Prices quoted above are for hair pad cushions. These pieces are also available with cushions filled with 50% goose down and 50% goose feathers, or 80% goose down and 20% goose feathers, at the following additional charges:

		50/50 cushion	80/20 cushion
CW12	Chair	$ 40	$ 50
CW23	Sofa	100	120
CW44	Chair	40	50
CW104	Chair	40	50
CW118	Sofa	120	150
CW163	Chair	40	50
CW166	Chair	40	50

†Enough fabric for two chairs.

Furniture Adaptations
(Finish samples available upon request)

		Standard Finish	Old Virginia Finish	Painted Finish
WA1002	Chest of Drawers....	$ 495	$ 525	$ 525
WA1003	Canopy Bed, Double.	375	395	395
WA1003½	Canopy Bed, Single..	355	375	375
WA1003-60	Canopy Bed, Queen size	450	470	470
WA1004	Table	310	330	330
WA1006	Pembroke Table	330	350	350
WA1008	Chest of Drawers....	650	685	—
WA1009	Table	210	220	220
WA1010	Table	210	220	220
WA1014	Table	220	230	230
WA1017-1	Sideboard	910	950	—
WA1020	Drop-leaf Table	315	345	—
WA1022	Drop-leaf Table	440	465	465
WA1024	Serving Table	380	395	395
WA1026	Drop-leaf Table	560	590	—
WA1029	Table	190	200	200
WA1030	Commode	315	335	335
WA1031	Bachelor's Chest	525	560	560
WA1033	Coffee Table	375	400	400
WA1034	Double Bed	355	375	375
WA1034½	Single Bed	335	355	355
WA1035	Coffee Table	350	365	365
WA1037	Desk	595	625	625
WA1038	Shelf	325	340	340
WA1038-24	Shelf	310	325	325
WA1039	Tea Table	200	230	230
WA1041	Sideboard	710	765	—
WA1042	Coffee Table	225	235	235
WA1043	Pedestal Dining Table, Center Section	505	550	—
WA1044	Pedestal Dining Table, End Section	470	515	—
	(1 Center, 2 Ends and 2 Leaves)	1,655	1,810	—
	(2 Ends and 1 Leaf)	1,045	1,145	—
	(2 Ends and 2 Leaves with support)....	1,215	1,325	—
WA1049	Console End	260	285	—
	(2 WA 1049 Ends and 1 WA 1026 Center)	1,080	1,160	—
WA1050	Double Chest	1,700	1,800	—
WA1057	Porringer Table	275	305	305
WA1058	Table	290	320	320
WA1059	Table	420	460	—
WA1060	Chest	750	850	—
WA1063	Double Bed	450	470	—
WA1063½	Single Bed	415	440	—
WA1063-60	Queen Size Bed	515	545	—
WA1066	Table	210	220	220

Upholstered Furniture Adaptations

Muslin prices of upholstered pieces include the cost of applying fabric provided by the purchaser. Yardage requirements of plain or small over-all patterns are listed below. Also listed below are prices of these particular pieces upholstered in top grain leather. Samples of leather and upholstery fabrics available upon request.

		Fabric Required 50"	Muslin Price	Upholstered in Top Grain Leather— Standard Finish	Extra Charge Old Virginia Finish	Extra Charge Painted Finish
WA1005	Sofa	9½	$775	$1,445	$12	$—
WA1011	Open Arm Chair	2½	310	477	8	—
WA1012	Wing Chair	6½	475	909	8	—
WA1016	Bench	¾	135	163	15	—
WA1018	Side Chair	⅔	210	243	20	—
WA1019	Side Chair	¾	235	273	20	20
WA1025	Open Arm Chair	3	370	592	8	—
*WA1040	Ladies Chair	1¾	395	536	15	—
*WA1046	Side Chair	1½	295	395	8	—
*WA1047	Wing Chair	6	470	883	8	—
WA1048	Side Chair	¾	210	248	20	—
*WA1055	Love Seat	7¾	625	1,164	10	—
WA1056	Open Arm Chair	2½	395	623	20	—
WA1118	Arm Chair	⅔	300	334	25	—
WA1119	Arm Chair	¾	325	364	25	25
WA1148	Arm Chair	¾	300	339	25	—

*Prices quoted above are for foam rubber cushions. These pieces are also available with cushions filled with 50% goose down and 50% goose feathers, or 80% goose down and 20% goose feathers, at the following additional charges:

	50/50 cushion	80/20 cushion
WA1005 Sofa	$75	$105
WA1012 Chair	25	35
WA1047 Chair	25	35
WA1055 Love Seat	50	70

Williamsburg Federal Furniture
Reproductions and Adaptations

THE CAPITAL OF VIRGINIA was moved to Richmond in 1780, and, as a result, Williamsburg ceased to be the center of political and social activity it had been during the previous three-quarters of a century. Not unexpectedly, population declined and prosperity waned, but the town did not fold up and die. In fact, several of the largest and most attractive houses surviving in Williamsburg today date from the last decades of the eighteenth century and the early years of the nineteenth. Among these are the Semple House on Francis Street, built before 1782, which was described in 1807 as "the handsomest house in town;" the rambling St. George Tucker House, constructed principally between 1788 and 1795; the brick Norton-Cole House on Market Square built between 1809 and 1812; and the spacious Coke-Garrett House near the Public Gaol, which was built in the nineteenth century, except for the eighteenth-century west wing.

While undoubtedly some of the furnishings of these newly constructed houses were in the earlier styles of the eighteenth century, by the 1790s examples of the new, classically inspired furniture styles popularized by Hepplewhite and Sheraton were to be found in Williamsburg. For this reason Colonial Williamsburg in recent years has acquired pieces of Federal furniture and accessories made before 1830, the generally accepted date for the beginning of the machine manufacture of furniture. Many of these items were chosen to furnish rooms in the Coke-Garrett House, now the official residence of Colonial Williamsburg's president.

Presented here are nineteen examples of furniture in the Federal style. Each is derived from an antique object in the Williamsburg collection, and every piece is faithfully copied by present-day craftsmen. Each object reflects the delicacy and lightness so characteristic of the Federal style, relying for its beauty on simplicity of line and form, embellished with exciting contrasts of inlay and veneer, rather than on the ornate curves and heavy carving of the preceding Chippendale style. This new collection enables Colonial Williamsburg to present a broader interpretation of life in Williamsburg, extending beyond the colonial period into the exciting early years of our national history.

The stately Coke-Garrett House is a blend of architectural styles and details representing a period from the mid-eighteenth century through the first third of the nineteenth century. The central portion was added in the 1830s. The house is furnished primarily in fine examples of American Federal furniture of the period 1780–1830 chosen by a team of historians, curators, and scholars. Selected pieces recently added to the Williamsburg Reproduction Program are illustrated and described on the following pages.

The fine examples of Federal furniture illustrated in this section are now being developed by the Kittinger Company. All pieces shown are the originals unless otherwise identified.

American
Circa 1810
Hepplewhite

cw 311 *Table*

Inside the lower drawer of the original of this small, two-drawer table is the cabinetmaker's label. Made by Matthew Egerton, Jr. of New Brunswick, New Jersey, about 1800, it was originally intended as a sewing or worktable, but today it would serve perfectly as a bedside table or small lamp table. The recessed front visually lightens the overall effect of the piece. The reproduction is illustrated on the right.
Height 28½"; width 19"; depth 19⅝".

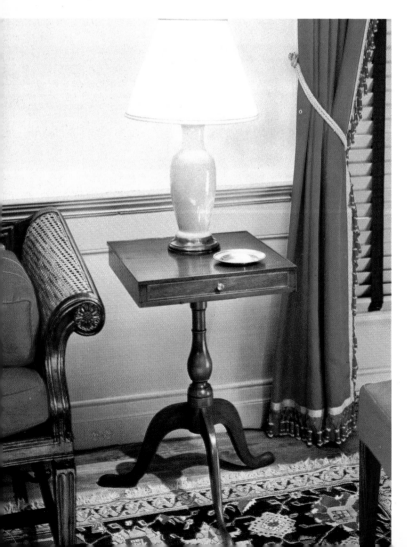

wa 3000 *Table*

The utility of this small stand is enhanced by the drawer in the top, an unusual feature. Essentially designed in an earlier style, the thin band of inlay outlining the drawer indicates it was made about 1790. The original was made of cherry, probably in Connecticut. The reproduction is on the left.
Height 25⅝"; width 16¼"; depth 16⅛".

American
Circa 1790
Hepplewhite

American
Circa 1800
Sheraton

American
Circa 1795
Hepplewhite

CW 316 *Table*

Small stands of this type are extremely versatile. With the top up they can be used to hold lamps, for serving drinks, and in many other ways. When not in use, the top can be folded down and the table placed against a wall where it takes up little space. This example, based on an original made in New York, is distinguished by fluted classical urn at the base of its pedestal.
Height 26¾"; length 18½"; width 18¾".

WA 3002 *Table*

The Federal period was noted for the variety of small, useful tables produced in its various cabinetmaking centers. One of the most important of these was Baltimore, where the original of this superb inlaid and veneered worktable was produced. Originally intended to hold sewing implements, it would be useful today as an end table or small bedside dressing table.
Height 30"; length 21"; width 19⅛".

American
Circa 1810
Sheraton

CW 314 *Table*

Small tables or stands with folding tops were made in the Queen Anne and Chippendale periods, and their popularity continued unabated into the early years of the nineteenth century. The work of an unknown New York cabinetmaker, the clover-leaf top, classical urn pedestal, and flared, reeded legs of the original of this example indicate it was made about 1800. The reproduction is on the left.
Height 28½″; length 25″; width 17⅜″.

American
Circa 1810
Sheraton

CW 313 *Nest of Tables*

Several new furniture forms were introduced during the Federal period. One of the most useful was the nest of tables. Ideal for use at parties and other social functions, when not in use these tables can be stacked unobtrusively in a corner and still present an attractive appearance. Like the English originals, the tops of these faithful copies are made of highly-figured rosewood.
Height 29⅜″ set; width 23 1/16″ set; depth 13″ set.

CW 318 *Table*

Card or gaming tables were one of the most popular forms of furniture in the Federal period and were made in great variety. The Massachusetts original on which this copy is based reveals most of the basic features of the Federal style: the elaborate use of cross-banded veneers and inlays, the lightness but strength of the overall construction, and the shaped, reeded legs terminating in high, delicately-turned feet. Useful for bridge or other card games, this table also looks well as a side or console table with its top folded against a wall. A pair of these tables is handsome when used in this manner.
Height 30⅜″; width 37⅝″; depth 17⅝″ closed, 35¼″ open.

English
Circa 1800
Empire

CW 309 *Table*

The Federal period was an era of change, not only in design but in mechanical innovation as well. This folding card table, based on an original in the Colonial Williamsburg collection attributed to the New York workshop of Duncan Phyfe, demonstrates new techniques of design and construction. The acanthus carving of the central pedestal is based closely on ancient classical design. The clover-leaf top and brass lion-paw feet are innovative features of the new style. When the folding top is closed, the table sits flat against a wall; when open, the two side legs swing to the rear to provide support for the top. Height 28⅞"; width 36"; depth 18" closed, 36" open.

CW 308 *Chair*

One of the features of the later Federal style was a reliance on architecturally correct copies of ancient Greek and Roman furniture. The English maker who crafted this graceful armchair about 1810 copied almost literally the design of an ancient Greek Klismos chair, but he updated it by painting it green and caning the seat and back. The running Greek key design on the front seat rail further underscores the reliance of the makers of Federal furniture on classical motifs.
Height 33"; width 21⅞"; over-all depth 22⅝".

English
Circa 1800
Early Empire

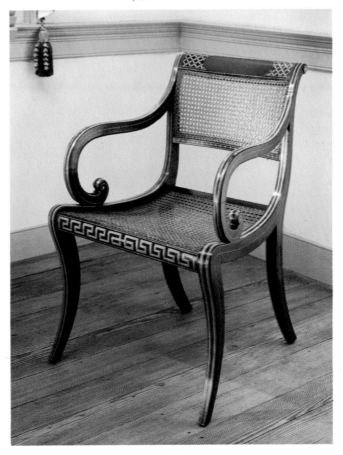

American
Circa 1815
Duncan Phyfe

American
Circa 1800
Hepplewhite

cw 300 *Sideboard*

The original of this finely detailed sideboard was made in South Carolina about 1800 and presently graces the dining room of the Coke-Garrett House. Of conventional form, the piece is distinguished by a virtual vocabulary of classically inspired inlaid motifs—husks, flutes, paterae—each meticulously done in holly against a figured mahogany ground. The reproduction is to the right above.
Height 36″; length 72″; depth 27⅝″.

cw 312 *Desk Table*

Many pieces of Federal furniture can be used a variety of ways. Made in Baltimore about 1810 by the noted cabinetmaker John Needle, the original of this piece was probably intended as a dressing table. Today it could serve its original purpose in a bedroom, or it could be used as a desk or as a small sideboard in a dining room. Each detail of the original has been faithfully copied.
Height 36⅝″; width 37¼″; depth 19½″.

American
Circa 1812
Hepplewhite

American
Circa 1800
Hepplewhite

cw 304 *Chair*

This is an unusual but extremely useful chair. It retains the clean, straight lines of Martha Washington type chairs such as CW 307, and also incorporates padded and rolled arms such as those on easy chair CW 305 for added comfort. The original was made in New England about 1800. The reproduction is to the left.
Height 44¼″; width 28¼″; over-all depth 26½″; arm height 25″.

American
Circa 1800
Hepplewhite

cw 305 *Chair*

Few easy chairs were made in the Federal period, as the form was almost out of fashion by the end of the eighteenth century. The Baltimore cabinetmaker who made the original from which this copy is derived admirably succeeded in lightening the essentially heavy lines of the form by banding the skirt of the front and sides in mahogany and inlaying the tapering front legs with boxwood husks.
Height 44½″; width 31¾″; over-all depth 33″; arm height 26½″.

English
Circa 1790
Sheraton

CW 315 *Canterbury*

Introduced in the Federal period as a rack to hold large folios of music, the canterbury remains essentially unchanged in form today. It can still be used for its original purpose, as well as to store and display magazines and large books so that they are readily at hand. This fine mahogany example copied from an original English canterbury looks well beside an easy chair or sofa. The reproduction is shown on the right.
Height 23″; length 20″; width 15⅞″.

American
Circa 1800
Hepplewhite

CW 307 *Chair*

The term "Martha Washington" used to describe a chair of this design is a modern one, but it accurately reflects the period when graceful chairs like this one were first made. The high back, flowing lines, and an overall feeling of lightness and delicacy are hallmarks of the Federal style superbly reflected in this example, copied from a Massachusetts chair made about 1800.
Height 43⅝″; width 25⅞″; over-all depth 27″; arm height 26⅜″.

American
Circa 1810
Sheraton

CW 303 *Sofa*

The compact proportions of this sofa greatly enhance its usefulness. Unusual features are the inlaid panels of bird's-eye maple
on the back crest rail. This is a faithful duplication of the original
Salem, Massachusetts, piece now in the Coke-Garrett House.
The reproduction is illustrated above.
Height 34⅜″; length 60⅛″; over-all depth 23¾″; arm height
28⅜″.

American
Circa 1810
Sheraton

CW 301 *Sofa*

The basic design of this sofa may be found in Thomas Shera
The Cabinet-Maker and Upholsterer's Drawing Book, first publi
in London in 1793. The Massachusetts craftsman who mad
original from which this copy is derived was obviously fam
with Sheraton's classic design as evidenced by the turned, v
shaped arm supports and the tapering, fluted legs.
Height 39½″; length 68″; over-all depth 28½″.

CW 306 *Secretary*

Few examples of furniture in the Colonial Williamsburg collection better exemplify the Federal style than this delicate secretary bookcase with the overall lightness of its design, the extensive use of the best crotch veneer and lightwood inlays, and the reverse-painted glass panels on its doors. Behind the doors of the upper section are seven pigeonholes and three drawers. The shelves are adjustable, and the folding writing surface of the lower section is lined with cabinet cloth. The brilliantly conceived original was made in Boston and its features have been faithfully copied in this meticulous reproduction.

Height 74¼"; width 37½"; depth 21⅜".

American
Circa 1810
Sheraton

American
Circa 1810
Hepplewhite

CW 302 *Bookcase*

The basic design of this winged breakfront bookcase is closely related to similar pieces made during the Chippendale period. However, the unknown Boston cabinetmaker who executed the original about 1800 has lightened the overall effect by a sparing use of wood. The influence of the Gothic Revival, which was introduced during the Federal period, can be seen in the pointed arches at the top of each door.
Height 87¼"; length 61¾"; depth 17⅜".

PRICE LIST

(*November 1, 1973*)

Williamsburg Federal Furniture

Furniture Reproductions

CW300 Sideboard—*Available* 1974

CW301 Sofa—*Available* 1974

CW302 Bookcase—*Available* 1974

CW303 Sofa—*Available* 1974

CW304 Chair—*Available* 1974

CW305 Chair—*Available* 1974

CW306 Secretary—*Available* 1974

CW307 Chair—*Available* 1974

CW308 Chair—*Available* 1974

CW309 Table—*Available* 1974

CW311 Table—*Available* 1974

CW312 Desk Table—*Available* 1974

CW313 Nest of Tables—*Available* 1974

CW314 Table—*Available* 1974

CW315 Canterbury—*Available* 1974

CW316 Table—*Available* 1974

CW318 Table—*Available* 1974

Furniture Adaptations

WA3000 Table—*Available* 1974

WA3002 Table—*Available* 1974

Williamsburg
Fabrics, Bedspreads and Wall Coverings

VISITORS to the exhibition buildings of Williamsburg never fail to be impressed by the rich and varied use of fabrics and decorative wallpapers. These wall, bed and window coverings maintain a long tradition in the colonial capital. Subdued or exuberant, simple or exotic, they established the background and set the tone for Williamsburg's historic rooms. The same fabrics and papers can lend a dramatic flair to contemporary rooms, whether they are to be part of a period decor or of one strikingly modern. They combine an eighteenth-century decorative genius with the timelessness of beauty and utility.

Wall and window hangings were designed as much to exclude cold and drafts from the room as to beautify it. For the same purpose, the colonial housewife often provided her tall post beds with a substantial array of hangings, in many cases matching the window fabrics. In today's bedrooms a similarly handsome effect is achieved by bedspreads that match or complement the window hangings.

In medieval times tapestries were hung over bare stone walls to give protection against the damp. In later centuries, as construction methods improved, these heavy, thick tapestries gave way to rich silk damasks, especially in the more elegant public and private settings. Hand-painted and hand-blocked wallpapers came into use around the time of Williamsburg's origins and extremely fine examples were to be found on the walls of some houses during the eighteenth century. A Chinese wallpaper of later date used in the supper room of the Governor's Palace is now available in a magnificent adaptation.

Williamsburg Fabrics are produced for Craft House by F. Schumacher and Company of New York City, and wallpapers by Katzenbach and Warren, Incorporated, also of New York City. Together, these firms have produced for the Reproductions Program a group of *Williamsburg* color-related fabrics and wallpapers. *Williamsburg* bedspreads are produced exclusively by Bates Fabrics, Incorporated, of New York City, in several patterns and a wide selection of colors.

The originals of these fabric and wallpaper designs have been gleaned from a variety of sources. Surviving examples of textiles, furniture coverings, bedspreads and damask window hangings are available for copying. Scraps of wallpaper turn up as lining of trunks or bible boxes where, protected from the light, colors have lasted undiminished. Paintings of the period show designs and colors, and drawings, prints and advertisements give further models. In restoring Williamsburg homes successive layers of wallpaper have been recovered by careful soaking and peeling.

Whereas the Williamsburg furniture tradition is English and American, it is not surprising that the ladies of colonial times looked also to France for their curtains and coverings as well as their frills and furbelows. Readers of this section will soon discover the French inspiration of many of the designs, for this was also the age of Aubusson wall hangings and rugs.

The curatorial staff of Williamsburg has made the identification and use of eighteenth-century fabrics a scientific and artistic life's work. In the restoration of a room, the nature of the background decoration is of overwhelming importance. The same considerations apply to furnishing today's rooms: Color, material and design all enter in, and the function of a room—whether sitting room, bedroom, dining room, even kitchen, den or playroom—helps to determine the choice. Then comes the mood that is desired: formal or informal, simple or elegant. Silk materials enhance the effect of a formal or elaborate decor; cotton may be used to emphasize a simpler or lighter mood. Thus, in the Palace ballroom in Williamsburg, summer hangings are made of Jones Toile—a printed cotton fabric with a charming pastoral design as illustrated in the catalogue. It is well known that larger rooms can use patterns that are bold in color and design, whereas the size of small rooms is enhanced by small and restrained designs.

Williamsburg Fabrics, faithfully reflecting the originals, come in a wealth of materials. There are the finest cottons (calicos and glazed chintzes); linens, (plain and printed); and gorgeous silks woven as damask, satin and velvet, each with its particular beauty and utility; and woolens woven into elaborate damask, as well as into simpler designs. Today, as in past centuries, weavers combine cotton and flax, cotton and silk, and cotton and wool for special effects.

The heavier materials are particularly suitable for the formal hangings of a sitting room or dining room, for upholstery, or for bed coverings. The lighter materials serve especially well in bedrooms, study or playrooms, or to mark a seasonal change in other rooms.

In addition to the restored homes and public buildings of Williamsburg that are open to the public, many privately occupied homes demonstrate a most felicitous free mixing of wall and window fabrics of colonial derivation in a variety of settings, together with paintings and accessories that know no period. These homes, some of which are illustrated in color in this catalogue, provide an abundance of decorating ideas that readers may wish to apply to their own homes and decor. For a formally appointed dining room or a casual sun room or parlor, an immense range of fabrics and wallpapers in colors and designs that have stood the test of time give unlimited opportunities for choice.

How Windows Are Treated

Reference has already been made to the selection of fabrics for a given room, considerations which apply also to the kind of wallpaper used. The practical treatment of windows is a matter for which Williamsburg provides a number of precedents. There are three basic types of window treatment:

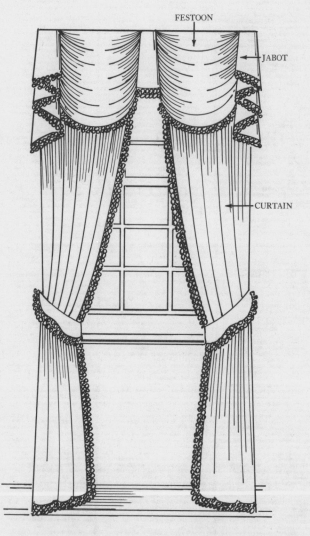

In the first, festoons and jabots (which are side frills) are placed over the floor-length curtains.

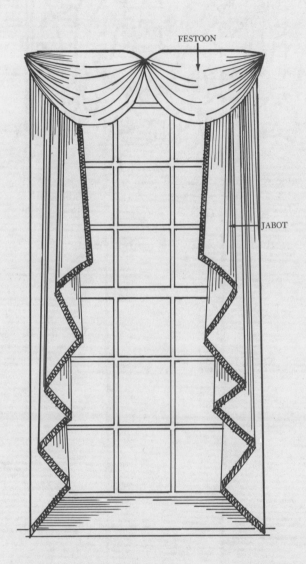

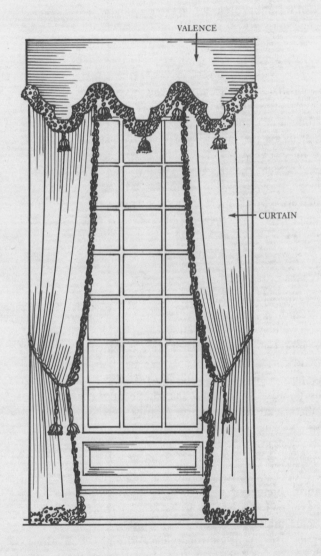

In the second, there are festoons and jabots only, and the jabots hang to the window sill or chair rail.

In the third, there is a more or less elaborately shaped valance covered by material. Curtains generally reach to the floor, although Williamsburg has many examples of valance treatment with curtains reaching to the window sill only.

Festoons

The number of festoons depends on the width of the window. In Williamsburg where windows are only 3½ feet wide there are two festoons, each of two feet or less (festoons may overlap).

The number of folds in the festoon determines the degree of formality; many folds convey depth and richness while few folds give a sense of lightness.

Curtains

Floor-length curtains are always elegant and formal, while hangings to the window sill are informal and at the same time functional, for they keep the curtains away from the floor in an area much used, or difficult to clean.

The most pleasing curtain effects are given by 100% fullness, which means that curtain width should be double that of the window. Most fabrics measure approximately 50 inches; a pair of curtains for a window four feet wide, therefore, requires two widths, one for each curtain.

Valances

Valances are subject to many variations. An elaborately shaped and deep valance like the one illustrated in Figure 5, which is in the dining room of the Governor's Palace represents one extreme, and conveys a sense of grandeur with ornateness. Valances used in less formal settings in Williamsburg are illustrated in a series of designs (a to f, page 99). The shape of the valance is also subtly related to the pattern and type of fabric used. A simple valance calls for cottons and small patterns, an intricate design for damasks, a bold design for large fabric patterns.

The proper length of a valance is determined partly by the fabric—longer if it is to accommodate a large and bold pattern, for example. Color is important because a dark color makes a valance seem smaller, a light color larger, in size. A decorator rule of thumb is to allow overall 1½″ to 1¾″ for each foot of window height, modified by the above considerations.

Trimmings

Effects, either formal or informal, can be obtained by trimming in the form of fringe, binding, or braid. When used, the trimming should relate to an important color in the fabric. The more ornate velvet and damask hangings are usually trimmed, both in valance and festoon as well as the curtains themselves. Ruffles, of course, always suggest lightness and a touch of frivolity.

Other Features

When maximum light is needed from the window, valances should be kept high up and shallow, and curtains, when drawn back, should not encroach too much on the window panes. Valances should cover everything at the top, including Venetian blind boxes, and should also extend close to the ceiling or molding.

Williamsburg Window Treatments

In the examples to follow, we see how the designers have treated selected windows in the homes of Colonial Williamsburg. These offer to the homemaker and decorator multiple suggestions of desirable effects to be obtained in one's own rooms.

Figures 1 to 12 illustrate the many combinations in actual use in Williamsburg.

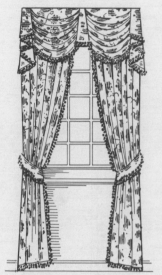

Figure 1

Craft House Dining Room
Formal. Multi-folded festoons and jabots over floor-length curtains. All are trimmed with fringes.

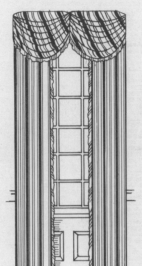

Figure 2

Brush-Everard House
Fringe on multi-folded festoon and curtain. Formal treatment.

Figure 3

Daphne Room, Raleigh Tavern
Multi-pleated festoon with jabots to window sill. Edges fringed in color of fabric.

Figure 4

Wythe House Hall
Jabots extend to chair rail and so complement an architectural feature of the room.

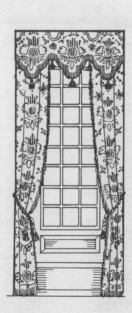

Figure 5

Dining Room, Governor's Palace
Elaborate valance with three deep scallops. Large patterned fabric determines height of valance. Heavy trimmings for a sumptuous effect.

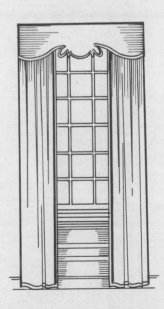

Figure 6

Northeast Bedroom of Wythe House
Shaped valance with plain fabric is formal but simple. Binding at edge of valance and front and bottom of curtains.

115

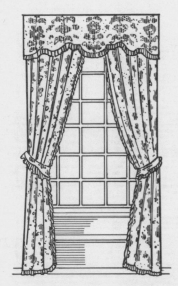

Figure 7

Living Room, Craft House
Shaped valance with designed fabric for a formal setting.

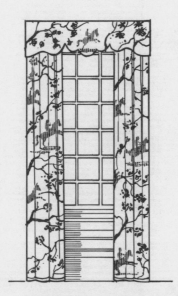

Figure 8

Northwest Bedroom of Wythe House
Shaped valance with designed fabric. Binding at edge of valance and curtains reflect dominant color of pattern. The whole gives a semi-formal effect.

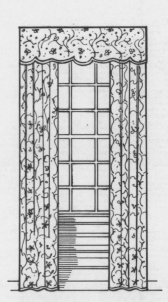

Figure 9

Northwest Bedroom of Wythe House
Informal winter draperies in cotton fabric. Simple valance.

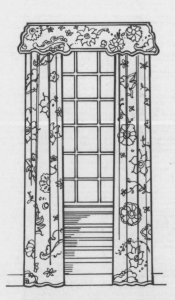

Figure 10

Southeast Bedroom of Wythe House
Bold free cotton fabric makes valance appear less formal in spite of its details.

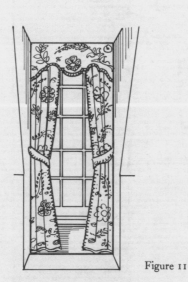

Figure 11

Dormer in Southwest Bedroom of Brush-Everard House
Short draperies may be enhanced by bold valance and fabric.

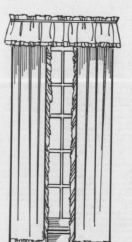

Figure 12

Dormer in Raleigh Tavern Bedroom
Simple valance with pleated material and bold trimming.

Typical Valance Designs used in Colonial Williamsburg

a. A soft-shaped valance of regular and inverted scallops. This relatively informal design calls for a small-patterned or figured fabric.

b. A more formal valance than *a*, and more suitable for a fabric with a large design.

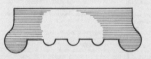

c. "Dog ear" valance, an English design. It is suited to fabrics with an over-all or flowing pattern.

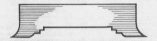

d. A more formal "dog ear" valance with an oriental motif in its pagoda shape. The design is used in the Wythe House parlor and is most appropriate for a formal fabric.

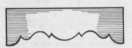

e. A Chippendale-type design. This valance is suitable with a large-patterned formal fabric.

f. A design in the European style. Large-patterned fabrics are suitable here.

g. A transitional shape. This valance is adaptable to most fabrics, whether the design is an over-all or a definite pattern.

h. A versatile design taken from an antique in the Williamsburg collection. It is suitable for a plain or small-patterned fabric.

i. Soft festoons calling for a damask or similar formal fabric. The shape is influenced by French designs of the eighteenth century.

j. A treatment similar to Jefferson's sketches of hangings at Monticello. This festoon and jabot design is formal and best suited to damasks.

k. A less formal treatment using festoons alone. This valance design can be adapted to most fabrics.

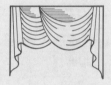

l. A very formal, heavily draped treatment with a French feeling. It is late-eighteenth-century and is most often used with damasks.

m. A single shirred valance. This simple, easy-to-make design is appropriate for an informal fabric.

Correct Method for Measuring the Most Usual Kinds of Windows

A. EXTREME WIDTH
B. INSIDE WIDTH
C. TOP OF TRIM TO CEILING
D. EXTREME HEIGHT
E. INSIDE HEIGHT
F. SILL TO FLOOR
G. RETURN

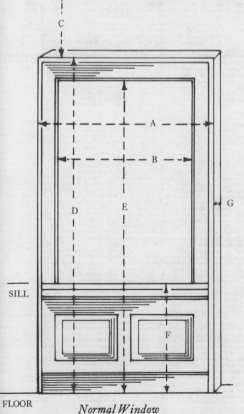
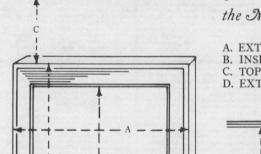

Normal Window

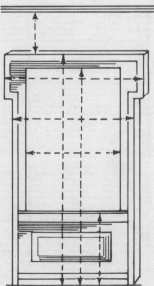

Crossetted Window

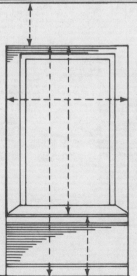

Casement Window

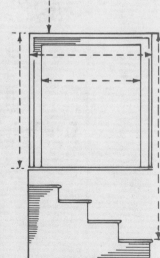

Stairway Window

Bed Hangings

The ideal treatment for beds can be seen in the Craft House and in the upper bedrooms of the Wythe House where the valances at the top of canopy beds have the same design as the window valance. Generally window fabrics are repeated in those of the bed. On field beds (those with a strongly arched canopy) gathered or shirred valances give a light, informal effect and this can be repeated at the windows.

The dressing of a bed, tall post or not, requires careful attention to the bedspread. It may complement or relate to the bed or window hangings. Solid color bedspreads may be used with printed fabrics in any decor.

Ordering
Williamsburg
Fabrics, Bedspreads and Wallpapers

Color samples of all *Williamsburg* Fabrics are available on request; cotton samples (2″ x 6″) ten cents per pattern with full color range included; damask samples (3″ x 6″) fifty cents deposit per sample. Large samples of all fabrics are also available on a loan basis; a deposit equivalent to the price per yard is requested. All deposits are refunded when samples are returned.

In addition to the authentic wallpaper reproductions, wallpapers commemorating Williamsburg art and life are available in a number of colors.

Most *Williamsburg* Wallpapers are manufactured with a protective stain-resistant coating for use in bathroom, kitchen, and nursery and are pretrimmed for ease in hanging.

A large wallpaper catalogue will be sent on loan for a $6.00 deposit plus $2.25 mailing charge. Deposit will be refunded if the catalogue is returned within 30 days. For those who wish to keep the catalogue for a longer period there is an additional charge of $14.00.

Please note that although wallpaper is priced by the single roll, it is packed only in double rolls or triple rolls.

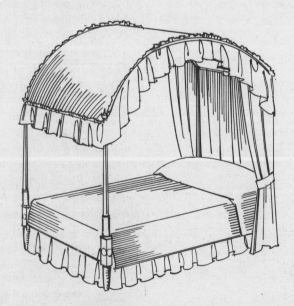

The harmonious combination of window fabric, wall covering and upholstery on the wing chair (cw 12) has a striking effect. Sometimes these three items can be used to contrast; other times, as seen here, to show great unity. The pattern is Floral Stripe, and it is shown to great advantage in a simply yet handsomely furnished room. On the bachelor's chest (wa 1031) is the cw 6 Footed Bowl, l 8 Lamp, and the ap 101 Tea Caddy. Next to the chair is the cw 149 Kettle Stand with an air-twist wine glass (cw 47). As alive today as in the eighteenth century, this room has a tailored, crisp look.

FABRICS
by
Schumacher

More than 45 different patterns in some 250 color variations make up the collection of Williamsburg Fabrics produced for Craft House exclusively by F. Schumacher and Company of New York. While most of these are authentic reproductions of antique textiles used in Colonial Williamsburg, some are commemorative patterns highlighting the life and art of eighteenth-century Williamsburg.

The bold colors, rich patterns, and lush textures of these fine fabrics reveal the vitality of this exciting period.

This amazingly versatile fabric collection offers a means of giving any home, however contemporary it may be, some of the charm of Williamsburg's restored houses and public buildings. An infinite number of combinations and colors is possible, and the name Schumacher, like the hallmark of Williamsburg Reproductions, has always symbolized quality.

Opposite page—left to right.

*Wythe House Floral

This fine cotton fabric is a delightful combination of two eighteenth-century textile designs. An overall pattern of thorny stems bearing numerous flowers, leaves, and buds, is teamed with slender side borders of alternate flowers and stripes. Look for the related wallpaper on page 140.
Width 48".

Dobby Weave

A versatile solid-color cotton fabric, Dobby Weave is a copy of an American woven diaper design. It is available in a wide range of fresh colors, all treated with stain-resistant Zepel to make them practical in any home.
Width 54".

*Apples

These stylized apples and narrow stripes on a natural background have been copied from an eighteenth-century quilt lining. The pattern has been reproduced in linen (shown here) and adapted in a woven cotton. Related wallpaper is shown on page 136.
†Woven cotton: width 54".
Printed linen: width 48".

Floribunda

This dramatic floral-design cotton has been reproduced from an eighteenth-century French textile. Its graceful branches bear an assortment of carnations, tulips, morning glories, roses, and other bright-hued flowers.
Width 36"; repeat 30½".

*†Bombay

A book or lining paper dating from the first quarter of the nineteenth century inspired the intricate design of this rich-looking cotton print. It has also been reproduced in a related wallpaper, as described on page 135.
Width 36".

†Adaptation
*Also available in related wallpaper

*All fabrics are available
in a choice of colors.*

Wythe House Border Resist

This fine cotton fabric, resist-dyed in two shades of blue, is shown here as it is used in a bedroom of the George Wythe House. Its striking pattern repeat of large leaves and sunflowers, with a two-inch border of trailing vines, has been copied from a mid-eighteenth-century textile. Note the use of the contrasting border to outline draperies and valances in this set of window and bed hangings.
Width 54"; repeat 17".

Grapes

One of the oldest and most popular of the *Williamsburg* reproduction fabrics, this cotton has stripes of grapes, vines, and leaves, alternating with a stripe of small flower-and-leaf design. The original is English, block-printed about 1790.
Width 54"; repeat 17".

Color samples of all *Williamsburg* fabrics are available upon request: cotton samples (2" x 6") ten cents per pattern with full color range included; damask samples (3" x 6") fifty cents deposit per sample. Large samples of all fabrics are also available on a loan basis; a deposit equivalent to the price per yard is requested. All deposits are refunded when samples are returned.

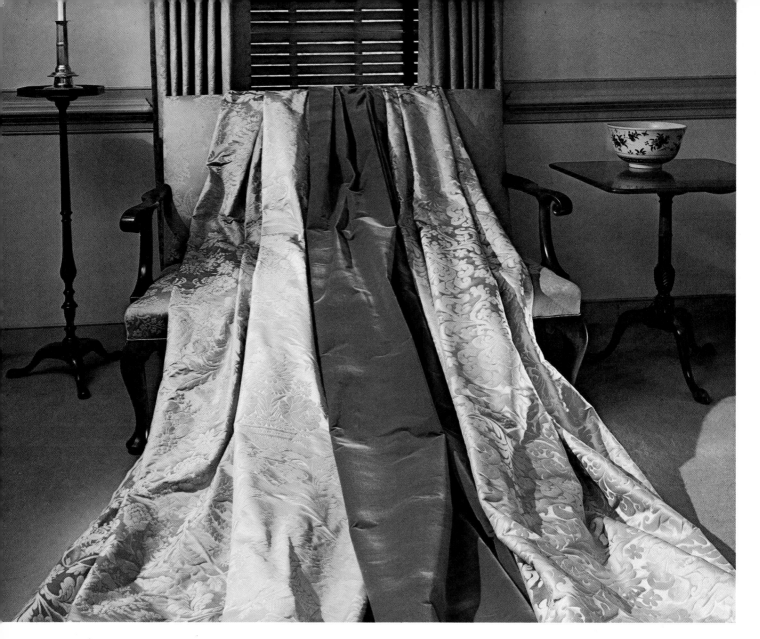

Fabrics left to right: Ludwell Damask (on draperies and on cw 154 Settee), Lord Dunmore Damask, Bruton Damask, Williamsburg Velvet, Gloucester Damask. *All fabrics are available in a choice of colors.*

Ludwell Damask

A central framed bouquet highlights the woven floral pattern of this elegant damask. Blue, the document color of this early-to-mid-eighteenth-century design, is reproduced on pure silk; adaptation colors, including the color shown above, are in cotton.

Silk (blue only): width 50″; repeat 17½″.

†Cotton: width 53″; repeat 18½″.

Lord Dunmore Damask

Undulating floral boughs frame individual flower motifs in this handsome damask design. Reproduced in silk, it has also been adapted in rayon and silk (as shown here).

Silk (blue only): width 50″; repeat 18″.

†Rayon and silk: width 53″; repeat 23½″.

Bruton Damask

Highlight of this rich silk fabric is a repeating central design of graceful flowers framed in a foliate cartouche. This fine damask is also available as an adaptation fabric in silk and cotton.

Silk: width 50″; repeat 23½″.

†Silk and cotton: width 52″; repeat 21¼″.

Williamsburg Velvet

This fine silk velvet with its vibrant colors and superb texture will add luxury to today's homes as its original did to those of colonial days. Like the original, the reproduction silk pile is backed by cotton. Width 50″.

Gloucester Damask

Symmetrical designs of stylized leaves and flowers highlight this fine silk damask, copied from a seventeenth-century antique fabric. It has been adapted in silk and cotton.

Silk: width 50″; repeat 28¾″.

†Silk and cotton: width 52″; repeat 28¼″.

*Flowered Print

This bright cotton was reproduced from an antique French textile, circa 1780. Its overall design of vine-like stems bearing berries, leaves, and exotic flowers, is copied in a related wallpaper described on page 136.

Width 36″; repeat 14½″.

*Also available in related wallpaper
†Adaptation

Fabrics left to right: Flowered Print, Flowering Tree, Green Spring Damask, Bluebell Stripe, Spotswood.
All fabrics are available in a choice of colors.

Flowering Tree

Bring Williamsburg charm to chairs, sofa, or draperies with this colorful glazed chintz copied from an antique English quilt. Its repeating pattern shows branches bearing peonies, roses, tulips and poppies as well as a variety of leaves. Width 54"; repeat 34".

Green Spring Damask

A compact, symmetrical design of tulips, lilies, and carnations with fanciful leaves forms the motif of this elegant silk damask. The original fabric is mid-seventeenth-century Italian. Also available as a silk and cotton adaptation fabric.
Silk: width 54"; repeat 8".
†Silk and rayon: width 54"; repeat 8½".

*Also available in related wallpaper
†Adaptation

*Bluebell Stripe

An English block-printed design of about 1770 inspired this delicate design which alternates a trailing vine of bluebells with a stripe of diamond shapes. The reproduction is treated with stain-resistant Zepel for modern practicality. The related wallpaper is shown on page 134. Width 36".

Spotswood

This symmetrical design of scrolls and stylized flowers, available in a number of rich colors adapted in woven cotton, as shown, is also reproduced as a silk and cotton fabric in its original colors of blue and gold. While the original is probably seventeenth-century Spanish, the fabric suits many types of furniture.
Width 54"; repeat 8¾".
†Cotton:
Silk and cotton.

*Williamsburg Stripe

Stripes of varying widths are woven in dramatic colors to create this luxurious silk and cotton fabric. A copy of an eighteenth-century Italian antique, it makes a striking addition to contemporary decor. Related wallpaper on page 142. Width 54".

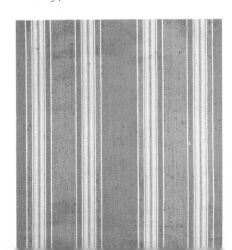

Fabrics, left to right: Floral Trails, Raleigh Tavern Resist, Country Linen, Pomegranate Resist, Plantation Calico. *All fabrics are available in a choice of colors.*

Floral Trails

A design reminiscent of needlework enhances this fine cotton, suitable for bedroom or sitting room. Like the original, copperplate-printed in England about 1770, the fabric has graceful vines bearing roses, daisies, crocuses, bachelor's buttons, lilies and thistles.
Width 54″; repeat 32″.

*Raleigh Tavern Resist

Adapted from an antique French design, resist-dyed, this linen and cotton fabric has a pattern of stylized floral bouquets alternating with a ribbon entwined with fruit and flowers. Its related wallpaper is described on page 138.
Width 50″; repeat 42″.

*Also available in related wallpaper

*Country Linen

A modern fabric with traditional texture and quality, this fine linen is available in a wide range of exciting colors. Its weave is a reproduction of an American antique textile. A related wallpaper is shown on page 135.
Width 50″.

Pomegranate Resist

A spectacular design of large pomegranate flowers and feathery leaves, copied from an eighteenth-century resist-dyed textile, distinguishes this linen and cotton fabric.
Width 50″; repeat 20½″.

Plantation Calico

Indian designs of exotic plants and flowers influenced this charming pattern, copied from a French document of the late eighteenth century. The fine cotton fabric would harmonize with French Provincial or eighteenth-century English style furniture.
Width 50″; repeat 13¼″.

124

Wood Floral

The bold and attractive design of flowers and foliage set against a dotted background is taken from a French printed cotton used in a coverlet made in the last decade of the eighteenth century. The reproduction is also cotton.
Width 54″; repeat 16″.

†Nassau Stripe

Broad stripes separated by narrow guard stripes give character to this fine silk fabric adapted from a textile made in France about 1800.
Width 54″.

Queen's Quilt

Marseilles quilting was included among textiles imported by Balfour and Barraud "to be sold . . . at their store in Norfolk . . ." as advertised in the *Virginia Gazette*, July 25, 1776. The goods advertised were, in all probability, the hand-quilted items that were later simulated in a loom-woven quilting technique such as the late-eighteenth or early nineteenth-century petticoat from which this 100% cotton fabric was copied.
Width 54″.

Edinburgh Check

The checked pattern of this linen fabric is copied from eighteenth-century bed hangings made in New England from a textile probably woven in Scotland.
Checks were among the most popular furnishing fabrics for upholstery, curtains, and bed hangings throughout the eighteenth century.
Width 48″.

Honeycomb

The distinctive weave of this unusual cotton fabric was taken from white cotton counterpane woven in North Carolina about 1800. The design is similar to other so called dimity coverlets from the same region.
Width 54″.

Williamsburg Tie Dye

A late eighteenth-century French cotton with a pattern achieved by warps tied and dyed in indigo is the original from which this handsome cotton fabric has been reproduced.
Width 52″; repeat 14½″.

†Adaptation

Fabrics, left to right: Wood Floral (shown on cw 12 Wing Chair), Nassau Stripe, Queen's Quilt, Edinburgh Check, Honeycomb, Williamsburg Tie Dye. *All fabrics are available in a choice of colors.*

Pondicherry

Delicate trailing vines and flowers inspired the airy design for this fine cotton fabric. The eighteenth-century example from which it is copied is an Indian mordant painted cotton.
Width 54″; repeat 17¼″.

Anthesis

This printed cotton fabric with its dramatic design of chrysanthemums, birds and branches has been copied from an English polychrome wood-block print of about 1780.
Width 54″; repeat 32″.

Wetherburn Cheque

This handsome silk bourette check will be a striking addition to any room. It is offered in large selection of colors, including that of the original mid-eighteenth century fabric now used as a chair covering in a bedroom of Wetherburn's Tavern.
Width 52″; repeat 4½″.

†Plantation Twill

The texture and weave of this handsome all-cotton fabric has been adapted from an eighteenth-century French bourette silk textile in the Williamsburg collection.
Width 54″.

Wool Satin

This plain and versatile all-wool fabric is copied from a mid-eighteenth century English quilted coverlet of wool and mohair satin. It is available in a wide wide range of attractive colors.
Width 52″.

Garden Floral

This cheerful and charming cotton fabric has a floral design as fresh as a summer garden. The original English wood-block print of about 1790 was used as a border fabric on an appliqué quilt.
Width 54″; repeat 9¼″.

†Adaptation

Fabrics, left to right: Pondicherry, Anthesis, Wetherburn Cheque, Plantation Twill, Wool Satin (shown on cw 13 His Lordship's Chair), Garden Floral. *All fabrics are available in a choice of colors.*

Fabrics, left to right: Wythe House Stripe; on the cw 44 Wing Chair is the Floral Bough; in background, Multi-Stripe, Solomon's Seal, Tulip. *All fabrics are available in a choice of colors.*

Wythe House Stripe

One is reminded of the gracious atmosphere of the Wythe House in this simple yet elegant cotton fabric. Two-tone red is the document color, with many other colors available.
Width 50″.

Floral Bough

A lavish flowering of iris, roses, chrysanthemums, lilies, carnations, lilacs and passion flowers blossom from gnarled stems against a plain background in this fine cotton. The antique, a French copperplate design, and the reproduction fabric are used in the Wythe House.
Width 36″; repeat 29½″.

*Multi-Stripe

Stripes were the fashion in the late eighteenth century, as demonstrated by this handsome chevron twill design on cotton. Related wallpaper by Katzenbach and Warren on page 136.
Width 50″.

Solomon's Seal

This fine cotton fabric may be seen in use in the Brush-Everard House. The antique was printed in England, about 1775. Its reproduction shows thorny stems abloom with roses, carnations and Solomon's seal.
Width 40″; repeat 35½″.

*Tulip

Dainty stylized tulips in neat geometric arrangement make up this attractive woven cotton fabric. The design, derived from a seventeenth-century document, has its related wallpaper pictured on page 138.
Width 54″.

*Also available in related wallpaper

127

All fabrics are available in a variety of colors.

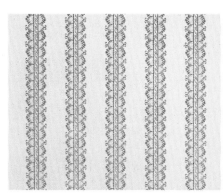

Pleasures of the Farm

Charming rural scenes of eighteenth-century France are illustrated in great detail in this fine printed cotton. It is a reproduction of a French toile de Jouy, copperplate-printed about 1783; a delightful choice for an eighteenth-century look in living room or dining room. Width 40"; repeat 40".

*Liner Stripe

This delicate design of stripes printed on 100% cotton is copied from the border tape used on antique bed hangings in the James Geddy House. The related wallpaper is on page 142. Width 50".

*Pintado Stripe

Left to right

Like so many fine cottons, this is of East Indian origin; its Indian name means painted cotton. Light and airy, the design comes from an antique cotton fabric, probably French, made about 1775. The reproduction is 100% cotton. A related wallpaper is shown on page 137. Width 36".

Peyton Randolph Wool Damask

Copied from an English damask of the last quarter of the eighteenth century, this reproduction is 100% wool and fully mothproof, practical for any home. Its repeating central design features a large palmette enclosed in scrolled sprays of flowers and feathery leaves. Width 52"; repeat 23".

Williamsburg Lateral Stripe

An unusual arrow-like effect is created by weaving wool and cotton with horizontal stripes. This fine fabric is copied from a tabby-weave blanket in the Williamsburg collection. Width 54".

Shir-O-Shakkar

This is the original East Indian name for seersucker, which literally meant "milk and sugar." Alternating plain and puckered stripes of 100% cotton make a simple, yet unusual fabric that would brighten any room. Width 54".

*Bruton Resist

Stylized chrysanthemums, lilacs and graceful fern-like leaves create a striking pattern on this linen and cotton fabric reproduced from an eighteenth century textile here shown on a WA 1047 chair. A related wallpaper may be seen on page 140. Width: 54"; repeat 13".

*Also in related wallpaper

128

Fabrics, left to right: Bellflower, Coverlet Cotton, Checks, Liverpool Birds (on WA 1046 Side Chair), Jones Toile, Nosegay. *All fabrics are available in a choice of colors.*

Bellflower

Alternate rows of full-blown bellflowers and half-open blooms entwined with leaves and ribbon make up this graceful pattern. It is reproduced in a linen-cotton combination, suitable for draperies or upholstery. Width 50″; repeat 14″.

Coverlet Cotton

A cherished American antique bedcovering was the inspiration for this reproduction in 100% cotton. A pronounced pattern in the weave distinguishes this sturdy and versatile fabric. Width 52″.

*Checks

Always in fashion, always adaptable to any environment, this small checked linen and cotton fabric is reproduced from an American antique document. Related wallpaper is described on page 141. Width 48″.

*Also available in related wallpaper

Liverpool Birds

Two popular eighteenth-century motifs, stripes and fanciful birds, are combined in this fine cotton fabric. A stripe of exotic, imaginary birds is alternated with a plain stripe.
Width 54″; repeat 7″.

Jones Toile

An English textile, made in 1761 by Robert Jones in his Old Ford factory in London, is reproduced in printed cotton used for summer hangings in the ballroom of the Governor's Palace. The legends "R.Jones/1761" and "R.I.& Co./Old Ford/1761" form an unobtrusive part of the design. Width 40″; repeat 77″.

Nosegay

Dainty bouquets are framed by trailing stems in this light and airy floral cotton fabric. Copied from a French design, it is charming for a lady's bedroom. Width 36″; repeat 14″.

Horse and Fox

A Wythe House bedroom is the showcase for this interesting reproduction of a design first printed in England about 1770. Animal vignettes are set among winding branches of a tree in this fine cotton fabric.
Width 36″; repeat 37″.

Fabrics, left to right: Floral Stripe, Diamond Floral, Potpourri, Taffeta Linen. *All fabrics are available in a choice of colors.*

*Tavern Check

This striking linen and cotton fabric brings the hospitable spirit of Williamsburg inns and taverns to your family room or breakfast room. Its bold checks were copied from an American antique. The related wallpaper is on page 142.
Width 48″; repeat 3″.

*Floral Stripe

This reproduction of an eighteenth-century French textile alternates dainty ribbon-looped bouquets with wide stripes of stylized flowers. This charming cotton fabric has its related wallpaper, as shown on pages 138 and 139.
Width 36″; repeat 12½″.

Diamond Floral

Originally from Provence in France, this restrained but lively pattern bespeaks continental European influences on eighteenth-century England and her American colonies. It suggests many contemporary usages.
Width 54″; repeat 8″.

*Potpourri

This popular reproduction fabric displays a gay medley of flowers and leaves, spiced with color. It is copied from a piece of antique block-printed cotton made in England. Related dinnerware by Wedgwood and wallpaper by Katzenbach and Warren are also available (pages 136 and 137).
Width 36″; repeat 22¼″.
Width 54″; repeat 26¼″.

Taffeta Linen

The texture of an eighteenth-century linen sheet was reproduced for this fine fabric.
Width 50″.

*Also available in related wallpaper

WILLIAMSBURG BEDSPREADS
by Bates Fabrics Inc.

Bates Fabrics Inc., weavers and printers of fine quality textiles, have reproduced for Craft House three beautiful bedspreads in different textiles and a wide selection of exciting contemporary colors. These versatile reproductions are as at home in today's contemporary settings as the originals were in the eighteenth century.

Lafayette Resist

The striking pattern of this bedspread is reproduced from a quilted coverlet of the late eighteenth century. Stylized pomegranates and acanthus leaves in a symmetrical repeating design are printed to duplicate the resist method of dyeing. The spread of 100% cotton can be machine washed and dried with no pressing required. It is available in a gift box in the following sizes and colors:

Twin: 82″ x 110″
Double: 95″ x 110″

Colors: Navy, Wine, Gold, Green, Lemon

Color samples of Williamsburg bedspreads are available upon request. A fifty-cent deposit is requested for each pattern. All deposits are refunded when samples are returned.

William and Mary

Mythological birds and animals combined with large symmetrical leaf and plant motifs provide the distinguished border design of this copy of a late seventeenth-century quilted coverlet. The center portion has an all-over diamond pattern. Of 100% cotton, this bedspread can be machine washed and dried with no pressing necessary. It is available in the following sizes and colors:

> Twin: 80″ x 110″
> Double: 96″ x 110″

Colors: Snow White, Antique White.

Wythe House

Copied from a coverlet thought to have been made in Virginia this bedspread of 100% cotton suggests the overshot patterns popular in the eighteenth and nineteenth centuries. It can be machine washed and dried with no pressing required. It comes in a gift box in the following sizes and colors:

> Twin: 80″ x 110″
> Double: 96″ x 110″

Colors: Snow White, Antique White, Green, Red, Russet, Ochre, Gold, Blue.

WALLPAPERS by Katzenbach and Warren

The skilled craftsmen of Katzenbach and Warren have copied many of Colonial Williamsburg's rare documents to produce their outstanding selection of exquisite *Williamsburg* Wallpaper Reproductions. Many of these designs derive from eighteenth-century wallpaper fragments found under layers of modern paint and paper on the walls of colonial buildings. Some were discovered lining old trunks and dispatch boxes. Still other patterns are based on antique textiles from the Williamsburg collection, and keyed to the modern fabric reproductions. Each design has been accurately reproduced in the colors of the original, as well as in a wide range of other colors.

In addition to the authentic reproductions, commemorative wallpapers which depict Williamsburg art, architecture, and life are available in a variety of color combinations.

Most *Williamsburg* wallpapers are manufactured with a protective stain-resistant coating for carefree use in bathroom, kitchen or nursery, and are pretrimmed for ease in hanging. A large wallpaper catalogue will be sent on loan for a $6.00 deposit plus $2.25 mailing charge. Deposit will be refunded if the catalogue is returned within 30 days. For those who wish to keep the catalogue for a longer period, there is an additional charge of $14.00.

Please note that although wallpaper is priced by the single roll, it is packed only in double rolls or triple rolls.

THE DUCKS

THE DOVES

Supper Room Commemorative Wallpaper

This paper is a superb adaptation by Katzenbach and Warren of the magnificent Chinese wallpaper in the Governor's Palace supper room. The hand-painted antique paper has been reduced in scale and a few panels eliminated in order to suit the homes of today. All the grace and color of the original are captured in this commemorative design, and most of the exquisite details of the old paper have been carefully copied.

For instance, all of the birds are in pairs, except for the owl who has no mate. Dragonflies, bees, a spider's delicate web, a caterpillar, and even a few flies and mosquitoes have been artfully reproduced in this fine paper.

The two panels that make up the paper, "The Doves", and "The Ducks" (both shown above) are available printed on a wide range of ground colors.

For additional information please write Craft House.

133

AVIARY

BIRD AND ACORN

BLUEBELL STRIPE

CHARLES II

BOMBAY

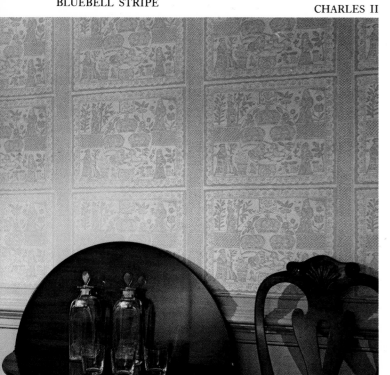

*All wallpapers
are available
in a choice
of colors.*

COLONIAL
MOLDINGS

†Aviary

A delight for bird lovers, this charming wallpaper depicts about a dozen birds, with notes on their care and habits. It was adapted from a linen handkerchief entitled "The Aviary or the Bird Fancyers Recreation." Originally copperplate-printed about 1770, the fine detail provides lasting interest in rooms that are frequently used. Sold in triple rolls.

Bird and Acorn

The document colors of black on deep curry enhance the clean-cut lines of this Bird and Acorn wallpaper, copied from a book paper printed about 1800. The design is available in other striking color combinations for use in today's homes. Sold in double rolls.

*†Bluebell Stripe

An eighteenth-century English quilt inspired this dainty pattern of stripes and trailing vines of bluebells. In addition to the wallpaper, Bluebell Stripe has been reproduced in a fabric, shown on page 123. Pleasant for young girls' rooms. Sold in double rolls.

*Bombay

An intricate East Indian pattern of closely-set leaves, vines, and flowers makes up this unusual wallpaper. Its original was a book or lining paper of the early nineteenth century. The related fabric is shown on page 120. The lively pattern brightens dark rooms and enlarges small rooms. Sold in double rolls.

Charles II

The original paper which inspired this charming reproduction probably dates from about 1660. Figures representing the four seasons surround a circle containing a lion, unicorn, and the crowns of England, Scotland, and Ireland. It is one of the oldest English lining papers extant. Sold in double rolls.

§Colonial Moldings

These unusual papers were inspired by architectural features frequently found in the homes and buildings of eighteenth-century Virginia, which you might want to simulate today. Cornice and Chair Rail (sold by the single roll containing 10 yards of cornice, 10 yards of chair rail and 10 pairs of profile ends). Wainscot (sold by the single roll containing 5 yards).

*†Country Linen

This linen-textured wallpaper is available in a number of rich colors to set off your furnishings and accessories. The document fabric is a linen grain bag, probably American in origin. The related fabric is shown on page 124. Sold in double rolls.

Diagonal Floral

This pleasing design, shown here in a white and putty combination, was copied from an antique wallpaper found in an American home of the post-Revolutionary period. Its graceful ordered pattern makes a charming background for any room. Sold in double rolls.

§Duke of Gloucester

Three sources contributed to this commemorative pattern. The vase and flowers were inspired by the lush floral arrangements used in the Governor's Palace, and the birds were copied from the Chinese wallpaper in the Palace supper room. The overall pattern is based on an eighteenth-century English textile. The result: a wall covering of great elegance. Sold in double rolls.

*Also available in related fabric
†Adaptation
§Commemorative

COUNTRY LINEN

DIAGONAL FLORAL

DUKE
OF
GLOUCESTER

HOMESPUN STRIPE

FLOWERED PRINT

FLORAL
SQUARES

†*Homespun Stripe*

Soft warm colors and homespun texture distinguish this unusual striped wallpaper. Its design was inspired by an eighteenth-century woolen blanket which was woven in America and is now part of the Williamsburg collection. Sold in double rolls.

*†*Flowered Print*

This cheerful design, shown here with related cotton fabric, was adapted from a French block-printed textile made about 1780. It is strewn with colorful flowers, vines, leaves and berries. For the fabric, see page 123. Sold in double rolls.

Floral Squares

A charming arrangement of delicately-drawn floral squares, this pattern is copied from a block-printed paper found as a lining in a seventeenth-century Bible box. The original was made in England about 1680. Sold in triple rolls.

Mandarin and Pine Tree

East meets West in this dramatic reproduction wallpaper, which gracefully combines English flowers with Oriental motifs. The antique from which it was copied was made about 1760-70 and used to line a trunk. Sold in double rolls.

Lafayette Floral

Another colonial town, Kennebunkport, Maine, is the source of the English eighteenth-century wallpaper fragment from which this charming floral design was copied. This antique paper now rests in the Williamsburg collection. Sold in double rolls.

*†*Pintado Stripe*

A light and airy wallpaper pattern taken from an antique fabric dating from about 1775, probably of French origin. (The name, from Portugese 'pinta' for "spotted," was used in the seventeenth century to designate painted cottons—chintz—from India). Related fabric is on page 128. Sold in double rolls.

*†*Multi-Stripe*

Crisp and fresh-looking, this striped paper was copied from an old fabric in the Williamsburg collection. A popular design in the eighteenth century, it is gaining popularity again in both paper and fabric (see page 127). Sold in double rolls.

*†*Potpourri*

Adapted from the cotton fabric of the same design (see page 110). This entrancing pattern is a rich medley of birds, flowers and fruits. A dinnerware pattern by Wedgwood has also been inspired by Potpourri. Sold in double rolls.

*†*Williamsburg Apples*

Slender stripes and stylized apples adapted from an eighteenth-century quilt lining make up this delightful wallpaper. The fabric reproduction is on page 120. Sold in double rolls.

§*Little Crowns*

Rows of miniature crowns march across this commemorative paper, inspired by the crown of William III, in whose honor the city of Williamsburg was named. Sold in double rolls.

†Adaptation
*Also available in related fabric
§Commemorative
All wallpapers are available in choice of colors.

MANDARIN AND PINE TREE

LAFAYETTE FLORAL

PINTADO STRIPE

MULTI-STRIPE

POTPOURRI

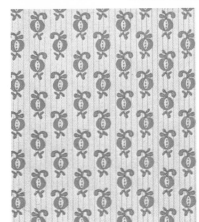

WILLIAMSBURG APPLES

LITTLE CROWNS

*All wallpapers are available
in a choice of colors.*

EDENTON

Edenton

This elegant pattern is a copy of antique wallpaper found in the Joseph Hewes House, Edenton, North Carolina. The design was printed in the first quarter of the nineteenth century, and the reproduction is available only in the document color shown. A formal wallpaper that shows up smartly in a hallway or dining room. Sold in double rolls.

RALEIGH TAVERN

*†Raleigh Tavern

Bouquets of stylized flowers alternate with undulating ribbon stripes entwined with blossoms in this striking paper. It was adapted from an antique French fabric, and is available in a variety of colors. The related fabric, Raleigh Tavern Resist, is shown on page 124. Sold in double rolls.

*†Tulip

This charming floral pattern has been copied from a European textile of the late seventeenth century. Its neat blocks of stylized flowers and leaves are reproduced in a related fabric, shown on page 127. Sold in double rolls.

TULIP

Bernardston

This handsome pattern is a reproduction of an early nineteenth century wallpaper from the Whithed home in Bernardston, Massachusetts. It makes a pleasant wall covering for a bedroom, sitting room, or hallway. Sold in double rolls.

*†Floral Stripe

An eighteenth-century French cotton fabric inspired this rich design, in which bouquets of flowers on undulating ribbons alternate with wide bands of stylized flowers. It can be seen again on page 119, and the related fabric is described on page 130. Sold in double rolls.

Brewster

A reproduction of the wallpaper found applied to pine sheathing in an old house in Brewster, Massachusetts. The original of this light and delicate design dates from about 1790. Sold in double rolls.

§Williamsburg Commemorative Scenic

This handsome hand-printed paper consists of seven strips, each 27 inches wide trimmed, for a total width of 15 feet 9 inches. As illustrated below, and on page 139, the strips show Bruton Parish Church, the Governor's Palace, the Magazine and the Guardhouse, the Courthouse of 1770, the Raleigh Tavern, and the Capitol. Not shown is the Garden, a filler strip which may be used anywhere to allow buildings or groups of buildings to be centered. Height of the patterns varies from 12½ inches in the Garden to 22¼ inches in the Governor's Palace. It is quite handsome as a decorative border on a painted wall, or also when used to paper an entire wall or room. Also available in double size. Write for further information.

Stencil Square

In hallway, kitchen, dining room or family room, this handsome geometric pattern suits today's way of life. Copied from an antique fragment in the Williamsburg collection, this classic paper is available in the document colors of blue on taupe and other rich color combinations. Sold in double rolls.

†Adaptation
*Also available in related fabric
§Commemorative

WILLIAMSBURG COMMEMORATIVE SCENIC

Bruton Parish Church

The Governor's Palace

The Magazine and Guardhouse

138

BERNARDSTON

BREWSTER

FLORAL STRIPE

STENCIL SQUARE

All wallpapers (except Edenton) are available in a choice of colors.

The Courthouse of 1770

The Raleigh Tavern

The Capitol

RIBBON FLORAL

WILLIAMSBURG BRUTON RESIST

WYTHE HOUSE FLORAL

WEST ST. MARY'S MANOR

Ribbon Floral

The original paper was a lining for an old cowhide trunk found in Harwichport, Massachusetts. As wallpaper, this reproduction of a late eighteenth-century pattern of ribbons and flowers is particularly pleasing in a bedroom or hallway. Sold in double rolls.

**†Wythe House Floral*

The borders of the Wythe House Floral cotton fabric (see page 120) inspired this graceful wallpaper pattern. In the wallpaper, the borders combine for a striped effect; in the fabric they simply frame a large flowering vine. Sold in double rolls.

**†Williamsburg Bruton Resist*

Reproduced from an 18th-century resist-dyed fabric, this unusual wall paper design is available in many stunning colors. Stylized chrysanthemums, lilacs, and fern-like leaves make up the pattern. The related linen fabric is on page 128. Sold in double rolls.

West St. Mary's Manor

This charming design of flowers and lacy scrolls is copied from a late-eighteenth-century wallpaper originally used in a colonial Maryland home, West St. Mary's Manor. The ribbon-like bands that resemble lace are often found in fabrics of the period. Sold in double rolls.

*Also available in related fabric
†Adaptation

Mary Lloyd

This airy and elegant floral pattern was copied from the lining paper of an antique leather box. A label in the box identifies Mary Lloyd as a trunkmaker "at the corner of Pudding-Row, Opposite Winetavern Street, Dublin". The delicacy of this wallpaper opens up long, narrow rooms and hallways. Sold in double rolls.

*†*Williamsburg Check*

An antique linen tabby-weave fabric in the Williamsburg collection inspired this crisp-looking checked wallpaper, available in a wide variety of fresh, attractive colors. The fabric reproduction is described on page 129. Sold in double rolls.

*Also available in related fabric
†Adaptation
§Commemorative

§*Williamsburg Military*

The historic buildings of Williamsburg, together with brightly-uniformed English soldiers, regular Virginia troops, cannon and military posters, appear in this colorful commemorative wallpaper. Naturally, this is the perfect wallhanging for a young boy's room. Sold in double rolls.

†*Palace Garden Damask*

This lavish pattern of flowers and leaves is inspired by a fabric document of the second quarter of the eighteenth century. Benjamin Bucktrout, Williamsburg cabinetmaker, advertised paper hangings, including damask, for sale in the *Virginia Gazette* of May 9, 1771. Sold in triple rolls.

All wallpapers are available in a choice of colors.

MARY LLOYD

WILLIAMSBURG MILITARY

WILLIAMSBURG CHECK

PALACE GARDEN DAMASK

WILLIAMSBURG LINER STRIPE

WILLIAMSBURG STRIPE

WILLIAMSBURG TAVERN CHECK

WINTERBERRY

*†*Williamsburg Liner Stripe*

This delicate pattern of lacy stripes is copied from the border tape used on antique bed hangings in the James Geddy House. The same design is used in a related fabric of 100% cotton, illustrated on page 128. Sold in double rolls.

Williamsburg Tavern Check

The crisp look of a starched tablecloth is carried over into this boldly checked wallpaper copied from an early American textile. It is available in a wide range of gay colors, suitable for kitchen, dining room or family room. A related fabric in linen and cotton is shown on page 130. Sold in double rolls.

*Also available in related fabric
†Adaptation

*†*Williamsburg Stripe*

An eighteenth-century Italian antique textile inspired both this hand-some wallpaper design and its related fabric, seen on page 123, in a rich silk and cotton combination. Stripes of varying widths are woven into a dramatic design, available in a wide range of colors. This striking wallpaper is attractive in a young man's bedroom, a den, or family room. Sold in double rolls.

Winterberry

Found in a late eighteenth-century home in Melrose, Massachusetts, this dotted stripe with vertical bands of a conventional leaf motif is a delight-fully delicate pattern. Crisp and cheerful, this wallpaper has the trea-sured quality of timelessness. Sold in double rolls.

Williamsburg Fabrics, Bedspreads and Wall Coverings

Fabrics

	Per Yard
Anthesis	$12.00
Apples (Printed linen)	12.00
†Apples (Woven cotton)	26.00
Bellflower	16.00
†Bluebell Stripe	11.00
†Bombay	9.00
*Bruton Damask (Silk)	90.00
*Bruton Damask (Silk and Cotton)	57.00
†Bruton Resist	16.50
†Checks	16.50
†Country Linen	9.00
Coverlet Cotton	25.50
Diamond Floral	8.00
Dobby Weave	9.00
Edinburgh Check—*Available* 1974	
Floral Bough	14.00
†Floral Stripe	10.00
Floral Trails	14.00
Floribunda	12.00
†Flowered Print	12.00
Flowering Tree	17.00
Garden Floral	12.00
*Gloucester Damask	100.00
*Gloucester Damask (Silk and Cotton)	57.00
Grapes	12.00
Green Spring Damask (Silk)	72.00
Green Spring Damask (Silk and Rayon)	57.00
Honeycomb—*Available* 1974	
Horse and Fox	12.00
*Jones Toile	12.00
†Liner Stripe	11.50
Liverpool Birds	20.00
*Lord Dunmore Damask (Silk)	80.00
*Lord Dunmore Damask (Rayon and Silk)	56.00
*Ludwell Damask (Silk)	70.00
Ludwell Damask (Cotton)	29.00
Multi-Stripe	22.50
Nassau Stripe—*Available* 1974	
Nosegay	12.00
Peyton Randolph Wool Damask	54.00
†Pintado Stripe	8.50
Plantation Calico	15.00
Plantation Twill—*Available* 1974	
*Pleasures of the Farm	10.00
Pomegranate Resist	13.00

*Although these particular fabrics are priced by the yard, orders should be for complete pattern repeats.
†These fabrics and wallpapers are color related.

	Per Yard
Pondicherry	$12.00
†Potpourri	12.00
Queen's Quilt—*Available* 1974	
†Raleigh Tavern Resist	14.50
Shir-O-Shakkar	15.00
Solomon's Seal	13.10
*Spotswood (Silk and Cotton)	53.50
Spotswood (Cotton)	30.00
Taffeta Linen	10.00
†Tavern Check	17.10
†Tulip	32.00
Wetherburn Cheque	36.00
Williamsburg Lateral Stripe	26.50
†Williamsburg Stripe	40.00
Williamsburg Tie Dye	14.50
Williamsburg Velvet	64.00
Wood Floral	12.00
Wool Satin	48.00
Wythe House Border Resist	10.00
†Wythe House Floral	14.00
Wythe House Stripe	20.50

Wallpaper

	Single Roll
Aviary	$ 6.60
Bernardston	6.00
Bird and Acorn	5.70
†Bluebell Stripe	5.70
†Bombay	5.70
Brewster	5.70
Charles II	6.00
Colonial Mouldings	
Cornice and Chair Rail	12.00
Wainscot	12.00
†Country Linen	5.10
Diagonal Floral	5.70
Duke of Gloucester	6.00
Edenton	36.00
Floral Squares	5.70
†Floral Stripe	5.70
†Flowered Print	6.60
Homespun Stripe	5.10
Lafayette Floral	6.30
Little Crowns	5.10
Mandarin and Pine Tree	5.40
Mary Lloyd	5.40
Multi-Stripe	5.70

All prices include shipping charges within the Continental United States and are subject to change without notice.

Wallpaper, *continued*

	Single Roll
Palace Garden Damask	$ 6.00
†Pintado Stripe	6.00
†Potpourri	6.60
†Raleigh Tavern	5.70
Ribbon Floral	5.70
Supper Room Commemorative	
Each Panel	90.00
Write for additional information	
Stencil Square	5.40
†Tulip	5.70
West St. Mary's Manor	5.70
†Williamsburg Apples	5.70
†Williamsburg Bruton Resist	6.30
†Williamsburg Check	5.70
†Williamsburg Liner Stripe	5.40
Williamsburg Military	6.00
†Williamsburg Stripe	5.70
†Williamsburg Tavern Check	6.30
Winterberry	5.70
†Wythe House Floral	6.30
Williamsburg Commemorative Scenic	
Individual Strip	18.00
Set of 7 Strips	120.00

Write for additional information.

†These fabrics and wallpapers are color related.

Bedspreads

7800	Lafayette Resist	
	twin size	$ 31.35
	double size	34.60
7801	Wythe House	
	White, Antique White	
	twin size	39.25
	double size	44.40
	Green, Red, Gold, Russett, Blue, Ochre	
	twin size	44.25
	double size	49.40
7802	William and Mary	
	twin size	77.00
	double size	92.10

Important Accessories from
Colonial Williamsburg

LIGHT . . . reflected light, direct light, even high-lights! The combination of reality and reflection can be the magic of any era, and is really the subject of this section.

Mirrors, for example, were a decorative wonder in the eighteenth century for only quite recently had it become possible to fabricate large pieces of plate glass. For the first time craftsmen were free to lavish their skills on mirrors of great size, and their products symbolized the newest in wealth and luxury. To this day, mirrors provide a superb addition to any decor. They are things of beauty in themselves, and, properly used, they add depth or dimension to a room, increase the natural lighting, re-flect artificial light and objects, and duplicate architectural details.

With mirrors from the Colonial Williamsburg collection one can reproduce in a modern setting the effects that the eighteenth century strove for, and obtained, in its hand-some rooms.

Colonial Williamsburg owns and displays magnificent period mirrors in their traditional settings—"looking glasses" as they were aptly termed. Selections of these antiques are available as reproductions and adaptations by Friedman Brothers Decorative Arts of New York. Great care has been taken with the details: beveled edges are appropriately heavy and the inclination just right. Gilded designs on lacquered frames are subtle and delicate (a skill that few master). Because of this attention to precision, the *Williamsburg* mirrors of today are successful reflections of their antique ancestors. This is a task not easily, but admirably, accomplished. The beauty of these mirrors is in design, the pleasure in unlimited use. Smaller ones may be hung over a chest of drawers or a dressing table, or simply displayed as an incidental piece in a hallway. Also, such a mirror serves handsomely for shaving in a man's dressing room. The complexity of a picture wall can be relieved by the addition of a simple looking glass, while mirrors of larger dimensions can become a major accent piece on a wall or over a mantel.

Examples begin with Queen Anne and follow the changing styles throughout the century. Wall mirrors faithfully reflected the changing times, as well as the furniture styles of the periods. However, fancies and ornaments were frequently added.

One Queen Anne mirror has a two-piece plate glass (typical of very tall mirrors) with a lacquered frame and gilded designs of birds and plants in the Chinese manner. A Chippendale mirror in the King's Arms Tavern in Williamsburg carries a gilded rosette of leaves, while one in the Raleigh Tavern is richly adorned with gilded Prince of Wales feathers. In the Williamsburg collection there is an elaborate late eighteenth-century oval mirror in the Adam style, surmounted by an urn with curlicues of foliage and flowers, covered with gold leaf. Like the other mirrors mentioned here, this one has been reproduced and is truly a distinctive touch of Williamsburg.

One special looking glass of the late eighteenth century —known today as the bull's-eye mirror—is round with its convex glass reflecting the entire room, a highly effec-tive piece over mantel or chest. Another example is framed in gilt wood and gesso, and bears two candle arms below and an American eagle at the top. It typifies the Federal style of America after the Revolution.

Reflections and light! The eighteenth century depended on candlelight after dark. But it did so in its own special style with gracious chandeliers, hanging lanterns, sconces, hurricane lamps and carriage lanterns. These fixtures, in brass, tin, pewter, and copper, are reproductions created by Virginia Metalcrafters of Waynesboro, Virginia.

Available for use with candles (which have their own modern vogue), or wired for electric lighting.

Antique candlesticks, delft vases, student's lamps and Williamsburg finials provide the inspiration for distinctive table and floor lamps manufactured by Knob Creek of Morganton, North Carolina, who have adapted a variety of authentic Williamsburg antiques to lighting accessories that complement a traditional decor and lend contrast to a modern one.

The fireplace, more a source of warmth than light, occupied a focal position in the rooms of eighteenth-century Williamsburg, upstairs and down, and was suitably provided with accessories.

The beauty and design of fire tools such as tongs, shovel, and poker, andirons, and fenders were very handsome during this period. Original examples of these durable objects are to be seen in restored Colonial Williamsburg homes. As reproductions by the Harvin Company of Waynesboro, Virginia, they form attractive (and still useful) additions to today's fireplace. The brass finials of andirons were brought to a high polish to reflect fire and candlelight. And the foot often suggested the style of the period—a Chippendale ball-and-claw, a Queen Anne slipper, or a William and Mary ball foot. The cast-iron firebacks, solid and utilitarian guards to protect the back of the fireplace and to reflect the heat, were often decorative and unusual pieces of eighteenth-century equipment. Whether it be a plain back with simple lines or a highly embellished coat of arms, these pieces surely add charm to a glowing fire.

Important accessories cast the light and warmth of the colonial period into our own rooms and hallways. Their ageless design is indeed contemporary.

Important accessories in a hall or in a living room, mirrors and lighting fixtures provide backdrops for gracious rooms. The hallway mirror (cwlg 4) adds a graceful note to the well appointed interior. Its ornamental frame gives it charm and lightness against the Stencil Square wallpaper. The Queen Anne mirror (wa 1028) in the living room reflects the beauty of the setting. Of special interest: the card table (cw 150) in the hallway provides a surface for the electrified student lamp (l 16) and the ap 102 Tea Caddy. In the main room, an l 6 Blue Delft Vase Lamp casts light on the cw 12 Wing Chair; from the ceiling hangs the sparkling k 12895 Chandelier, and the wall sconces are cw 16–22. Decorating the fireplace are the cw 103–1A Firetools and the Davis Andirons (cw 100–4). Other pieces shown here can be found throughout this catalog.

Williamsburg MIRRORS by Friedman Brothers Decorative Arts

The decorative value of mirrors has been known and artfully used since the Middle Ages. Once a status symbol of great wealth and luxury, these "looking glasses" were sometimes used to line an entire wall or room.

Today's homemaker is even more inventive. She knows the space expanding value of a mirror, and its subtle touch of doubling the beauty of a flower arrangement or unusual accessory by reflection. A mirror adds life and sparkle wherever it is used.

Included in this selection of *Williamsburg* Mirror Reproductions by Friedman Brothers of New York are examples of the more elaborate as well as the simpler styles of the colonial period. The originals hang in the restored buildings of Colonial Williamsburg. The copies have been faithfully reproduced by master craftsmen.

All mirrors are available with antiqued glass excepting CWLG 2 on page 127.

As if framing a portrait, this handsome mirror (CWLG 7) reflects part of a lovely room . . . always changing from different angles. The lacquered frame, two-plate mirror is comfortably at home above the CW 19 Lowboy. Draperies shown and reflected are Ludwell Damask, and the CW 104 Wing Chair is upholstered in Wythe House Stripe.

CWLG 7   CWLG 4

CWLG 7

This two-plate mirror of the Queen Anne period is enhanced by the black lacquer frame, richly decorated with Chinese birds and plants. The original, made in England about 1715, may be seen today in the West Advance Building of the Governor's Palace. This mirror is also available with a red or green lacquer frame. Glass 15″ x 44¼″; overall size is 18¾″ x 48″.

CWLG 4

This two-plate mirror is a handsome example of the long Queen Anne looking glasses, with gilded birds and plant life applied on the black lacquered frame. Use it in a foyer or in the dining room over a sideboard. The original was made about 1715 in England. It is available with a red, green, or black lacquer frame. Glass 14½″ x 39½″; overall size 18″ x 43″.

CWLG 10 *and* CWLG 11

The clean, simple lines of these graceful Queen Anne mirrors add their gracious touch to a variety of settings, blending smoothly with modern designs as well as more traditional ones. They are exact copies of English antiques, made about 1725 and now in the Williamsburg collection. The glass is beveled to follow the delicate lines of the frame in these fine reproductions. Both are available as wall mirrors, or with an easel back for use on a dressing table or chest of drawers.

CWLG 10. Frame available in either polished or antique gold. Glass 15″ x 21¼″; overall size 15¾″ x 22″.

CWLG 11. Frame available in antique gold, polished gold or black. Glass 13¼″ x 23¼″; overall size 14¾″ x 24¾″.

CWLG 15

This ornate mirror is a careful copy of an English antique that was made about 1740. Because of the intricate gilt and gesso details, this mirror deserves a prominent place in the home. It could easily be hung in a master bedroom or dressing room as well as the dining room or living room. It is made of the finest walnut and walnut veneer.
Glass 22″ x 34″; overall size 28½″ x 58″.

CWLG 15

CWLG 10

CWLG 11

CWLG 3

This Adam-style mirror, with its intricately detailed ornamentation, is a copy of a late-eighteenth century antique. The oval glass is framed in gold leaf with an elaborate design of urn, flowers and leaves.
Glass 15½" x 25½"; overall size 22" x 49½".

CWLG 5

This Georgian mirror is framed in delicately carved burl walnut, adorned with Prince of Wales feathers in gold leaf. The original was made in England between 1740 and 1750, and now hangs in the Raleigh Tavern.
Glass 20¼" x 27¼"; overall size 28¾" x 46½".

CWLG 9

This fine mahogany mirror reflects the mature Chippendale style. The original was made in Philadelphia between 1756 and 1762, and may be seen today in the George Wythe House in Williamsburg. This exact reproduction would be charming over a chest of drawers in an Early American bedroom.
Glass 12½" x 21¾"; overall size 18¾" x 35¼".

CWLG 8

This delicate Chippendale mirror is framed in mahogany, with a gilded rosette of stylized leaves. It is an exact copy of the original, which was made in England about 1760, and now hangs in the King's Arms Tavern in Williamsburg.
Glass 15½" x 27¼"; overall size 22" x 42¼".

CWLG 3

CWLG 5   CWLG 9   CWLG 8

CWLG 6

This magnificent Queen Anne looking glass is a faithful copy of an original dating from the reign of George I. The entire frame is made of rich gilded gesso, and is decorated with a carved shell and two eagle heads.
Glass 16½" x 28½"; overall size 22¼" x 41".

CWLG 14

Fanciful gilded chinoiserie figures and flowers decorate the lacquered frame of this strikingly beautiful Queen Anne mirror. The eighteenth-century American original now hangs in the hallway of the Peyton Randolph House. It is available with a red, green or black lacquer frame with either regular or antiqued glass.
Glass 34⅜" x 15⅜"; overall size 44" x 18¼".

WA 1032

Serenely beautiful, the antique American looking glass which inspired this graceful adaptation hangs today in the Raleigh Tavern in Williamsburg. The mahogany adaptation has the soft curves of the original Chippendale piece made between 1750 and 1775. Beveled glass optional.
Glass 15¼" x 27¼"; overall size 21½" x 40¾".

WA 1028

The pleasing simplicity of this Queen Anne mirror faithfully retains the feeling of the original piece, made in England about 1710 and now in the Williamsburg collection. Available with either mahogany or gold frame. Beveled glass optional.
Glass 21¼" x 29½"; overall size 23½" x 31½".

CWLG 2

CWLG 6

CWLG 14

WA 1032

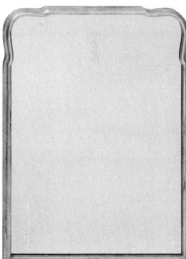

WA 1028

CWLG 2

This eye-catching piece would make a delightfully different focal point for a wall gallery. The Federal-style mirror has convex glass, and is framed in gilt wood and gesso. Two candle arms balance a fiery eagle with outspread arms. The original was probably made in America in the early nineteenth century, and now hangs in the Williamsburg Inn.
Glass diameter 11¾"; overall size 17½" x 38¾".

Williamsburg LAMPS
by Knob Creek of Morganton

You will find the perfect lamp to light both traditional and contemporary settings with drama and distinction in this magnificent collection of exciting lighting accessories. Some are careful adaptations of priceless antiques, others were inspired by the classic architectural detail of the Historic Area. All are magnificently fashioned, and add grace and distinction to any setting.

L 1 *Pulpit Finial Lamp*

This ruggedly handsome lamp takes its inspiration from the urn-shaped finial on the canopy of a colonial church pulpit. Base is available in pine.
Shade: Off-white silk piped in gold.
Height 36″.

L 2 *Delft Brick and Mahogany Lamp*

Two flower bricks, exact replicas of an English antique, are stacked and combined imaginatively with dark mahogany. An inspired accent to a contemporary setting.
Shade: Hand-sewn beige silk.
Height 27″.

L 4 *17th-Century Brass Spool Lamp*

An adaptation of a seventeenth-century brass candlestick with spool turning gleams against the dark mahogany base.
Shade: Stretched white silk.
Height 24″.

L 3 *Pewter and Mahogany Candlestick Lamp*

Glowing pewter and shining dark mahogany combine to form this graceful lamp. Derived from an old English candlestick in the Brush-Everard house
Shade: Antique dark green.
Height 20″.

L 6 *Blue Delft Vase Lamp*

An English antique of about 1700 was copied and placed upon a dark mahogany pedestal to create this charming lamp. Three painted scenes make it attractive from any angle.
Shade: Hand-sewn off-white silk.
Height 28″.

L 1

L 2   L 4   L 3   L 6

150

L 8 *17th-Century Mahogany Candlestick Lamp*

The elegantly turned shaft of a rich dark mahogany candlestick in the Governor's Office inspired this distinguished adaptation.
Shade. Hand-sewn, off-white silk.
Height 32".

L 12 *17th-Century Candlestick Lamp*

A massive, polished brass candlestick set in a heavy dark mahogany base makes a magnificent lamp. Stunning on an executive's desk at home or in the office.
Shade: Stretched white silk.
Height 25".

L 15 *Octagonal Pewter Candlestick Lamp*

A stately pewter candlestick copied from an antique in the Brush-Everard House surmounts a dark mahogany base in one of the most recent lamp adaptations.
Shade: Stretched off-white silk.
Height 28".

L 10 *Candle Stand Floor Lamp*

A rare hexagonal English mahogany candlestand from the Williamsburg collection joins the familiar octagonal pewter candlestick from the Brush-Everard House to inspire this delightful lamp.
Shade: Off-white silk.
Height overall 52"; table height 25".
Table diameter 10½".

L 5 *Kettle Stand Floor Lamp*

A swirl-base candlestick replaces the kettle on this pedestal base dark mahogany stand. Usually attractive, perfect for a small space where there is no room for a lamp and a table.
Shade: Hand-sewn white silk.
Height overall 54"; table height 28".
Table diameter 12".

L 8   L 12   L 15

L 10   L 5   151

L 16   L 14   L 19   L 13

The student lamp (L 16) of the 1800s has moved through the centuries from candlelight to electrification. As seen here, it gives a businessman's office a pleasant personal feeling as do the cw 164 Bookcase and the cw 44 Wing Chair.

L 16 *Student Lamp*

This handsome mahogany adaptation of a nineteenth-century student lamp is equally at home on desk or table.
Shade: Black metal.
Height 25″.

L 14 *Pewter Chamberstick Lamp*

Classically simple, the pewter chamberstick set in dark mahogany makes a delightful bedside lamp, or library desk light.
Shade: Dark green parchment.
Height: 19″.

L 19 *Carolina Tobacco Jar Lamp*

A Dutch delft tobacco jar of the late eighteenth century has been adapted as a lamp to command attention wherever it might be placed.
Shade off-white silk piped in blue.
Height: 29″.

L 13 *Delft Polychrome Lamp*

This hand-painted lamp with dark mahogany took its inspiration from an apothecary jar. Creamy white, with polychrome trim in delicate blues and gold.
Shade: Off-white silk piped in gold.
Height 27½″.

This gracious Williamsburg
dining room is lighted by a
Governor's Office Chandelier
(K 12939). Fine brass
fireplace reproductions
on the hearth include
the Firetools (CW 103-1),
the Andirons (CW 100-1),
and the Fender (CW 102-1).
The room is in the
Robert Carter House,
a privately occupied
restored house
of Colonial Williamsburg.

K 12700
Campbell's Tavern Lantern

An unusual six-sided lantern of antiqued
wood and tin, copied from a New England antique of the late eighteenth century. Height
14½"; width across corners 7¾"; height including canopy and suspension chain 28½".

Williamsburg
LIGHTING FIXTURE REPRODUCTIONS

The soft glow of candlelight, once a necessity for the eighteenth-
century homeowner, is used today to create a feeling of warmth,
leisure and gracious relaxation. You will find, in this collection,
chandeliers, sconces and lanterns which may be used today much
as they were two hundred years ago. Each of these reproductions
is a careful copy of a lighting fixture used in the restored buildings
of Colonial Williamsburg, and in each case the character of the
original has been faithfully preserved by the master craftsmen
of Virginia Metalcrafters.

Available for use with candles, all fixtures have also been
adapted to electricity to meet modern lighting requirements,
conforming to underwriters specifications.

153

K 12895   K 12891   K 12939

K 11758

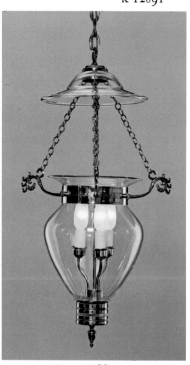

K 12880

Chandeliers and Lanterns

K 12895 *Raleigh Tavern Chandelier*

Polished or antique brass, or polished or antique pewter. Available with four lights (like the original), five lights, or six lights (as illustrated). Height 18½″; width 22½″, total length 44″, with three suspension links.

K 12891 *Governor's Palace Chandelier*

Your choice of polished or antique pewter. Available with four lights (like the original), five lights or eight lights. Height 20″; width 28¾″. Total length 44″, with 2 feet of extension cord.

K 12939 *Governor's Office Chandelier*

Polished or antique brass, with eight arms. Two indirect lights inside base. Height 40″; width 32″; total length 52″; with one foot of suspension chain.

Gaoler's Lantern

Lanterns of this type were popular in the eighteenth century. They are now available in two styles, with softly gleaming antique tin finish.

K 12800 *Hand Lantern*

5½″ x 5½″; height 16″. One light, candle (illustrated).

K 12801 *Wall Lantern*

5½″ x 5½″; height 14″. One light, electrified (for indoor use).

K 12800

K 11758 *Tayloe House Lantern*

Polished brass or verdigris brass, with three lights. Height 23″; width 10⅛″, total length 47″, with two feet of suspension chain.

K 12880 *Wythe House Lantern*

Polished or antiqued brass, with three electrified lights. Height 23″; width 12″; total length 47″ with two feet of suspension chain.

154

K 12596   K 12580   K 12894

K 12596 *Capitol Chandelier*

This brass chandelier is a fine reproduction of the kind that brought light and cheer to colonial houses since the early years of the eighteenth century. The original one was probably first made in Holland about 1710. Height 25⅛"; width 27"; total length 51½" with 27½" suspension chain. Twelve lights.

K 12580 *Tin Chandelier*

This sophisticated, six-arm chandelier was copied from an American antique of the late 1700's. The graceful spareness of the design could add a charming touch of Williamsburg to a contemporary dining room. Height 27"; width 24"; height with canopy and suspension chain 41½".

K 12894 *Apothecary Shop Chandelier*

Polished or antique brass. Available with six lights (like the original) or five lights. Height 18"; width 19"; total length 42" with 2 feet of suspension chain.

K 11751 *Brush-Everard Lantern*

Polished or antique brass. Height 23"; width 10½"; total length 47" with two feet of suspension chain. Available with four lights or one light.

*K 11751S *Brush-Everard Lantern, Small*

Polished or antique brass. Height 16"; width 7½"; total length 40" with 2 feet of suspension chain. Three lights, electrified.

K 12893 *Governor's Palace Hall Lantern*

Polished or antique brass, with beveled glass panels. Height 32"; width 9½"; total length 56" with 2 feet of suspension chain. Four lights, electrified.

K 12921 *Watchman's Lantern*

Antique tin or antique brass. Height 21"; width 9"; total length 45" with two feet of suspension chain. Two lights, electrified.

K 12892 *Governor's Palace Lantern*

Polished or antique brass. Height 34"; width across corners 18"; total length 58" with two feet of suspension chain. Six lights, electrified.

*K 12892S *Governor's Palace Lantern, Small*

Polished or antique brass. Height 18"; width across corners 11"; total length 42" with 2 feet of suspension chain. Not Shown. Four lights, electrified.

*Adaptation

K 11751

K 12893

K 12921

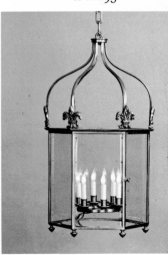

K 12892

155

K 12579 *Printing Office Chandelier*

Antique tin or tin painted black. Available with four lights; five lights or six lights (like the original). Height 15″; width 26½″; total length 54″ with six suspension links.

K 12578 *Raleigh Tavern Bar Chandelier*

Antique tin or tin painted black. Available with four lights, five lights, six lights, or eight lights (like the original). Height 11½″; width 27½″; total length 50½″ with six suspension links.

CW 16-3 *Palace Warming Room Sconce*

Polished or antique brass. Backplate height 10½″; backplate width 4⅛″; arm projects 10⅝″. Electrified or unwired for candles.

CW 16-74 *House of Burgesses Sconce*

Polished or antique brass, or polished or antique pewter. Backplate height 6¼″; backplate width 3¼″; arms project 7″. Electrified or unwired for candles. Mounted on walnut backplate when electrified.

CW 16-22 *Bruton Hurricane Sconce*

Polished or antique brass with handmade crystal globe. Total height with 10″ globe, 17″; with 13″ globe, 20″; backplate diameter 3¾″; arm projects 12″. Electrified or unwired for candles.

*CW 16-22D *Double-Arm Bruton Hurricane Sconce*

This adaptation has the same design and measurements as CW 16-22 Sconce, but with double arms. Available with 10″ globe only. Electrified or unwired for candles.

CW 16-23 *Double-Arm Sconce*

Polished or antique brass with handmade crystal globes. Total height with globes 17″; total width 15½″; backplate diameter 3⁵⁄₁₆″ arms project 9″. Available only for candles.

*Adaptation

cw 16-3

cw 16-74

cw 16-22

cw 16-22D

cw 16-23

K 12600 *Campbell's Tavern Chandelier*

This handsome two-tiered lighting fixture has been copied from one of a pair of wood and iron chandeliers now hanging in Christiana Campbell's Tavern. The originals were made in New England about 1785. Height 26″; width 30″; total length 52″ (suspension chain 26″).

K 12879 *West Carriage Gate Lantern*

Polished copper or copper finished black. Height 22½″; width 11″; projects 9½″. Two lights, electrified.

K 12878 *Guardhouse Lantern*

Polished copper, or copper finished black. Height 17⅜″; width 14¾″; projects 10½″. One light, electrified.

K 13161 *Wythe House Kitchen Sconce*

Antique tin or tin painted black. Backplate height 8½″; width 2½″; projects 2¾″. Candle. Electrified available in antique tin only.

K 13162 *Servants' Quarters Sconce*

Antique tin or tin painted black. Height 10″; width 4½″; projects 4¾″. Candle. Electrified available in antique tin only.

*Adaptation

*K 12601 *Campbell's Tavern Chandelier, Small*

A one-tiered adaptation of the K 12600 chandelier. Height 17½″; width 22½″; total length 43½″ (suspension chain 26″).

K 12877 *East Carriage Gate Lantern*

Polished copper or copper finished black. Height 17¾″; width 11⅜″; projects 7″. Two lights, electrified.

*K 12877s *East Carriage Gate Lantern, Small*

Size adaptation of K 12877 East Carriage Gate Lantern. Height 13″; width 6¾″; projects 4½″. Not shown. Two lights, electrified.

K 13158 *Palace Kitchen Sconce*

Antique tin or tin painted black. Height 12″; diameter 10″; projects 4½″. Candle. Electrified available in antique tin only.

K 13159 *Palace Crimped-Edge Sconce*

Antique tin or tin painted black. Height 13½″; diameter 11½″; projects 5¼″. Candle. Electrified available in antique tin only.

K 13160 *Palace Saucerback Sconce*

Antique tin or tin painted black. Height 10⅜″; diameter 9⅜″; projects 5½″. Candle. Electrified available in antique tin only.

K 12879 · K 12878 · K 13161 · K 13162 · K 12877 · K 13158 · K 13160 · K 13159

Williamsburg
FIREPLACE ACCESSORIES
by The Harvin Company

Through the ages, man has used fire for his comfort and delight. The pleasures of the fireplace make it a natural focal point in any room, a source of light and heat and unequalled charm. The handsome accessories shown in this collection of Williamsburg treasures will enhance the beauty of your own fireplace, and dramatize this important area of your home.

CW 103-1 *Firetools*

These graceful brass and polished steel tools were copied from an antique set made in England in the first quarter of the nineteenth century. Like the originals, which are now in the Moody House, they have ball finials. They are also available with finials to match the CW 100-1 Claw-and-Ball Andirons, the CW 100-2 Raleigh Tavern Andirons, and the CW 100-4 Davis Andirons. Average height 29″.

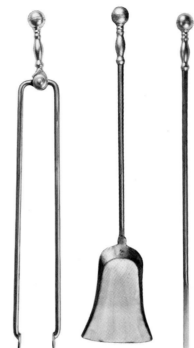

cw 103-1 Ball Finials

CW 100-1 *Claw-and Ball Andirons*

These handsome reproductions were copied from a pair of brass andirons made in the late eighteenth century, and now used in the Wythe House student's room.
Height 24″; depth 22½″.

CW 16-05 *Jamb Hooks*

The polished brass "chimney hooks" from which these are reproduced support fire tools on either side of the fireplace in the Brush-Everard House. Used singly or in pairs, each comes with four brass screws for mounting. Backplate length 2⅞″; width 1⅛″; hook projects 3¾″.
Right or left hook.

CW 102-1 *Serpentine Fireplace Fender*

A simple pierced pattern with a scalloped edge distinguishes this handsome brass fender. It was copied from an English antique, circa 1780.
Height 6¾″; width 49¼″; depth 11⅝″.

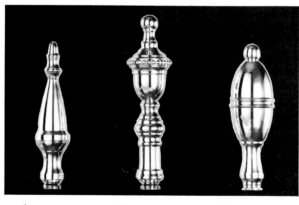

* cw 103-1A Davis Finials	* cw 103-1B Claw-and-Ball Finials	* cw 103-1C Raleigh Tavern Finials

*Adaptation

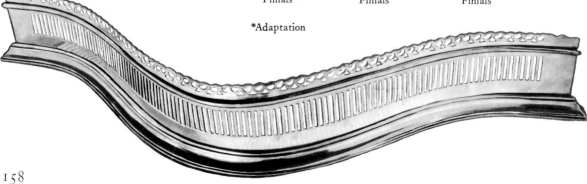

CW 100-4 *Davis Andirons*

The ball-and-steeple finials on these reproductions are unusually graceful. The brass andirons were copied from a pair of antiques in the Williamsburg collection. The antiques are marked "J. Davis, Boston," and were made between 1803-1823.
Height 17″; depth 15½″.

CW 100-2 *Raleigh Tavern Andirons*

Boldly designed with large brass steeple tops, these brass andirons were copied from a pair of American antiques. The originals were made in the late eighteenth century, possibly in New York or Pennsylvania.
Height 23½″; depth 22″.

CW 26-11 *Iron Kettle*

This authentic hearth accessory adds a nostalgic touch to any fireplace, or makes an unusual planter for porch or patio. It has slightly concave sides and rounded bottom, copied from an old English piece in the Williamsburg collection.
Height 6⅜″; diameter 6½″.

Firebacks may be used as unusual decorative pieces, and their original use, to reflect heat and protect the back wall of the fireplace, is still valid.

CW 101-3 *Panel Fireback*

This cast-iron fireback was copied from an antique used in the Governor's Palace. Fragments of a duplicate fireback were excavated at the site of the Palace; experts believe the two might have come from the same foundry and mold. The antique was made in the first half of the eighteenth century.
Height 24″; width 18½″.

CW 101-2 *Virginia Fireback*

The legend "Virgᵃ 1737" decorates the face of this cast-iron fireback. The reproduction was copied from antique fragments excavated at the site of the Red Lion on Duke of Gloucester Street in Williamsburg.
Height 24″; width 20¾″.

CW 101-1 *Charles Rex Fireback*

The royal arms of King Charles I of England embellish this elaborate cast-iron fireback. The reproduction was copied from an antique made in England in the second quarter of the seventeenth century, now used in the Governor's Palace.
Height 23″; width 21″.

159

BRASS HINGES
and RIM LOCKS
by Folger Adam

Careful attention to detail is the distinguishing mark of a beautiful home. These reproductions are careful copies of locks used in eighteenth century Williamsburg, now seen again in Williamsburg's restored houses and exhibition buildings. This handsome hardware, carefully crafted by Folger Adam in the classically simple style, will be a tribute to your good taste.

Keeper   Left-hand medium lock with drop handle

The Williamsburg Rim Lock (above), so called because the entire lock is exposed, is made of heavy brass, hand-fitted and polished by expert craftsmen. It is available with solid brass knobs or drop handles (below). It includes a complete lock assembly with one large brass or stainless-steel key (below). For those who do not wish to carry a large colonial key, the #1 and #2 locks are also made with a covered key escutcheon (below), and with a modern cylinder lock unobtrusively fitted to the large lock, and operated by a small key. Knob or drop handle sets for use with modern mortise latches are also available.

The locks are made in three different sizes to fit the scale of individual doors with right-hand or left-hand openings. The side of the door on which the keeper is placed determines whether the lock is right or left hand. Orders should specify lock size, whether right or left hand, the thickness of door, and preference for either brass or stainless steel key.

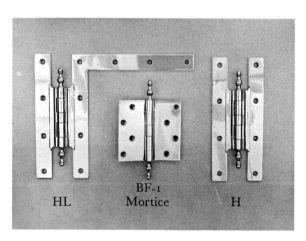

HL   BF-1 Mortice   H

KEY
#1 Large. 10" x 5¾" x 1⅜"
#2 Medium. 8" x 4½" x 1"
#3 Small 6¾" x 4" x ⅞"

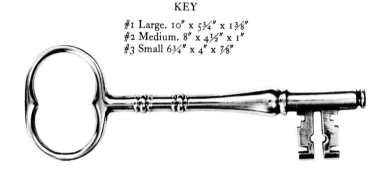

These handsome polished brass HL and H hinges are reproductions of antiques found in Tazewell Hall, a Williamsburg house built about 1725. The original of the BF-1 is in the Peyton Randolph House. Available in different sizes and combinations to accommodate any door.

	Length	Overall Width
HL-1	11¾"	14⅞"
HL-2	8¾"	11¼"
H-1	11¾"	4½"
H-2	8¾"	3⅝"
BF-1	4¼"	4½"

KEY ESCUTCHEON
AND FLAP WITH
CYLINDER LOCK
Optional with the Brass
Rim Locks #1 and #2 only.

KNOB
Solid brass, optional to
use with lock above, and
throughout the house.

DROP HANDLE
AND ROSE
Optional with the Brass
Rim Lock shown above.

Williamsburg Important Accessories

Mirrors

		Regular Glass	Antiqued Glass
CWLG 2	Convex	$505	$ —
CWLG 3	Oval	450	475
CWLG 4	Queen Anne	305	340
CWLG 5	Chippendale	450	485
CWLG 6	English	370	400
CWLG 7	Queen Anne	370	420
CWLG 8	Chippendale	340	370
CWLG 9	Chippendale	250	275
CWLG 10	Queen Anne, Easel	215	240
CWLG 10	Queen Anne, Wall	190	215
CWLG 11	Queen Anne, Black Easel	205	230
CWLG 11	Queen Anne, Black Wall	175	200
CWLG 11	Queen Anne, Gold Easel	215	240
CWLG 11	Queen Anne, Gold Wall	190	215
CWLG 14	Queen Anne	340	370
CWLG 15	Georgian	610	640
*WA 1028	Queen Anne, Mahogany		
	Standard Finish	140	165
	Old Virginia Finish	153	178
*WA 1028	Queen Anne, Gold	150	175
*WA 1032	Chippendale, Mahogany		
	Standard Finish	180	210
	Old Virginia Finish	197	227

*Additional charge for beveled glass
WA 1028....Regular.. $30   WA 1032........ $20
Antique.. 40

Lamps

L 1	Pulpit Finial Lamp	$115
L 2	Delft Brick and Mahogany Lamp	135
L 3	Pewter Candlestick and Mahogany Lamp	99
L 4	17th-Century Brass Spool Lamp	119
L 5	Kettle Stand Floor Lamp	215
L 6	Blue Delft Vase Lamp	155
L 8	17th-Century Mahogany Candlestick Lamp	95
L 10	Candlestick Floor Lamp	215
L 12	17th-Century Candlestick Lamp	105
L 13	Delft Polychrome Lamp	135
L 14	Pewter Chamberstick Lamp	95
L 15	Octagonal Pewter Candlestick Lamp	195
L 16	Student Lamp	155
L 19	Carolina Tobacco Jar Lamp	185

Lighting Fixtures

CHANDELIERS

		Candles	Electrified
K-12578	Raleigh Tavern Bar Chandelier		
	4 arms	$ 95.00	$115.00
	5 arms	105.00	125.00
	6 arms	110.00	135.00
	8 arms	120.00	155.00
K-12579	Printing Office Chandelier		
	4 arms	95.00	115.00
	5 arms	105.00	125.00
	6 arms	110.00	135.00
K-12580	Tin Chandelier	120.00	145.00
K-12600	Campbell's Tavern Chandelier—*Available* 1974		
K-12601	Campbell's Tavern Chandelier—*Available* 1974		
K-12891	Governor's Palace Chandelier		
	4 arms	425.00	470.00
	5 arms	450.00	505.00
	8 arms	540.00	605.00
K-12894	Apothecary Shop Chandelier		
	5 arms	315.00	405.00
	6 arms	345.00	435.00
K-12895	Raleigh Tavern Chandelier		
	Brass 4 arms	295.00	355.00
	Brass 5 arms	320.00	395.00
	Brass 6 arms	345.00	435.00
	Pewter 4 arms	335.00	395.00
	Pewter 5 arms	365.00	440.00
	Pewter 6 arms	395.00	485.00
K-12896	Capital Chandelier	1050.00	1150.00
K-12939	Governor's Office Chandelier		
	8 arms	835.00	945.00

LANTERNS

K-11751	Brush-Everard Lantern		
	1 light candle		$275.00
	4 lights electrified		305.00
K-11751S	Brush-Everard Lantern—Small		
	3 lights electrified		255.00
K-11758	Tayloe House Lantern		
	1 light candle		225.00
	3 lights electrified		260.00
K-12700	Campbell's Tavern Lantern		
	Candles		80.00
	Electrified		95.00
K-12800	Gaoler's Hand Lantern		
	Candles		31.30
K-12801	Wall Lantern		
	Electrified		65.00

All prices include shipping charges within the Continental United States and are subject to change without notice.

K-12802	Hanging Lantern	
	Electrified......................	$ 80.00
K-12877	East Carriage Gate Lantern	
	2 lights electrified................	210.00
K-12877S	East Carriage Gate Lantern—Small	
	2 lights electrified...............	185.00
K-12878	Guardhouse Lantern	
	1 light electrified.................	210.00
K-12879	West Carriage Gate Lantern	
	2 lights electrified...............	255.00
K-12880	Wythe House Lantern	
	1 light candle...................	225.00
	3 lights electrified...............	260.00
K-12892	Governor's Palace Lantern	
	1 light candle...................	620.00
	6 lights electrified...............	660.00
K-12892S	Governor's Palace Lantern—Small	
	4 lights electrified...............	485.00
K-12893	Governor's Palace Hall Lantern	
	1 light candle...................	620.00
	4 lights electrified...............	660.00
K-12921	Watchman's Lantern	
	2 lights candles, tin..............	260.00
	2 lights tin or brass electrified......	285.00

SCONCES

		Candles	Electrified
CW 16-3	Palace Warming Room		
	Sconce.............	$ 41.00	$ 51.00
CW 16-22	Bruton Hurricane		
	Sconce		
	10″ Globe........	56.75	66.75
	13″ Globe........	62.00	72.00
CW 16-22D	Double-Arm Bruton		
	Hurricane Sconce...	103.00	123.00
CW 16-23	Double-arm Sconce....	93.20	—
CW 16-74	House of Burgesses		
	Sconce		
	Brass...........	50.75	63.35
	Pewter..........	60.75	73.35
K-13158	Palace Kitchen Sconce.	14.15	22.65
K-13159	Palace Crimped-Edge		
	Sconce............	14.25	22.75
K-13160	Palace Saucerback		
	Sconce...........	12.75	20.75
K-13161	Wythe House Kitchen		
	Sconce............	6.35	14.35
K-13162	Servants Quarters		
	Sconce............	10.35	19.85

Fireplace Accessories

CW 100-1	Claw and Ball Andirons..............	$170.00
CW 100-2	Raleigh Tavern Andirons.............	145.00
CW 100-4	Davis Andirons....................	100.00
CW 101-1	Charles Rex Fireback...............	45.00
CW 101-2	Virginia Fireback...................	45.00
CW 101-3	Panel Fireback....................	45.00
CW 102-1	Fireplace Fender...................	205.00
CW 103-1	Firetools (with any finial)...........	128.50
CW 16-05	Jamb Hook....................Each	17.35
	Pair	33.00
CW 26-11	Iron Kettle......................	16.85

Hinges

Orders should specify thickness of door.

H-1	Hinge............................Each		$ 81.50
H-2	Hinge............................Each		73.10
HL-1	Hinge............................Pair		170.40
HL-2	Hinge............................Pair		151.40
BF-1	Mortice Hinge ....Pair		116.70

Brass Rim Locks

	With two knobs and colonial key	With one knob, one drop handle, and colonial key	With two drop handles and colonial key
#1 Large.................	$163.60	$168.10	$175.20
#2 Medium..............	130.40	134.90	142.00
#3 Small................	106.40	110.90	117.90
Inclusion of modern cylinder lock (for #1 or #2 Lock only).....................			$27.80
Extra key, large (stainless steel or brass)			
for #1 Lock................................			18.00
for #2 Lock................................			16.25
for #3 Lock................................			14.50

Matching Hardware (for closet doors, and for use with any standard make of tubular or mortise latch; orders should specify thickness of door and indicate whether a square or diagonal spindle is desired)

Two Knobs..................................	$22.10
One Knob and one Drop Handle..............	26.90
Two Drop Handles..........................	35.30

Decorative Items
from
Colonial Williamsburg

EIGHTEENTH-CENTURY householders surrounded themselves with items of usefulness, convenience, and beauty. Two hundred and fifty years later, their counterparts, living in suburban homes or in city apartments would like to do the same. Not surprisingly, some articles then in common use have now become exceedingly rare. Many cups, mugs, and glasses are known only by archaeological fragments, which reveal the shape, pattern and color of the originals. Such objects possess great archaeological interest and value because they record the daily life of people of another day.

There is no doubt that the walls of eighteenth-century rooms were decorated with contemporary prints, engravings, and maps. The Dietz Press of Richmond, Virginia, publishes a superb series of reproductions of early eighteenth-century hand-tinted prints originally prepared by the English naturalist Mark Catesby and the English nurseryman Robert Furber (flowers and fruits). These original prints of Catesby and Furber were valued in their time and are rare today. Although Robert Furber did not visit Virginia, Mark Catesby traveled widely and lived in Williamsburg between 1712 and 1717. All of these prints are exquisite in detail and add an elegant touch to a formal or semi-formal setting. They become the small but important things that "make the past alive." Maps and Williamsburg military prints also are historically valid material for informal decorations, perhaps in the bar or den.

As jardinieres, bricks (for flowers), vases, pitchers, inkwells and apothecary jars, among other pieces, modern delftwares are attractive additions to period or modern interiors.

Decorative ceramics were popular in the eighteenth century. The tradition is continued in the "figures"—delightful representations of Colonial Williamsburg personalities, and the character jugs of craft and tradesmen in the direct tradition of the period's Toby jugs. These exquisitely modeled and hand-painted ceramic pieces are created by Doulton and Company, a firm that dates back to 1815.

In colonial times, the art of drying flowers for use in the winter months was well advanced, as was the growing of blossoms that lent themselves to this treatment. These used to be called "everlastings" and have achieved new popularity in today's decor. Williamsburg dried flowers are prepared by 18th Century Bouquet, Incorporated, of Princeton, New Jersey, and today are used to add a splash of color to an interior in winter, as well as in summer.

Never obtrusive, always correct, these decorative items from Colonial Williamsburg add a gracious touch to today's good living.

Many articles of wood used in eighteenth-century Williamsburg become attractive accessories in the modern home. It's interesting that small wooden objects often reflect the style of a furniture period. Some shaving mirrors and clocks were recognizably Chippendale while some butlers' trays bore the character of Georgian. They are as functional today as when they carried their cargo of punch bowls, posset pots, or tea ware. Copied meticulously by local artisans of Victorius, Inc., Waynesboro, Virginia, these articles embody high standards of wood craftsmanship.

A wide range of decorative articles were made of brass. Eighteenth-century brass was generally whiter than most of the modern metal. Colonial Williamsburg's reproductions are made by Virginia Metalcrafters, Inc. Candlesticks in a variety of designs are seen in the exhibition buildings of Colonial Williamsburg. They are faithfully reproduced and finished so as to be resistant to tarnish. Particularly decorative are the elegant Urn and "S" door knockers to grace a principal entrance.

Featured as decorative items in the Williamsburg collections are a rare assemblage of delftware. Now recognized for their exceptional charm, color and utility, these pieces are made by Oud Delft of Nijmegen, Holland with such fidelity that reproductions bear an identifying date so as to avoid confusion with the antique! As jardinieres, bricks (for flowers), vases, pitchers, inkwells and apothecary jars, among other pieces, modern delftware is an attractive addition to period or modern interiors.

Regardless of what they are called or their purpose, these items are all outstanding decorative pieces. Some of them are made of china, others of brass, glass, wood, or pewter. All of the accessories featured in this section, or other sections of the book, can bring a warm touch of Williamsburg to your home.

BRASS CANDLESTICKS AND ACCESSORIES

by Virginia Metalcrafters

The graceful designs of antiques in the Williamsburg collection have been carefully duplicated by master craftsmen, proud of their skill and the beautiful pieces they produce. Ancient techniques are used, and the eighteenth-century metal, whiter and brighter in color than modern brass, has been painstakingly reproduced. In addition, a special finish is applied to each piece. This closes the pores of the metal so that it resists tarnish, and gives it a distinctive mellow patina.

Used alone, in pairs, or displayed with fruits and flowers, these gleaming accessories will add a glowing touch of warmth wherever you place them.

cw 16-12 *Mid-drip Candlestick*

The drip-pan on this handsome candlestick is not only graceful but practical. It has been reproduced from an antique, circa 1680, now used in the parlor of the George Wythe House.
Height 8½".

cw 16-20 *Baluster Candlestick*

Perfect proportions and purity of line distinguish this simple candlestick. It was copied from an early eighteenth century English antique now in the Raleigh Tavern. Use it alone, or with the cw 9 Hurricane Shade (page 206).
Height 5¾".

cw 16-13 *Brush-Everard Candlestick*

A seventeenth-century English candlestick now in the parlor of the Brush-Everard House was the model for this handsome reproduction. Its bold curves, sausage turning and flaring trumpet base are lovely and distinctive.
Height 8".

cw 16-5 *Square Base Candlestick*

The original of this fine reproduction may be seen in one of the committee rooms of the colonial Capitol. A Queen Anne design of about 1720, it is square based with ridged ball feet.
Height 6¾".

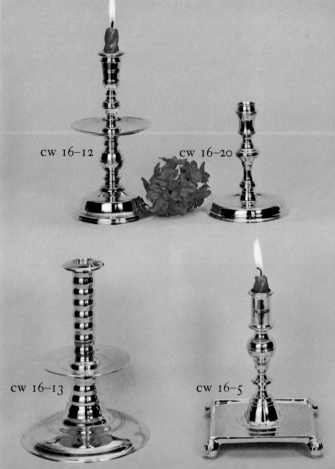

cw 16-12   cw 16-20

cw 16-13   cw 16-5

cw 16-33 *Spiked Candlestick*

Massive and magnificent, this candlestick with wrought-iron spike was copied from a seventeenth-century English antique now in the Palace. It is dramatic alone or with the cw 10 Hurricane Shade (page 206). A white candle is included. For other candles please see page 219.
Height 7½", exclusive of spike.

cw 16-73 *Candleholder with Snuffer*

This delightful reproduction has been copied from an old English piece now at Carter's Grove. It is perfect with colonial furnishings, charming in a contemporary room.
Diameter 6".

cw 16-21 *Chamberstick*

The original of this graceful chamberstick was made in the mid-eighteenth century and is now in the Raleigh Tavern. It adds a bit of old-fashioned charm in bedroom or bathroom.
Length, including handle 8½"; height 2½".

cw 16-36 *Candlestick*

A handsome antique, probably of French origin, has been copied to make this fine brass candlestick. The reproduction faithfully matches the graceful lines of the original, which may be seen in the Governor's Palace.
Height 8¾".

cw 16-34 *Tall Candlestick*

More than a foot tall, this will add drama to any setting. It is a careful copy of a Continental antique now in the Capitol. The reproduction is also available as two-light lamp, without shade.
cw 16-34   Height 12½".
cw 16-34E.   Lamp height 27½".

cw 16-10 *Swirl Base Candlestick*

The special detail of this striking candlestick has been copied from an English antique made about 1750. The original is now in the Governor's Palace.
Height 8¾".

cw 16-35 *Octagonal Base Candlestick*

The original of this eighteenth-century candlestick, of Dutch origin, is now in the Governor's Palace. It fits neatly under the cw 9 Hurricane Shade (page 206), and is charming in pairs on a small mantel.
Height 7".

cw 16-63 *Candelabra*

A serpent's head decorates each branch of this elegant reproduction, and it has arms that move up or down and swivel to give an entwined effect. The original is now in the Governor's Palace.
Height 16".

cw 16–18

cw 16–27

cw 16–24

cw 16–38

cw 16–39

cw 16–2

cw 16-27 *Candle Extinguisher*

Conical devices of this type were known as extinguishers in the eighteenth century. Snuffers were of scissors form. This reproduction, with its free-swinging brass cone and long burnished steel handle, is especially well suited for extinguishing candles surrounded by hurricane shades. Also handy for putting out tall tapers.
Length 12″.

cw 16-2 *Round Base Candlestick*

The classic lines of this serenely lovely candlestick add charm to any room. Use it alone, in pairs, or with the cw 10 Hurricane Shade (page 206).
Height 8″.

cw 16-39 *Taperstick*

This miniature brass candlestick holds a tiny taper, and the original was made in England in the late 1600's to melt the wax used to seal documents and letters. It may be used for the same purpose today, or simply as a pretty accessory on desk, coffee table, or by the bedside. Use it alone, or with the cw 8 Hurricane Shade (page 206).
Height 4″.

R 10 *Hand-Dipped Beeswax Candles* are available for use in cw 16-39 taperstick.
Height 6¾″.

BRASS DOOR KNOCKERS

cw 17-67 *Urn Door Knocker*

These fine reproductions are used on a number of Colonial Williamsburg's restored houses. The plain bar area is an appropriate place to engrave your name.
7¾″ x 4¼″.

cw 17-67

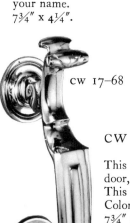

cw 17-68

cw 16-24 *Trumpet Base Candlestick*

Contemporary in spirit, this fine reproduction is a replica of an early eighteenth-century English design. The original is now in the George Wythe House.
Height 8¼″.

cw 16-18 *Scissors Candle Snuffer*

This delightful Williamsburg reproduction was copied from an English candle snuffer, made circa 1720-1735, and used today in the library of the Brush-Everard House.
Length 6¼″.

cw 16-38 *Candleholder*

This enchanting little candleholder, with a simple six-star design on the handle was copied from an eighteenth-century piece. It may be hung on a wall, or used as an ash tray.
Height 6½″.

cw 17-68 *"S" Door Knocker*

This classic, distinctive design enhances any door, of traditional or contemporary design. This knocker is also used on many doors in Colonial Williamsburg.
7¾″ x 2¾″.

AP 104

AP 109

AP 104 *Chippendale Mirror*

Scrolled and curved in the distinctive Chippendale manner, the mahogany frame of this fine mirror was copied in detail from the original, hand-cut in about 1770.
Overall height 19½″; width 9½″.

AP 109 *Wall Bracket*

A fine copy of an antique made about 1760, this mahogany bracket is excellent for displaying a small clock, a candlestick, or a small floral arrangement.
Height 9″; width 12½″; depth 8″.

AP 131 *Spoon Rack*

A mahogany adaptation of a late eighteenth-century antique, this spoon rack has two horizontal racks with slots for twelve spoons. Illustrated with six cw 56 pewter spoons (page 196).
Height 23″; width 12½″; depth 5⅜″.

Williamsburg WOODEN ACCESSORIES

In today's world of production line assembly, it is unusual to find beautiful objects, carefully made by hand. Each wooden accessory in the Reproductions Program is handmade by skilled craftsmen. Copied in exquisite detail from eighteenth-century antiques belonging to Colonial Williamsburg, these fine accessories are meticulously cut, assembled, and finished by hand in the old tradition of superb craftsmanship.

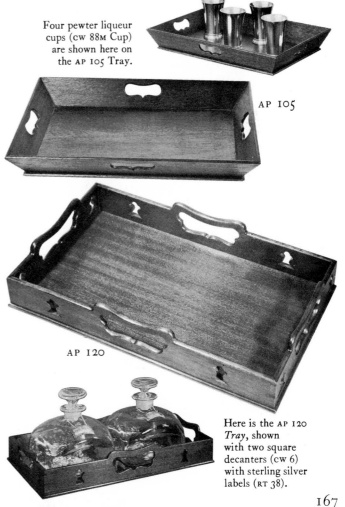

Four pewter liqueur cups (cw 88m Cup) are shown here on the AP 105 Tray.

AP 105

AP 120

Here is the AP 120 *Tray*, shown with two square decanters (cw 6) with sterling silver labels (RT 38).

AP 105 *Small Tray*

This fine mahogany tray is particularly suited to serving liqueurs. It is a meticulous copy of the antique.
6½″ x 9½″.

AP 120 *Gallery Serving Tray*

This unusual mahogany tray, copied from an antique now used in the Governor's Palace, has a pierced and mitered rim with carved hand holes. Alcohol and heat resistant, it serves as an excellent cocktail or tea tray. Two trays make handsome "in and out" baskets on an executive's desk.
9½″ x 16½″.

*AP 102 *Oblong Tea Caddy*

This handsome caddy can hold cigarettes or cards, and it is also available velvet lined and fitted as a jewel box. It has three compartments with removable partitions. The original was made in England about 1760, and was veneered. The adaptation is solid mahogany. Height 6"; length 10"; depth 6".
AP 102-J Jewel Box.

AP 101 *Octagonal Tea Caddy*

This mahogany container has more than 25 hand-assembled parts. Complete with foil lining and polished brass hardware, it is copied from an English piece made about 1760 and can hold jewelry, cards, or tobacco.
Height 4¾"; diameter 6¼".

AP 130 *Wall Sconce*

The gleam of candlelight is reflected from the mirrored back of this unusual dark mahogany sconce, copied from an antique in the Peyton Randolph House. The curved glass front slides up for easy access to the candlestick. Shown here with the cw 16-20 Baluster Candlestick (page 164). Also Available Electrified.
Height 18"; width 13⅝"; depth 6½".
Inside shelf depth 4½".

AP 16-81 *Wooden Wall Lantern*

This pleasing mahogany wall lantern, reproduced from an English example of about 1775, will be an attractive addition to any room. Shown here with a cw 16-37 traveling candleholder (page 219).
Height 16⅛"; width 6⅞"; depth 6⅞".
Inside shelf 4¾" x 4¾".

cw 16-80 *Hurricane Candleholder*

The pedestal of this unusual candleholder is made of mahogany and supports a 10-inch, mouth-blown hurricane globe. It is a handsome accessory for any table, indoors or on porch or patio.
Overall height 16¼".

AP 125 *Queen Anne Tray*

The simple grace of this mahogany tray with hand-carved corners and square bracket feet is reminiscent of silver trays of the Queen Anne period. Reproduced with a heat and alcohol resistant finish, it becomes a welcome asset at coffee, tea or cocktail time.
Height 1¼"; Length 18⅜"; width 13".

*Adaptation

168

AP 101

AP 102

AP 130

AP 16—81

cw 16—80

AP 125

Shown at left with teapot, creamer and sugar bowl (cw 80, cw 81, and cw 82).

AP 127 *Gaming Board*

The parquet squares of this handsome board are made of rich contrasting woods, meticulously fitted. A fitting complement to your finest chess or checker set. It is copied from an antique now in the Wythe House.
17¼″ square.

AP 126 *Wine Server*

A very special conceit for the man who thought he had everything! This wine server not only cradles the wine at the proper angle, but also catches any drops that might fall. It is a reproduction of an antique.
Height 4⁵⁄₁₆″; length 13¼″; width 4½″.

AP 129 *Candlestand*

The exquisite turnings, solid base and tray top of this mahogany candlestand are copied from an English antique of about 1770. Useful as well as ornamental, candlestands were often placed on side tables to raise candlesticks to greater height. (Shown here with the CW 87 Pewter Chamberstick.) Today they often hold flower arrangements or trailing plants.
Height 8½″; diameter of top 6″.

AP 127

AP 129

AP 126

Wythe House Clock

The Wythe House Clock is an authentic reproduction of a late eighteenth-century English clock in the George Wythe House. Its hand-rubbed solid mahogany cabinet is enriched with an inlaid design of holly wood. The feet, face-frame, and top handle are of solid brass. Modern mechanisms are of the finest quality.
Height (with handle extended) 10½″; width 7½″; depth 4″; diameter of dial 3⅞″.

8-Day Nonstriking
8-Day Striking

A Wythe House Clock
on an
AP 109 Wall Bracket (page 167).

Williamsburg DELFT By Oud Delft of Nijmegen

Delftware was a common pottery of the colonial housewife; today it is treasured in the finest homes for its grace, coloring, and style. Messrs. Oud Delft of Nijmegen, Holland have been commissioned by Craft House to copy a selection of rare delft antiques in the Colonial Williamsburg collection. So close are these copies that Colonial Williamsburg has asked the manufacturer to impress an identifying date into each piece so that none may be mistaken for an antique. The discriminating collector and decorator will find many pieces of interest in these pages.

Williamsburg Delft Reproductions, imported for Craft House by Foreign Advisory Service Corporation, are made with essentially the same techniques as were used two hundred years ago in Holland. Each piece is lightly fired before it is dipped in tin-enamel glaze, which is allowed to dry. The decoration is then applied by a skilled artist. After another firing, a lead glaze is applied for brilliance, and one last firing completes the meticulous process.

C 10 *Delft Plate*

The Chinese influence is shown here in the design, in two shades of blue. Copied from an eighteenth-century English plate found at the site of the Chiswell-Bucktrout House. Use it as a wall decoration, even as a very special ash tray. Diameter 10¼".

C 48 *Pitcher*

Two Chinese figures, a distant town, and a delicate tree decorate this graceful pear-shaped pitcher. It is a copy of an English antique, circa 1760.
Overall height 9¼"; capacity 2 quarts.

C 5 *Jardiniere*

This square polychrome brick is adaptable to a variety of flower arrangements. It is a faithful copy of a Lambeth delft jardiniere, made about 1750. Height 4".

*C 33 *Pitcher*

This delightful pitcher proves once again that useful objects can also be beautiful. Filled with milk or waffle batter, it will brighten the breakfast table. Multicolored flowers decorate this gay adaptation of a salt-glazed antique made about 1750–60. Height 6¼"; capacity 1¼ quarts.

*Adaptation

C 51 *Porringer*

Copied from a Lambeth delft antique in Colonial Williamsburg's Apothecary Shop, this pleasing replica makes an unusual consommé bowl, and is equally suitable for serving nuts and candies. The original was made circa 1720–30.
Height 2⅛"; overall diameter 5½".

C 31 *Cream Jug*

This adaptation was hand-painted in brilliant polychrome, inspired by a smaller jug made in Liverpool about 1760. The original is in the Raleigh Tavern public dining room.
Height 4½".

C 32 *Jar*

The original of this delicate vase was made in Liverpool in the mid-eighteenth century. In the summer months it is charming filled with sweet peas or small daisies; in the winter, with small dried flowers.
Height 5½".

C 10 C 48 C 5 C 51 C 31 C 33 C 32

c 49 *Vase*

This versatile vase can be used to hold a large floral arrangement or converted into an unusual lamp base. Decorated with three scenes of figures and landscapes, it can also add a touch of Williamsburg to a shelf grouping. Copies from an English antique, made about 1700, now in Williamsburg's Apothecary Shop.
Height 10¼"; top diameter 4½".

c 53 *Caster*

Useful for sugar or cinnamon, or a delightful holder for bath powder, this caster is a copy of a piece of Dutch delft made in the eighteenth century.
Height 6⅜"; overall base diameter 3".

c 52 *Oval Dish*

Painted with a design of birds, rocks and flowers, this unusual reproduction is often used as a small planter or a distinctive nut dish. The original, circa 1690, was probably used for potted meat.
Height 3¼"; length 7".

c 54 *Mug*

This bell-shaped mug is a copy of an antique made in Lambeth about 1760. A set of eight or twelve, together with the c 44 Punch Bowl (page 173) make a charming and most distinctive party table.
Height 5"; capacity 12 ounces.

c 57 *Candlestick*

Unusually attractive, with hand-painted designs in varying shades of blue. It is a replica of an antique made in Liverpool about 1750.
Height 7".

*c 38 *Candlestick*

An engaging candlestick has been adapted from the top section of a mid-eighteenth-century Lambeth delft food warmer. Like the antique, this copy has been meticulously hand painted in a crisp blue design.
Height 2½".

c 30 *Vase*

The original of this Bristol delft piece was designed between 1710 and 1720. The classic urn shape has been deftly decorated with a stylized motif.
Height 6".

c 45 *Vase*

This is a reproduction of a magnificent Bristol delft antique, made about 1760. Fill it with large flowers or leaves, or use it as a planter.
Height 9¾".

*Adaptation

Williamsburg Bricks

Round, square, or oblong, ceramic bricks were popular in the eighteenth century as inkwells or flower vases. Delft bricks—including some of these reproductions—are used as flower containers in the exhibition buildings of Colonial Williamsburg.

c 29

c 27 *Polychrome Brick*

This is a reproduction of a Bristol delft piece of the mid-eighteenth century. The subtle shades of soft blue and purple make a refreshing background for flowers in the same colors. Filled with plants, two make excellent bookends. Height 3½"; length 6".

c 29 *Blue Brick*

The Mimosa design is hand painted in the familiar delft colors on this fine replica of an English antique. The original dates from the second quarter of the eighteenth century. Height 3½"; length 5¾".

c 26 *Chinese Brick*

These delightful bricks, gaily decorated in soft delft colors, are perfect containers for small flowers or greens. The original, a piece of Bristol delft, was made about 1740. Height 2½"; length 4½".

c 47 *Shell Tray*

A Chinese scene decorates this appealing shell, a copy of an antique made in Liverpool circa 1750. It may be used to serve sweetmeats, its original purpose, or it makes a charming ash tray for the dining table. Width 3¾".

c 41 *Polychrome Saucer*

This tiny saucer displays an intriguing hand-painted design; two or four make a fine set of individual ash trays. It was copied from an antique excavated in Williamsburg. Diameter 4½".

c 47

c 55

c 41

c 55 *Sweetmeat Tray*

The stylized flowers on the border, and the blue and white house in the center are typical of English delft motifs of about 1740. Side length 4¾".

c 58

c 59

* c 58 *Mug*

A small adaptation of the "porter" mug, this one is just the right size for hot or cold drinks. Height 4½"; diameter of base 3¼"; capacity 12 ounces.

c 59 *"Porter" Mug*

Made to quench a man-sized thirst, this delft mug was copied from an English antique which bears the name "porter," a popular beverage of the time. Today it would also serve as a vase for flowers. Height 6"; diameter of base 4¾"; capacity one quart.

*Adaptation

172

c 28

c 40

c 37   c 36

c 44

CAROLINA

c 60

c 61

c 28 *Inkwell*

A fine copy of an antique in the Williamsburg collection, this inkwell is not only a fine desk accessory, but looks delightful filled with a small nosegay. The original is a piece of Continental tin-enameled earthenware.
Height 1¾″; width 4¾″.

c 40 *Round Brick*

Use it without the top as a serving bowl, or with the top to hold your favorite flower arrangement. It is a copy of a piece of Lambeth delft, circa 1700, decorated with an abstract design. Diameter 6″.

c 36 *and* c 37 *Wallpockets*

Perfectly reproduced, these wallpockets are copied from antiques made in Lambeth about 1750. They were designed to be used in pairs with plants or flowers, but may be used singly for an unusual wall decoration. Alone or in pairs, they add dimensional interest to a wall gallery of pictures.
c 36 Chinese Boy. Height 8″.
c 37 Chinese Girl. Height 8″.

c 44 *Punch Bowl*

The generous size of this punch bowl is enhanced by the nicely scaled design of birds, flowers and leaves in the traditional shades of blue. Fill it with punch for a festive occasion, or use it year round as a centerpiece, filled with fruit or flowers. The original was excavated in fragments from the site of the Coke-Garrett House in Williamsburg, and carefully restored.
Height 5⅝″; diameter 10½″.

c 60 *Tobacco Jar*

The original of this tin-enameled earthenware piece was made in the second half of the eighteenth century. Characteristic of Dutch delft, the colors are blue and white. The inscription reads, "Carolina."
Height 10⅜″.

c 61 *Cup and Saucer*

This cup and saucer is polychrome delft and has been finely reproduced from an antique that was made about 1750. The original is a type known as Fazackerly. Attractive alone as a decorative object, and most impressive when used as a set for after dinner service.
Saucer diameter 4⅝″.
Cup height 2⅜″.

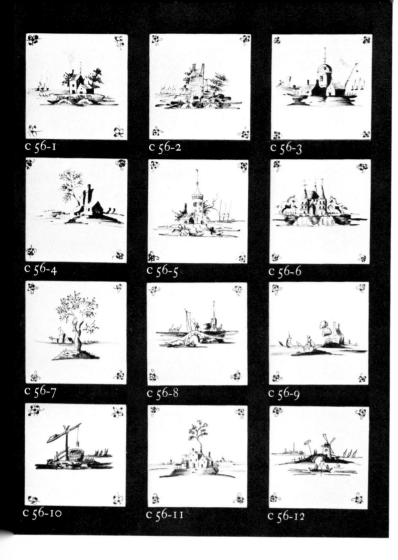

c 56-1   c 56-2   c 56-3

c 56-4   c 56-5   c 56-6

c 56-7   c 56-8   c 56-9

c 56-10   c 56-11   c 56-12

Williamsburg Delft Tiles

Cobalt blue on white, these attractive tiles are copied from those used as facing for the fireplace opening in the northeast bedroom of the Governor's Palace. They may also be used on table tops, as decorative wall ornaments, or to tile areas in kitchen, terrace or bathroom. 5¼″ square.

FANCIES by Wedgwood

c 4 *Posy Holder*

Reproduced from an English Staffordshire "finger vase" made about 1770, the famous *Williamsburg* Posy Holder is a delight to the flower lover. Fanciful arrangements can be made in it with only a few flowers. Height 7¾″.

c 21 *Monteith*

The sepia side engravings on this cream-colored commemorative monteith or punch bowl were copied from a 1740 copperplate, and show the Governor's Palace and Wren Building in Williamsburg. Designs of native Virginia plants, and the arms of colonial Virginia are graceful embellishments. Length 12″; depth 5¾″.

c 23 *Melon Dish*

The cream-colored dish has been copied from an eighteenth-century mold. The covered melon-shaped bowl is fixed to a leaf tray. It is delightful for individual servings of soup and dessert, and for jellies and marmalade. Capacity 8 ounces.

*c 22 *Cornucopia*

Effective as wall ornaments with or without flowers, these wall pockets have been adapted in size from a pair belonging to Colonial Williamsburg. The originals are Staffordshire saltglaze, made in England *circa* 1760. Height 10″.

*Adaptation

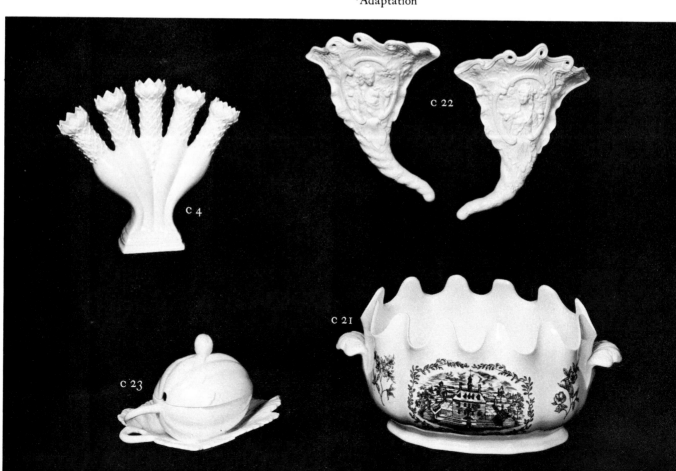

c 4   c 22   c 21   c 23

Figures and Character Jugs of Williamsburg

by Royal Doulton

FIGURES

Doulton and Company, Incorporated, has created a group of delightful figures modeled after men and women who lived in Williamsburg two hundred years ago. These exquisite bone china figures are modeled and painted by hand by Doulton's master craftsmen. These authentic Royal Doulton figures embody the perfection, skill and artistry of years of English craftsmanship.

Top row, left to right:
RD 1 *Standing Hostess*
Height 7½"
RD 2 *Gentleman*
Height 6¼"
RD 6 *Wigmaker*
Height 7½"

Second row, left to right:
RD 3 *Cook*
Height 6"
RD 9 *Boy from Williamsburg*
Height 5¾"
RD 8 *Child*
Height 5½"

Bottom row, left to right
RD 5 *Seated Lady*
Height 6"
RD 7 *Blacksmith*
Height 7"
RD 4 *Silversmith*
Height 6¼"

CHARACTER JUGS OF WILLIAMSBURG

These character jugs are vigorous characterizations of seven Williamsburg craftsmen of today, who wear the dress and ply the trades of their eighteenth-century predecessors. Fine collectors' items, the larger size is an unusual container for flowers or leaves, and the two smaller versions hold cigarettes, matches or pencils. All of these commemorative jugs are hand-painted.

Left to right: Night Watchman; Blacksmith; Gunsmith; Apothecary; Guardsman; Bootmaker; Gaoler.
Available in three sizes:
Large   Height 7"
Medium   Height 4"
Miniature Height 2½"

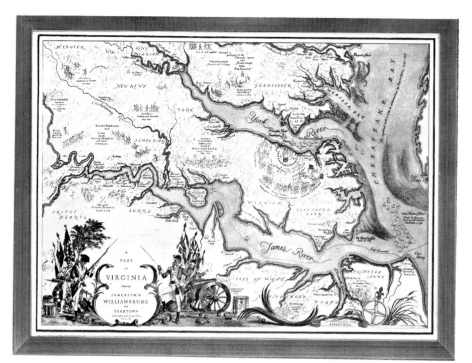

P 7 *Historical Map*

This hand-colored map of colonial Tidewater Virginia shows Jamestown, Williamsburg, and Yorktown, with historic events in the area from 1585 to 1781. Also included are the settlement at Jamestown, Bacon's Rebellion, the surrender at Yorktown, and other memorable events in early American history. The map was executed by Robert Ball. Unframed, 24¾″ x 18″ including margins. Framed in natural pine (shown), 26″ x 19¾″.

1. Officer—Virginia Regiment and Virginia Militia, French and Indian War

P 20 *Williamsburg Military Prints*

These eight colorful prints have been executed in France by the well known military artist Eugene Leliepvre. The uniforms and equipment of the soldiers are shown in meticulous detail, and each print is brilliantly hand-colored. The regiments illustrated were important in pre-revolutionary Virginia history. A description and history of the individual regiment featured accompanies each print.

P 20 *Williamsburg Military Prints* 1 *through* 8:

Unframed, 9¾″ x 12¾″.
Framed, ½″ gold frame with red mat, 13½″ x 17½″.
Framed, ¾″ walnut frame with green mat, 14″ x 17¾″.

2. Officer—44th Regiment of Foot, 1755

3. 48th Regiment of Foot, 1755

4. British Marines, 1775

5. Minute Battalion, Culpeper County 1775–1776

6. 6th Virginia Regiment, Continental Line 1776

7. Virginia Light Dragoons—Bland's Troop 1776

8. Virginia County Militia 1775

P4 *Bodleian Plate*

This is a copy of a print from a copperplate of about 1740, preserved by the Bodleian Library, Oxford, and given by them to Mr. John D. Rockefeller, Jr. It shows the then existing public buildings of Williamsburg and native Virginia flora and fauna. It provided important evidence for the restoration of Williamsburg. Black and white.

17¼" x 13¾" Unframed
18½" x 15" Framed in black and gold

P 18

Watercolor Prints
by
Kenneth Harris

P 17

The well-known Virginia artist, Kenneth Harris, painted the originals from which these fine prints were taken. Mr. Harris is a member of the American Watercolor Society, and has exhibited his work in more than 50 museums and galleries from New York to Texas. The pleasing colors and meticulous detail of these delightful scenes make them treasured mementoes of a Williamsburg visit.

P18 *Along Duke of Gloucester Street*

Unframed, 34½" x 25½" including margins
Framed in mahogany and gold leaf, 27¾" x 37".

P17 *Bruton Parish Church*

Unframed, 25¾" x 18⅞" including margins
Framed in mahogany and gold leaf, 28" x 21".

P16 *Wren Building*

Unframed, 25¾" x 18⅞" including margins
Framed in mahogany and gold leaf, 28" x 21".

P 16

P II *Frenchman's Map*

This is an exact copy of a map of Williamsburg as it appeared about 1782, drawn by a French cartographer after the battle of Yorktown. The original map has been of tremendous value to the architects and archaeologists of Colonial Williamsburg in verifying the location of numerous eighteenth-century sites.

Unframed, 29½" x 22½" including margins

Framed in black and gold molding, 29½" x 24"

Maps of Early Virginia

These three detailed maps, similar to the 200-year-old originals now in the Williamsburg collection.

P 22 NOVA VIRGINIA TABULAR
24¼" x 19⅛" Unframed

P 23 VIRGINIAE ET FLORIDAE
22⅞" x 19⅛" Unframed

P 6 MAP OF VIRGINIA
18" x 15¾" Unframed
19¼" x 17" Framed in black and gold

Etchings by Samuel Chamberlain

Four magnificent drypoint etchings by Samuel Chamberlain capture in sepia the beauty and charm of four familiar scenes of Williamsburg. Each is signed and numbered by Mr. Chamberlain.

E 1 The CAPITOL
Unframed, 19¾" x 12¾" including margins

E 2 The RALEIGH TAVERN
Unframed, 16¾" x 12⅜" including margins

E 8 The GOVERNOR'S PALACE
Unframed, 19½" x 12¾" including margins

E 11 DUKE of GLOUCESTER STREET
Unframed, 10½" x 14¾" including margins

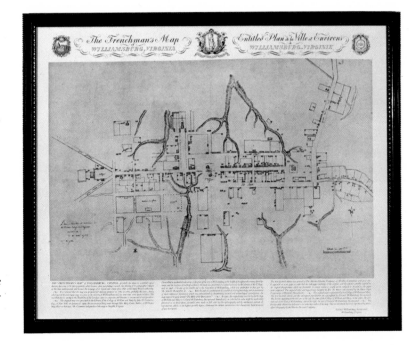

P II

P 22

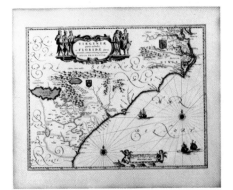

P 23

P 6

E 8

E 11

E 2

E 1

Williamsburg
HAND-TINTED PRINTS
by The Dietz Press

Fine reproductions of Robert Furber's floral and fruit prints, and Mark Catesby's prints have been made available through the Dietz Press. Modern connoisseurs will appreciate the detail and care taken in reproducing these famous eighteenth-century prints. Each one has been reproduced on the highest quality rag paper, then hand-tinted by artists who have duplicated the original rich colors. In their day, they were used in sales catalogs and reference books, and soon became collectors' items. Today these reproductions are in great demand as decorative accessories. A wall with an entire set of twelve is an impressive sight, but a single print or a pair stand well alone.

A different flower and fruit print is available for each month of the year. Please specify month desired.

P 8 FLORAL PRINTS
Framed 18″ x 23″

P 10 BIRD PRINTS
Framed 18″ x 23″

P 14 FRUIT PRINTS
Framed 20½″ x 26½″

P 8 *June Floral Print.* Framed in black with gold leaf trim.

P 3 *Four O'Clock in the Country*

P 2 *Four O'Clock in Town*

P2 and P3 ROWLANDSON PRINTS

Not only did daily life in the country differ markedly from that in town, these delightful cartoons show that there was a significant difference at 4 A.M. too. Designed and etched by Thomas Rowlandson in 1788, the originals now hang in the bar of the Raleigh Tavern. Colored in muted tones of blue, yellow, and beige, the reproductions are amusing and attractive decorations.

Unframed, 19″ x 16″ including margins.
Framed in black and gold molding (shown) 18½″ x 15¼″.

180

P 8 *December Floral Print*. Framed in black with gold-leaf trim.

P 8 *Floral Prints*

Unframed 18½" x 24" (including margins)
Framed 18" x 23"

P 14 *Fruit Prints*

Unframed 18½" x 24" (including margins)
Framed 20½" x 26½"

P 14 *November Fruit Print*. Framed in fruit wood with gold-leaf trim.

P 14 *May Fruit Print*. Framed in fruit wood with gold-leaf trim.

P 10-2
*The American
Partridge*

P 1 0 *Catesby Prints*

Unframed 18″ x 24″ (including margins)
Framed 18″ x 23″ (black frame with
gold-leaf trim)

P 10-13
*The Golden Wing'd
Woodpecker*

P 10-5
The Painted Finch

P 10-11
The Crested Jay

P IO-I
The Partridge

P IO-6
The Chatterer

P IO-16
*The Red Crested
Woodpecker*

P IO-12
*White Bill'd
Woodpecker*

P IO-3
The Red Bird

P IO-4
The Blew Grosbeake

P 10-7 *Bahama Pintail*

P 10-8 *Buffle Head Duck*

P 10-9 *The Little Owl*

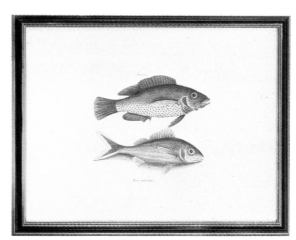

P 10-17 *Brown and Black Tail Fish*

P 10-15 *Pork and Schoolmaster Fish*

P 10-10 *Croaker and Squirrel Fish*

184

LIMITED EDITION PRINTS

by John A. Ruthven

John A. Ruthven has earned international recognition as an artist who paints wildlife with anatomical exactness and attention to infinite detail. Ruthven's paintings possess a living quality that few wildlife artists have been able to capture. He has painted this series exclusively for Colonial Williamsburg. Available unframed only, 16″ x 20″.

CARDINALS

MOCKINGBIRDS

BLUE JAY

DRIED FLOWERS

A large box of dried flowers was used to make this arrangement in the c 4 Posy Holder (see page 152). During the winter months, bouquets of dried flowers may be seen in the Exhibition Buildings of Colonial Williamsburg. Called "ever-lastings" in colonial days, these flowers lend warmth and excitement to cold sunless days when fresh flowers are scarce.

The use of dried flowers in Williamsburg's colonial buildings has its precedent in the eighteenth century when mass bouquets of bright everlastings were widely used to harmonize with the elaborate furnishings, spacious rooms, and forthright colors of the period.

Today's flower arranger will take equal delight in creating arrangements with the dried flowers offered at Craft House. Adaptable to both contemporary and traditional designs, the selection in each box includes a wide variety of leaves and bright blossoms such as cockscomb, strawflowers, magnolia, celosia, babies-breath, yellow yarrow, and larkspur.

To make a massed arrangement with these dried flowers fill a container with sand. Against a background of leaves, arrange tall spikes of material, then come forward with filler material. Next add strawflowers, celosia, and other round, weighty flowers and work them into an S curve or crescent design. Small pieces of spike material should then be arranged at the base of the arrangement to give depth to the design.

s 84 l *Dried Flowers.* Large box. This generous bouquet of dried flowers and leaves is available in the following predominant colors: red, pink, gold, pastel, or mixed.

s 84 m *Dried Flowers.* Medium box. Approximately two-thirds the amount of flowers in the large box in the same choice of predominating colors.

s 84 s *Dried Flowers.* Small box. Nearly one-third the amount of flowers in the large box, this selection does not include leaves. Mixed colors only.

Williamsburg Decorative Pieces

Brass Candlesticks and Accessories

		Each	Pair
CW 16-2	Round Base Candlestick...	$20.50	$ 39.00
CW 16-5	Square Base Candlestick...	27.50	53.00
CW 16-10	Swirl Base Candlestick....	26.00	50.00
CW 16-12	Mid-drip Candlestick......	27.50	53.00
CW 16-13	Brush-Everard Candlestick.	31.00	60.00
CW 16-18	Scissors Snuffer...........	13.30	—
CW 16-20	Baluster Candlestick......	15.35	29.00
CW 16-21	Chamberstick............	18.35	—
CW 16-24	Trumpet Base Candlestick.	19.50	37.00
CW 16-27	Candle Extinguisher.......	9.00	—
CW 16-33	Spiked Candlestick........	36.25	70.00
CW 16-34	Tall Candlestick..........	50.50	99.00
CW 16-34E	Tall Candlestick electrified.	89.40	—
CW 16-35	Octagonal Base Candlestick	20.50	39.00
CW 16-36	Candlestick..............	28.50	55.00
CW 16-38	Candleholder.............	13.05	—
CW 16-39	Taperstick...............	10.50	20.00
CW 16-63	Candelabra..............	81.45	160.00
CW 16-73	Candleholder with snuffer..	22.95	—
CW 17-67	Urn Door Knocker........	18.35	—
CW 17-68S	Door Knocker............	23.35	—

Prints and Maps

		Each
E 1	The Capitol....................	$40.50
E 2	The Raleigh Tavern.......................	40.50
E 8	The Governor's Palace...............	40.50
E 11	The Duke of Gloucester Street..............	32.50
P 2	Four O'Clock in Town, Unframed...........	3.30
	Framed......................	22.40
P 3	Four O'Clock in the Country, Unframed.....	3.30
	Framed......................	22.40
	Pair, Unframed..................	6.00
	Pair, Framed....................	42.30
P 4	Bodleian Plate, Unframed...............	2.30
	Framed......................	21.40
P 6	Map of Virginia, Unframed.................	2.30
	Framed......................	21.70
P 7	Historical Map.................... Not Available	
P 8	Floral Prints, Unframed	
	Each......................	12.95
	Pair......................	24.45
P 8	Floral Prints, Framed	
	Each......................	35.90
	Pair......................	68.80

		Each
	Catesby Prints	
P 10-1	The Partridge	
P 10-2	The American Partridge	
P 10-3	The Red Bird	
P 10-4	The Blew Grosbeake	
P 10-5	The Painted Finch	
P 10-6	The Chatterer	
P 10-7	Bahama Pintail	
P 10-8	Buffle Head Duck	
P 10-9	The Little Owl	
P 10-10	Croker and Squirrel Fish	
P 10-11	The Crested Jay	
P 10-12	White Bill'd Woodpecker	
P 10-13	The Golden Wing'd Woodpecker	
P 10-15	Pork and Schoolmaster Fish	
P 10-16	The Red Crested Woodpecker	
P 10-17	Brown and Black Tail Fish	
	Unframed:	
	Each.............................	$12.95
	Pair...........................	24.45
	Framed:	
	Each.............................	35.90
	Pair...........................	68.80
P 11	Frenchman's Map, Unframed...............	5.30
	Framed........................	46.00
P 14	Fruit Prints, Unframed:	
	Each................................	12.95
	Pair................................	24.45
P 14	Fruit Prints, Framed:	
	Each................................	43.00
	Pair................................	79.00
P 16	Wren Building	
	Unframed..........................	5.30
	Framed...........................	34.50
P 17	Bruton Parish Church	
	Unframed..........................	5.30
	Framed...........................	34.50
P 18	Along Duke of Gloucester Street	
	Unframed.........................	12.60
	Framed...........................	64.90
P 20	Williamsburg Military Prints	
	Unframed..........................	2.65
	Set of four, unframed..................	8.70
	Framed in gold with red mat or walnut with green mat.....................	18.00
	Set of four, framed...................	66.00
P 22	Nova Virginia Tabular	
	Unframed..........................	11.50

All prices include shipping charges within the Continental United States and are subject to change without notice.

P 23 Virginiae Et Floridae
       Unframed............................ $ 11.50
    Ruthven Prints
       Williamsburg Blue Jay................. 52.00
       Williamsburg Cardinals................ 52.00
       Williamsburg Mockingbirds............. 52.00

Wooden Accessories

AP 16-81	Wooden Wall Lantern—*Available* 1974	
AP 101	Octagonal Tea Caddy................	$ 49.35
AP 102	Oblong Tea Caddy..................	66.00
AP 102-J	Jewelry Case.....................	80.50
AP 104	Chippendale Mirror.................	59.30
AP 105	Tray...........................	19.15
	Set of 105 and 4 CW 88M pewter cups.	39.50
AP 109	Wall Shelf.......................	45.50
	Set of AP 109, AP 104 and CW 16-20	
	Candlestick....................	113.50
AP 120	Gallery Tray.....................	50.65
AP 125	Queen Anne Tray..................	45.90
AP 126	Wine Server.....................	39.25
AP 127	Gaming Board....................	45.90
AP 129	Candlestand.....................	40.75
AP 130	Wall Sconce.....................	156.65
	With CW 16-20 Candlestick......	171.15
	Electrified....................	210.00
AP 131	Spoon Rack	80.50
CW 16-80	Hurricane Candleholder.............	46.00

Wythe House Clock

Key Wound........................	$283.00
Key Wound—Striking.................	333.00
Key Wound with AP 109 Shelf..........	324.50
Striking with AP 109 Shelf............	374.50

Dried Flowers

S 84 L	Large Box......................	$28.00
S 84 M	Medium Box....................	20.25
S 84 S	Small Box......................	12.50

Ceramics

DELFT AND FANCIES

C 4	Posy Holder	
	Each.........................	$27.80
	Pair..........................	54.00
C 5	Jardiniere	
	Each.........................	23.30
	Pair..........................	45.00
C 10	Delft Plate.......................	23.30
C 21	Monteith	70.45
C 22	Cornucopia	
	Each.........................	27.80
	Pair..........................	54.00
C 23	Melon Dish......................	20.80

C 26	Chinese Brick	
	Each.........................	$13.30
	Pair..........................	25.00
C 27	Polychrome Brick	
	Each.........................	25.30
	Pair..........................	49.00
C 28	Inkwell.........................	32.30
C 29	Blue Brick	
	Each.........................	21.80
	Pair..........................	42.00
C 30	Delft Vase......................	16.80
C 31	Delft Jug.......................	13.30
C 32	Delft Jar.......................	12.80
C 33	Polychrome Jug..................	23.30
C 36 &		
C 37	Wallpocket	
	Each.........................	25.80
	Pair..........................	50.00
C 38	Candlestick	
	Each.........................	10.05
	Pair..........................	18.50
C 40	Round Brick.....................	30.80
C 41	Small Plate.....................	8.45
C 44	Punch Bowl.....................	62.00
C 45	Vase...........................	78.00
C 47	Shell Tray.......................	5.45
C 48	Pitcher.........................	44.50
C 49	Vase...........................	45.50
C 51	Porringer.......................	12.30
C 52	Oval Dish.......................	20.80
C 53	Caster..........................	25.80
C 54	Mug...........................	20.80
C 55	Sweetmeat Tray..................	7.95
C 56	Delft Tiles	
	Each.........................	5.80
	Set of six (any combination)...........	30.00
C 57	Candlestick	
	Each.........................	27.30
	Pair..........................	53.00
C 58	Small Mug......................	16.05
C 59	Porter Mug.....................	23.80
C 60	Tobacco Jar.....................	58.50
C 61	Cup & Saucer...................	23.45

ROYAL DOULTON FIGURINES

RD 1	Hostess.........................	$48.45
RD 2	Gentleman......................	53.45
RD 3	Cook...........................	52.70
RD 4	Silversmith......................	60.95
RD 5	Lady...........................	53.45
RD 6	Wigmaker......................	60.95
RD 7	Blacksmith......................	60.95
RD 8	A Child From Williamsburg.........	30.80
RD 9	Boy From Williamsburg............	30.80

ROYAL DOULTON CHARACTER JUGS

Large.............................	$19.00
Medium	10.65
Miniature.........................	7.25

Colonial Williamsburg
Decor for Dining

I N COLONIAL VIRGINIA, hospitality was unstinted. Records show that people visited friends or relatives for weeks—not infrequently for months. After all, travel time itself could occupy days or weeks. Travelers armed with proper letters of introduction could expect to stay with perfect strangers for prolonged periods of time.

Private hospitality was supplemented by that of colonial taverns and inns—where one could find accommodations for himself and his horse, meet friends, dine, talk politics, complain about and even agitate against the royal government. Not least of all, inns and taverns were places to carouse. Parties to welcome incoming officials, for example, might extend far into the night.

Despite some boisterousness of manners, hospitality of the day demanded the setting of a fine table in homes or taverns. In every aspect of dining and hospitality the colonists demonstrated an appreciation of the arts in their choice of silver, pewter, glass, and in their pottery and porcelain. The products of these same arts are available today in the careful reproductions and adaptations made for Colonial Williamsburg. Because of the Reproductions Program, many value-conscious Americans are setting a gracious table, mixing and matching the eighteenth and twentieth centuries as their tastes and habits dictate.

Silver and Pewter

Even people of modest means in colonial Virginia owned sterling silver, imported in large part from England, but also fabricated locally. Williamsburg counted some fifteen men who in one way or another dealt in silver in the seventy-year period before the Revolution. There were silversmiths and goldsmiths, jewelers, engravers, and watchmakers. Like the most famous of their number, James Geddy, Jr., all imported wares from England and advertised them for sale in the *Virginia Gazette*. The gentry bought silverware as a form of investment as well as a symbol of status, and their silver possessions are recorded in inventories. Theirs was the age of "Georgian," the greatest period in the history of domestic silver.

Pewter, an alloy of ancient origin (composed of tin, copper and antimony) was widely used in the American colonies for articles of domestic use.

Both silver and pewter pieces have come down intact from the eighteenth century. Many originals command extravagant prices as prized and sought-after articles of both rarity and beauty. From such museum treasures, the Stieff Company of Baltimore has made superb reproductions in silver and pewter. The pewterware is cast, turned, burnished, and polished to produce lustrous bowls, spoons, plates, sugar casters, and inkwells. The silverwares, produced by casting, spinning, and hammering, and meticulously brought to a high polish, include full tea and coffee services, sugar bowls, spare bowls, and creamers; table accessories such as sauce boats, salt cellars, pepper and mustard pots, sugar casters, and candlesticks. Available as reproductions are the Queen Anne and Shell patterns of sterling flatware. These were popular throughout much of the eighteenth century and today their traditional and handsome designs of knives, forks, and spoons are highly distinctive.

Plated silverware follows an English traditional method of plating silver. Several items of silverplate are available as adaptations of eighteenth-century antiques.

Silverware, solid or plated, is timeless and brings to our dining table the same richness, the same quality it lent to the good tables of our colonial forebears.

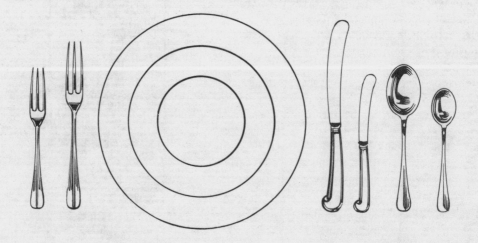

Glassware

Treasured and well guarded glasswares of two hundred years ago are in the Colonial Williamsburg collections. Many comparable fragments have been recovered from archaeological excavations. From these fragments came, for example, the pattern for the now famous baluster glass reproductions. The first glassmakers in America were "eight Dutchmen and Poles" who landed at Jamestown, Virginia, in 1608. They used techniques of glassmaking developed many centuries ago. Similar techniques are used today by the artisans at Royal Leerdam, one of the few glass manufacturers continuing the delicate art of off-hand glass blowing. Williamsburg glassware is made of lead glass, a strong, translucent material with a high capacity for light diffusion. The stemware adds classic distinction to modern table settings with goblets, wine glasses, and champagne/sherbet glasses in patterns of airtwist, teardrop, and baluster. These are contributions of the glass blowers' art. Additionally, reproductions or adaptations of colonial decanters in graceful and sophisticated shapes serve to furnish bar or side table in a fashionable decor.

Colored glass, a favorite of our present age, was known and enjoyed in the eighteenth and nineteenth centuries. Today colored glass has been fashioned again as wine bottles, vases, pitchers, and drinking glasses.

In the eighteenth century hurricane shades were used to protect candles from drafts. Hurricane shades especially used in combination with silver, brass, or glass candlesticks form a particularly pleasing accessory for hallway table, side table or dining table and are available in three sizes and several colors.

Dinnerware

From its earliest days, Williamsburg imported ceramic wares from England as a necessity of life. Dinnerwares ranged from a common pottery called delftware (made in England at the time in spite of its Dutch name) to the sophisticated products of Josiah Wedgwood, who founded his factory at Burslem, in Staffordshire, in 1759. The Wedgwood saga became a success story following the invention of the famous "cream ware," later called Queen's Ware to honor Queen Charlotte, wife of George III. She patronized Wedgwood and named him "Potter to Her Majesty."

Bone china was developed in English potteries during the last few years of the eighteenth century, and by the beginning of the nineteenth century this refined translucent porcelain ware had gained the popularity it still retains. The Wedgwood Company has today produced for Colonial Williamsburg dinner service of the same fine bone china, including reproductions of early Wedgwood pieces in the Colonial Williamsburg collection and in the Wedgwood company's own museum.

As in the earlier day, these beautiful pieces set their own standards of excellence in table fashions for the modern home. Williamsburg's decor for dinner-time establishes the pattern for a good table of the twentieth century.

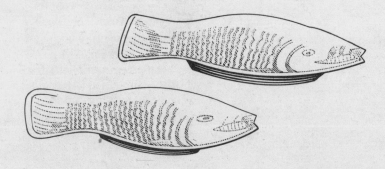

The table in this beautiful room is set for elegant dining. The china pattern is Chinese Flowers accompanied by Williamsburg Shell pattern sterling silver flatware. The crystal is Air Twist.

cw 6   cw 7   cw 5   cw 10

PEWTER by the Stieff Company

Pewter was one of the more widely used metals in early colonial days. Now this lustrous, durable metal is being used by the Stieff Company of Baltimore to create a group of fine pewter pieces copied from the treasured antiques on display in Colonial Williamsburg's exhibition buildings.

Footed Bowls

These simple, graceful footed bowls copied from an English antique of the eighteenth century find many uses in the modern home. Use the smaller bowls for nuts, candy, sauces, or consomme. The larger sizes are ideal for serving fruits or vegetables, cw 7 is a handsome container for flowers.

*cw 6........Diameter 9¼"	*cw 5.......Diameter 7¼"
*cw 7.........Diameter 11"	cw 10.......Diameter 5½"

cw 47 *Taperstick*

This charming little candlestick, copied from one of a pair of English antiques that date from about 1690, would have been used to melt sealing wax. Today it becomes a delightful decorative accent when placed under a cw 8 Hurricane Shade (page 206). Height 3¹/₁₆".

cw 32 *Candlestick*

This substantial octagonal candlestick copied from a seventeenth-century pewter antique will reflect the glow of candlelight with warmth and elegance. Impressive when used in pairs on a sideboard or dining table. Height 9".

cw 87 *Chamberstick*

In colonial days, this type of candlestick was carried up to one's bedroom. Now the reproduction makes a decorative table accessory, useful for candlelight dining, or as an ash tray or pipe rest. The original English antique is in the Williamsburg collection. Diameter 5¾"; height 3¼".

cw 30 *Candlestick*

The unusual faceted base distinguishes this handsome candlestick, meticulously copied by Stieff's craftsmen from a pair of rare Queen Anne candlesticks. The originals made in London about 1715 can be seen in the Brush-Everard House. Height 7¼".

cw 47   cw 32   cw 87   cw 30

*Adaptation

cw 60 *Porringer*

The original of this porringer, now in the Wythe House kitchen, was made by Edward Nash of London (circa 1717–1738). This detailed reproduction makes a superb nut or candy bowl, flower container or large ash tray.
Diameter 5¼".

cw 16 *Porringer*

This bowl is the ideal size for serving candy, nuts, or cocktail dip. It also makes a thoughtful christening present of lasting beauty and usefulness.
Diameter 3¼".

cw 15 *Porringer*

An excellent small serving dish, this handsome porringer was copied from an eighteenth-century English antique now displayed in the public dining room of the Raleigh Tavern.
Diameter 4¼".

cw 55 *Tankard*

Useful as well as ornamental, a handsome tankard in classic eighteenth-century design makes a wedding gift to be treasured. Each tankard holds a pint. A set of six makes an elegant decoration for bar or recreation room.
Height 5".

*cw 95 *Pitcher*

A silver pitcher made by Samuel Hitchcock in London in 1728–1729 inspired this smoothly rounded pewter adaptation. The original is in the Williamsburg collection. This copy holds 90 ounces.
Height 9½".

cw 85 *Sugar Scoop*

This generous scoop can be used with the cw 10 Bowl (opposite page) to serve nuts, mints or condiments. Its antique original bore the crowned X, symbol of English pewter of high quality.
Length 4⅞".

cw 51 *Berry Spoon*

This unusual slim-handled spoon is an exact copy of an English antique dating back to the late sixteenth or early seventeenth century. It is particularly effective used with the cw 7 Lipped Finger Bowl (page 207).
Length 6¾".

*cw 92 *Sugar*

This gracefully rounded adaptation was patterned after the cw 91 Creamer, its companion piece in spirit and style.
Over-all height 3¾".

*Adaptation

cw 91 *Creamer*

The fanciful, scalloped lip on this graceful creamer gives it special charm. Its antique prototype was probably made in England in the last half of the eighteenth century.
Over-all height 4".

cw 14 *Dressing Spoon*

The perfect gift for those who like to entertain lavishly, this handsome, heavy spoon is impressive in size and design. More than a foot long, it makes an elegant addition to any table service.
Length 13¼".

193

*cw 93 *Humidor*

This size adaptation of the larger cw 94 Humidor makes a handsome desk accessory. Both are copied from an eighteenth-century English antique.
Over-all height 6"; diameter of base 5".

cw 94 *Humidor*

This beautifully crafted humidor is an exact copy of an English antique now used in the Apollo Room of the Raleigh Tavern. The original was made by Anthony Jenner (circa 1770-1780). This handsome Stieff copy holds cigars, tobacco, matches.
Over-all height 7¼"; diameter of base 6".

cw 78 *Helmet Inkstand*

The original, now in the secretary's office of the Governor's Palace, was made in England by Bush and Perkins, around 1770-1790. The reproduction, which comes complete with quill pen, adds charm to any desk. Diameter 5".

cw 49 *Cup*

Copied from an eighteenth-century English beaker, this graceful cup is equally suitable for a cocktail or a small bouquet. It can also be used on a coffee table to hold cigarettes, or on a desk to hold pencils and pens. Height 3".

*cw 49m *Cup*

This two-ounce adaptation of the cw 49 Cup is an excellent jigger for the bar, or a charming cigarette cup for the dining room table. Height 2".

cw 64 *Pap Boat*

The original of this unusual piece has the crowned X found on good-quality eighteenth-century English pewter. It is here used as a pipe holder, but also makes a fine ash tray. Length 4⅜".

*cw 80 *Teapot*

An eighteenth-century antique teapot made in London by Samuel Ellis inspired this distinctive adaptation. The original, somewhat smaller teapot, is now displayed at the Raleigh Tavern. Capacity 2¼ pints; height 8¼".

cw 81 *Creamer*

This graceful pear-shaped creamer is an exact reproduction of an English or American antique now in the Raleigh Tavern. Height 3¼".
   *cw 83 LARGE CREAMER (not shown). A size adaptation of the cw 81. Height 4¼".

*cw 82 *Sugar*

This softly rounded sugar bowl was designed as a charming companion piece for the cw 81 Creamer. Height 2¾".
   *cw 84 LARGE SUGAR. A size adaptation of the cw 82. Height 3½".

*Adaptation

194

cw 93

cw 78

cw 94   cw 49   cw 49m

cw 64

cw 80

cw 82   cw 81

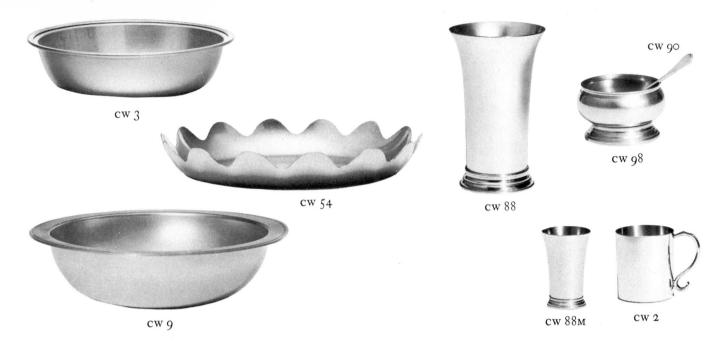

cw 3

cw 54

cw 9

cw 90

cw 98

cw 88

cw 88m

cw 2

cw 3 *Bowl*

An excellent bowl for fruit, vegetables, or flowers, this fine reproduction is a copy of a basin made by Thomas Badger of Boston about 1800.
Diameter 8″.

cw 54 *Strawberry Dish*

This unique scalloped bowl, particularly suitable for fresh strawberries, is spectacular piled high with any fresh fruit. Its original was an Irish antique made circa 1690–1700 by William Bancks.
Diameter 11½″.

cw 9 *Bowl*

This design of classic simplicity is copied from an antique bowl bearing English marks of the second half of the eighteenth century. It can be used alone as a serving dish or teamed with the cw 5 Mahogany Basin Stand.
Diameter 10⅜″.

cw 88 *Beaker*

This lustrous pewter piece can be used as a large drinking glass, like its original, or as a vase for flowers. Many have also found it useful for mixing cocktails. It is a careful reproduction of a graceful English antique.
Height 6¾″.

*cw 88m *Cordial Cup*

A size adaptation of the cw 88 Beaker, this smaller version makes a charming cordial cup. It also serves as a vase for tiny bouquets on a desk or table.
Capacity 1 ounce; height 2¼″.

cw 2 *Cup*

This first cup for baby has an easy-to-grasp curved handle and thumb rest; it makes a charming christening gift. A Queen Anne style reproduction, it could also be used for coffee or hot toddy. It looks most handsome with the cw 76 Plate (page 196) placed underneath it, and accompanied by cw 89 Coffee Spoon (page 196).
Height 2⅞″.

*Adaptation

cw 98 *Open Salt*

Gently rounded curves and graceful proportions distinguish this attractive Open Salt, a welcome accessory to any table. Copied from an antique now in the Governor's Palace kitchen, it is shown here with the cw 90 Salt Spoon (page 196).
Diameter 2¾″.

*cw 96 *Salt and* cw 97 *Pepper*

These matched salt and pepper shakers have been adapted from the larger cw 99 Caster by Stieff's master craftsmen. Use them as a pair to dress up your table settings. The cw 99 Pepper may also be used with the cw 98 Open Salt (above).
Height 5⅛″.

cw 99 *Caster*

A late eighteenth-century English antique now used in the Raleigh Tavern inspired this reproduction. A caster or muffineer, it is used now as it was 200 years ago, to serve sugar and spices at the table.
Height 7″.

cw 43 *Sundial*

An eighteenth-century American craftsman made the original of this pewter piece. It is an unusual paperweight or ornament, and can also be attached to a window ledge or garden table to serve its original purpose.
Diameter 3″.

cw 56 *Tablespoon*

This simple yet handsome pewter serving spoon takes its classic lines from a seventeenth-century English antique. It can also be used as a soup spoon. Length 7″.

*cw 53 *Teaspoon*

This is a size adaptation of the cw 56 Tablespoon, slightly smaller. Handsome copies of this spoon are used in Chowning's Tavern in Williamsburg.
Length 6″.

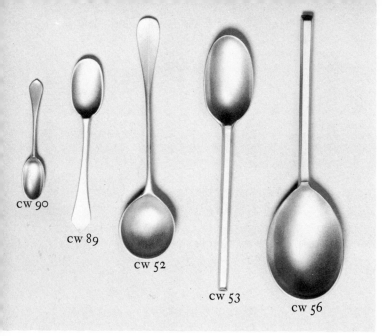

cw 52 *Ladle*

This is an authentic copy of a type of ladle widely used in England and colonial America in the late eighteenth century. Its size and shape are especially suited to use with the cw 10 Bowl (page 192). Length 5¾".

*cw 89 *Coffee Spoon*

Today's coffee drinkers will enjoy using this graceful spoon, as did those of the late seventeenth or early eighteenth century. Its design is adapted from an English antique.
Length 4¼".

*cw 90 *Salt Spoon*

This tiny spoon is a miniature of the handsome cw 89 Coffee Spoon shown above. It is used ideally with the cw 98 Open Salt. Length 3".

cw 76 *Plate*

This graceful small dish finds many uses in contemporary homes as a small ash tray, a card tray, or bread-and-butter plate. It has been copied from an eighteenth-century antique now used in the Governor's Palace kitchen. Diameter 5¼".

cw 58 *Soup Plate*

Superb as a soup plate or serving dish, this graceful reproduction makes a stunning large ash tray for your coffee table. It was copied from an eighteenth-century plate, probably of Continental origin. Diameter 8¾".

*cw 12 *Tray*

The original from which this tray was adapted was part of a miniature pewter service, probably of Continental origin. The adaptation, simple and unadorned, is a distinctive serving tray that blends with any decor. Diameter 10½".

cw 59 *Place Plate*

An antique from the Wythe House kitchen was the forerunner of this classically simple place plate. The original was made in London circa 1766–1777. The reproduction is excellent for serving sandwiches, cold meats and hors d'oeuvres.
Diameter 11".

*Adaptation

RT 18 RT 19 RT 16 RT 15 RT 29

STERLING SILVER REPRODUCTIONS by Stieff

WILLIAMSBURG SILVER REPRODUCTIONS combine the balance, strength, and satisfying proportions of the best eighteenth-century craftsmanship. Patterned after the silver used in a gracious, hospitable society, the hollow ware and flatware shown on the following pages have the direct simplicity and superb design characteristic of that elegant age. These handsome copies of colonial antiques, equally suitable in traditional and contemporary settings, increase in beauty with each day's use.

Even persons of modest means in colonial Virginia are known to have owned sterling silver. For the wealthy, sterling silver was a form of investment as well as a symbol of status and a necessary and appropriate part of table service. The graceful pistol-handled knives, three-tined forks, and rat-tailed spoons, and the handsome coffeepots, bowls, and pitchers now reproduced and available at Craft House, are as satisfying to own today as they were two hundred years ago.

*RT 18 *Creamer*

This is a size adaptation of a creamer thought to have been made by John Allen (1671-1760). Its shape echoes the soft curves of the RT 15 Sugar Bowl. Capacity 10 ounces; height 4½".

RT 33 SMALL CREAMER (not shown). Smaller than the creamer mentioned above (RT 18), this is the companion to the small sugar bowl (RT 34). The small creamer has a capacity of 4 ounces; height 3½".

RT 19 *Teapot*

The melon-shaped body of the *Williamsburg* teapot is balanced by the sweeping curve of its ebony handle. Delicate hand engraving around the top is its only ornament. The antique it copies was made by Boston silversmith, Jacob Hurd.
Capacity 1½ pints; height 6".

*Adaptation

RT 15 *Sugar Bowl*

Simple yet elegant, this bowl was copied from one made 200 years ago by John Burt, a Boston silversmith. Capacity 10 ounces; height 2¾"; diameter 4".

*RT 34 SMALL SUGAR BOWL (not shown). A small adaptation of the RT 15 Sugar Bowl. Capacity 5 ounces; height 2¼"; diameter 3¼".

RT 16 *Sugar Bowl Cover*

The unusual shape of this smoothly rounded cover is both practical and charming. It has its own foot and may be used separately as a small dish. It fits the RT 15 Sugar Bowl. Height 1¼"; diameter 4¼".

*RT 35 SMALL SUGAR BOWL COVER (not shown). A small adaptation of the RT 16 Sugar Bowl Cover. It fits the *RT 34 Small Sugar Bowl. Height 1"; diameter 3⅜".

RT 29 *Coffeepot*

The original of this magnificent coffeepot was made by Charles Le Roux, a New York silversmith. The straight spout and straight tapered sides contrast dramatically with the curves of its ebony side handle. Capacity one quart; height 11".

RT 71

RT 71 *Cup*

Simple lines and a graceful handle distinguish this silver cup copied from an American example of about 1795. It is perfect for serving punch and equally serviceable as a baby's cup.
Height 2⅞".

| GS 10 | GS 11 | GS 9 | GS 7 | GS 1 | GS 4 | GS 13 | GS 8 | GS 54 | GS 5 | GS 12 |

Williamsburg
REPRODUCTION
FLATWARE

This Shell Pattern silver service is based on an assembled set of English, Georgian flatware in the Colonial Williamsburg collection. It dates from about 1760. The raised shell on each piece is characteristic of the period, and is found on many English produced items during the middle years of the eighteenth century. Various forms, unknown in colonial times, have been adapted from the antique pieces. And note, the fork has four tines rather than three.

Williamsburg Shell Pattern

†GS 1 Dinner Knife
*GS 2 Luncheon Knife
†GS 4 Service Spoon
  GS 5 Tablespoon
*†GS 7 Bread and Butter Knife
  GS 8 Coffee Spoon
†GS 9 Dinner Fork
†GS 10 Luncheon Fork
*GS 11 Cocktail Fork
*†GS 12 Teaspoon
*GS 13 Iced-Tea Spoon
*GS 14 Roast Carving Set
*GS 54 Salt Spoon
*GS 60 Cold Meat Fork
*GS 61 Steak Knife
*GS 62 Steak Carving Set
*GS 63 Gravy Ladle
*GS 64 Fish Knife
  GS 65 Salad Fork
*GS 68 Baby Spoon
*GS 69 Baby Fork
*GS 70 Sugar Shell

†Six Piece Place Setting
*Adaptation

RT 65   RT 9   RT 10   RT 3   RT 2   RT 7   RT 4   RT 13   RT 12   RT 5   RT 6

The *Williamsburg* Queen Anne sterling silver pattern has been recognized for years as a most distinguished reproduction of eighteenth-century flatware. Copied from a design popular throughout most of the eighteenth century, the rat-tailed spoons, three-tined forks and pistol-handled knives are cherished today as then for their graceful shapes and clean lines.

Queen Anne Pattern

RT 1 Dinner Knife
RT 2 Medium Knife
*†RT 3 Small Dinner Knife
†RT 4 Dessert Spoon
RT 5 Tablespoon
RT 6 Tablespoon (notched)
*†RT 7 Butter Spreader
RT 8 Coffee Spoon
†RT 9 Dinner Fork
†RT 10 Medium Fork
*RT 11 Oyster Fork
*†RT 12 Teaspoon
*RT 13 Iced-Tea Spoon
*RT 14 Roast Carving Set
RT 51 Ladle
*RT 54 Salt Spoon
*RT 60 Cold Meat Fork
*RT 61 Steak Knife
*RT 62 Steak Carving Set
*RT 63 Gravy Ladle
*RT 64 Fish Knife
*RT 65 Salad Fork
*RT 68 Baby Spoon
*RT 69 Baby Fork
*RT 70 Sugar Shell

†Six Piece place setting
*Adaptation

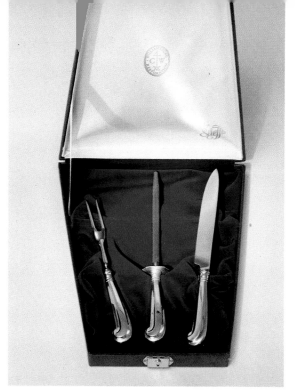

RT 14 *Three-Piece Roast Carving Set*

RT 61 *Set of Six Steak Knives*

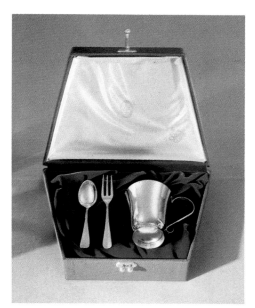

Three-Piece Baby Set

A "Queen Anne" pattern spoon and fork accompanied by a graceful cup make an excellent christening gift for the new arrival.
RT 69 Baby Fork
RT 68 Baby Spoon
RT 71 Cup

RT 38 *Labels*

Boxed set of six sterling silver decanter labels. Specify your choice of bourbon, scotch, gin, vodka, rye, rum, brandy, sherry or port. The individual label may be seen on page 222.

RT 23 *Finger Bowl*

A copy of an unusual bowl made by Jacobus Van der Spiegel, a New York silversmith, this reproduction serves as an elegant finger bowl. With the RT 27 Tray, it is a charming dish for a child. Height 2″; diameter 3¾″.

RT 28 *Bowl*

A design of classic simplicity copied from a bowl made by Philip Syng (1676–1739). This fine reproduction serves beautifully as a waste bowl for the *Williamsburg* tea or coffee service, or as a candy dish. Capacity 18 ounces; height 2⅝″; diameter 5½″.

RT 26 *Syrup Pitcher*

The original of this beautifully proportioned pitcher was made by Paul Revere, Sr., father of America's most renowned silversmith. It has an unusual handle design, and a generous capacity of 10 ounces. Height 6¼″.

RT 27 *Tray*

This versatile small tray may be used with either the RT 26 Syrup Pitcher or the RT 23 Finger Bowl. It also makes a handsome bread-and-butter plate. Diameter 5″.

RT 66 *Skewer*

Originally a skewer, now a handsome letter opener, this reproduction is carefully hand-engraved with a bright-cut decoration. Its original was made in York, England, in 1780 by J. Hampton and J. Prince. Length 9″.

RT 30 *Muffineer*

Tall, graceful, elegantly decorated, this caster was designed for sprinkling salt, sugar or spices over food. Today it's an attractive way to serve powdered sugar. The antique bears the London hallmark of 1709–1710. Capacity 10 ounces; height 8⅞″.

RT 32 *Individual Coffeepot*

For those who like to linger over their coffee, this charming spout cup makes a gracious touch on a breakfast tray or table. The raffia-covered handle is heat-resistant. Capacity 10 ounces; height 5¼″.

RT 23

RT 28

RT 66

RT 26

RT 27

RT 32

RT 30

201

RT 67

RT 22

RT 21

RT 54

RT 31

RT 24

RT 25

RT 67 *Brandy Warmer*

An old English saucepan made by John Eckford in 1723 inspired this graceful reproduction. An excellent way to serve melted butter or hot sauces.
Capacity 8 ounces; height 2¼"; length including handle 6¾".

RT 22 *Sauce or Gravy Boat*

The jaunty sweep of its curved handle balances the long, graceful lip of this fine reproduction. The original was made in Boston by John Burt. Capacity 10 ounces; overall length 8".

RT 21 *Compote*

An old definition of a salver or compote says it was used in serving vessels of liquids "to save the Carpit and Cloathes from drops." Today we use it for serving nuts, mints, petit fours and other delicacies. This is an authentic copy of a compote made by Jacob Hurd of Boston (1702-1758). Height 3⅛"; diameter 8½".
    *RT 20 COMPOTE. A smaller adaptation of the RT 21 Compote (not shown). Height 2¼"; diameter 6⅝".

RT 31 *Trencher Salt*

An antique made in London circa 1706-1707 was copied in this graceful open salt dish, glass-lined to guard the silver from corrosion. Shown with the *RT 54 Salt Spoon, it is a natural mate for the RT 36 Pepper Shaker (below).
Height 1¼"; diameter of base 2⅜".

RT 24 *Candlestick*

Silversmith Timothy Bontecou (1693-1784), made the original of this classic candlestick, which harmonizes so well with any setting. The oval of its removable cup reflects the shape of the base. Height 5½".

RT 25 *Mustard or Horse-Radish Pot*

A row of beading is the only embellishment on this simple, yet graceful mustard pot. Glass-lined to protect the silver, it is a useful addition to any table. Height 2½"; diameter 2¼".

RT 36 *Pepper Shaker*

A perfect partner for the RT 31 Trencher Salt, this handsome caster can also be used as a muffineer for nutmeg or cinnamon. The antique was made in Boston by Benjamin Burt (1729-1805). Height 5¼".

*Adaptation

RT 36

PLATED SILVERWARE

Plated silverware has had its place in the finest homes since about 1742, when an English cutler first discovered that silver and a base metal could be fused and worked like solid silver. The Stieff Company has produced several handsome pieces of plated silverware, copied from the original antiques with skill and care. These pieces surpass the best grade of superfine silver plate.

*J 1 *Bowl*

This classic bowl is a silver plate adaptation of an antique made by Richard Gurney and Thomas Cook of London. It makes a fine centerpiece or serving dish for hors d'oeuvres.
Height 3⅛″; diameter 7⅛″.

*J 2 *Candlestick*

The original from which this handsome candlestick was adapted was made in London in 1723–1724 by David Green.
Height 6¼″; width 3¾″.

*J 3 *Sugar Bowl*

A simple, graceful bowl made by a Boston silversmith over 200 years ago has been adapted in silver plate by Stieff craftsmen.
Height 2¾″; diameter 4″.

*J 4 *Sugar Bowl Cover*

The unusual cover of the sugar bowl shown above will also serve as a small footed dish for candy or nuts.
Height 1¼″; diameter 4¼″.

*J 5 *Creamer*

This dainty little creamer with its slender looped handle has softly rounded lines to match those of the J 3 Sugar Bowl.
Height 4½″; capacity 10 ounces.

*J 6 *Compote*

The beautiful and the practical combine in the simple design of this small compote, ideal for serving nuts, candies, or hors d'oeuvres.
Height 2¼″; diameter 6⅝″.

*J 8 *Coffeepot*

The chaste, unadorned look of this distinguished coffeepot was copied from a sterling silver pot made in London in 1740–1741.
Height 10¼″; capacity 2½ pints.

*J 9 *Standing Cup*

Copied from a Charles II silver goblet made in 1687–1688, this handsome standing cup has a nearly cylindrical bowl supported by a baluster stem and spreading circular foot. The English antique is in the Palace dining room.
Height 6″.

*Adaptation

WILLIAMSBURG GLASSWARE by Royal Leerdam

AIR-TWIST

cw 3s

cw 3w

cw 3g

TEARDROP

cw 2g

cw 2w

cw 2s

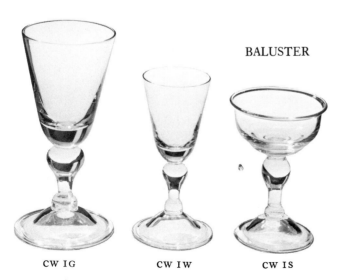

BALUSTER

cw 1g

cw 1w

cw 1s

With their timeless simplicity of line, *Williamsburg* glass reproductions harmonize with contemporary as well as traditional table settings. This fine glassware is unequalled for beauty of design, purity of materials, and superb hand craftsmanship. Interpreted from fragments excavated in Williamsburg and copied from antiques in the exhibition buildings of Colonial Williamsburg, these reproductions are made of lead glass, strong yet translucent, with an extraordinary power to diffuse light. Only the finest, most experienced craftsmen are entrusted with making these mouth-blown and hand-formed pieces. Each piece has its individual characteristics, reflecting the skill of the artisan who produced it.

STEMWARE

Air-Twist

This spiral air-twist form was developed about 1735 and was popular throughout the middle of the eighteenth century. Many fragments have been discovered in Williamsburg. In making the air-twist stemware, a wire is introduced into the molten stem to form a channel. Several channels are successively formed and then combined and twisted into a graceful spiral by the use of wooden paddles and other special tools in the hands of a master craftsman.

		Height
*cw 3s	Sherbet/Champagne	5¾"
cw 3w	Wine Glass	6½"
cw 3g	Goblet	7⅞"

Teardrop

The teardrop in this intriguing pattern is formed by first introducing a wire into the molten stem. When a channel forms, a wet stick is applied and the steam develops a "tear," which the craftsman pushes up the stem to the desired spot. The teardrop sherbet or champagne glass is copied from an antique in the Williamsburg collection. Many fragments of teardrop stems were revealed in Williamsburg archaeological excavations.

		Height
cw 2g	Goblet	7⅞"
*cw 2w	Wine Glass	6½"
cw 2s	Sherbet/Champagne	5¾"

Baluster

There is ample evidence that this was one of the favorite types of stemware in the colonial capitol. Among the common stem forms found during Williamsburg excavations was this inverted baluster with sloping domed foot, an English style of the first half of the eighteenth century. The handsome reproductions of this baluster shape are still popular today because the simplicity of style complements both modern and traditional settings.

		Height
cw 1g	Goblet	7⅜"
cw 1w	Wine Glass	5⅞"
*cw 1s	Sherbet/Champagne	5"

*Adaptation

CW 5W

CW 5T CW 5M CW 5S

The first glassmakers in America were "eight Dutchmen and Poles" who landed at Jamestown, Virginia in 1608. They introduced to America the ancient techniques of glassmaking developed more than 2000 years ago. Those same age-old techniques are used today by the artisans at Royal Leerdam, one of the few glass manufacturers continuing the delicate art of off-hand glass blowing.

Tavern Glasses

This handsome set of glasses was inspired by a fragment uncovered during excavations at Williamsburg, now in the archaeological collection. Simple, graceful, these glasses will dress up any party or table setting. CW 5M is an exact reproduction; the others are size adaptations. All are available in amber, amethyst, sapphire and emerald, as well as crystal.

			Height
*CW 5T	Iced Tea	....	6⅛"
*CW 5W	Water	....	5⅛"
CW 5M	Old-Fashioned	....	4⅛"
*CW 5S	Cordial	....	2⅞"

*CW 2P *Pilsener Glass*

This tall, graceful glass is excellent for serving beer or ale. Although it is an adaptation of the teardrop design, its tapered shape is in the best eighteenth-century tradition. Available in crystal only. Height 7⅞".

CW 2V *Teardrop Vase*

A fine reproduction in the style of teardrop stemware, this vase is ideal for long-stemmed flowers. It is also available in a taller adaptation. Height 10".

*CW 2VL (not shown). A size adaptation of the CW 2V Teardrop Vase. Height 11½".

*Adaptation

CW 15 *Plain Flip Glass*

This simple, handsome glass, available in crystal, and in amber, emerald, amethyst, and sapphire, makes a stunning tall vase. Its shape is copied from an English antique. Height 7½".

*CW 46 *Plain Wine Glass*

This superbly crafted wine glass will add elegance to any table setting. The bell-shaped bowl rising from a tall, graceful stem is of a generous size, to please connoisseurs. Height 7".

CW 47 *Air Twist Wine Glass*

A set of these handcrafted lead crystal glasses would greatly enhance any formal setting. The bell-shaped bowl is supported by a particularly attractive air-twist stem. Height 7".

CW 15

CW 2P CW 2V CW 46 CW 47

CW 42S Decanter is a fine complement for CW 47 Air Twist Wine Glasses.

Hurricane Shades

Originally used to shield candles from wind and drafts, hurricane shades are popular today for the same practical reason, as well as for decorative purposes. A hurricane shade may be used on its side filled with colorful fruits and nuts and pine cones, or upright surrounded by flowers, as a charming holiday decoration or centerpiece. These fine hurricane shades are size adaptations of a graceful antique used in the upstairs hall at the Governor's Palace. They are available in crystal, amber, amethyst, sapphire and emerald.

*cw 8 HURRICANE SHADE—A tiny shade to fit small spaces. Can be used with cw 16-39 Brass Taperstick or cw 47 Pewter Taperstick. Height 9".

*cw 9 HURRICANE SHADE—Height 14"; inside diameter of base 4⅞".

*cw 10 HURRICANE SHADE—Height 17¾"; inside diameter of base 5⅝".

*Adaptation

CW 10

CW 8

CW 9

CW 45

CW 11

cw 45 *Baluster Candlesticks*

The English antique which inspired these fine crystal pieces was created about 1720. The simple rounded lines of the baluster design are just as appealing now in any table setting. Height 8½".

cw 11 *Teardrop Candlesticks*

An exquisite pair of candlesticks reflecting the skill of modern craftsmen working by hand in the eighteenth-century manner. Eight separate pieces of glass are carefully joined to form the shaft of each candlestick where a "teardrop" resides. Particularly lovely on a dinner table or mantel. Height 8¹/₁₆".

To produce the fine glassware for the *Williamsburg* Reproductions program, Royal Leerdam craftsmen blow a "gather" of molten glass into a bubble on a blowpipe, then swiftly turn the bubble of glass and manipulate it into the shape that satisfies the skilled eye of the craftsman.

CW 12 *Wine Bottle*

A distinctive flask or carafe, this shapely bottle is copied from an antique in the Williamsburg collection. It also makes a charming ornamental flower vase or container for growing ivy. Available in four glowing colors, as shown. Height 8⅞".

CW 12

*CW 40 *Wine Bottle*

This fascinating bottle bears a bottle seal with the inscription: "Jno. Greenhow Wmsbg. 1770". Its original was excavated at the site of the John Greenhow House and Store. It is available in amethyst, emerald, sapphire and amber to lend color and charm to today's homes.
Capacity 26 ounces; height 8".

CW 7 *Lipped Finger Bowl*

Our forefathers used lipped bowls to rinse their wine glass between wine courses. Today these dainty bowls serve as finger bowls, and for ice, dessert, nuts, or flowers. The reproduction was copied from an antique in the Williamsburg collection. It is available in crystal as well as jewel-like tones of amethyst, emerald, amber and sapphire.
Height 4¼"; diameter at top 4½".

*Adaptation

*CW 36L *Pitcher*

Shown here in sapphire, this pitcher is a larger size adaptation of the 36s Pitcher. It is also available in crystal, amber, amethyst and emerald.
Height 5".

CW 36L   CW 36S

CW 36s *Pitcher*

This reproduction of a miniature eighteenth-century antique pitcher in the Williamsburg collection can be used as a small creamer or a vase for tiny flower arrangements. It is available in crystal, amber, sapphire, emerald and amethyst. Height 3⅝".

Williamsburg GLASSWARE FOR ENTERTAINING

The hospitality of two centuries ago is echoed in these handsome *Williamsburg* Glassware Reproductions. Their traditional designs are ideally suited to today's entertaining, since attractive bar accessories and dining glassware are still in demand.

*cw 38p *Water Jug*

Simplicity is the keynote of this gently rounded pitcher, carefully reproduced and copied from a cherished antique. Etching which decorates the original has been omitted. The pitcher or jug is available in crystal, amber, emerald, amethyst or sapphire.
Capacity 1½ quarts; height 7⅞".

cw 6 *Square Decanter*

This charming decanter with its wide base and low, rounded lines was copied from an antique designed to fit a cellarette. It is delightful alone or used in pairs on the AP 120 Tray.
Capacity 1½ quarts; height including stopper 6¼"; base 6 x 6".

*cw 42s *Decanter*

A very large decanter has been reduced in size to make this graceful adaptation. This version handles and pours with ease.
Capacity 1¼ quarts; height including stopper 11".

*Adaptation

cw 13 *Tall Decanter*

An antique once owned by a colonial resident of Williamsburg was copied for this handsome decanter. Its clean, modern-looking lines are available in crystal, amethyst, sapphire, emerald or amber.
Capacity 1⅓ quarts; height including stopper 11¼".

*cw 43 *Highball Glass*

Any table or bar would be enlivened by these handsome glasses, the perfect size and shape for today's entertaining. Available in crystal as well as the four vivid colors shown.
Height 5½"; capacity 12 ounces.

*cw 31s *Old Fashioned Glass*

A size adaptation of the 31L Double Old Fashioned Glass, this is especially popular for cocktail parties because of its compact size. Available in crystal and four jewel colors.
Height 3¼".

cw 31L *Double Old Fashioned Glass*

This handsome copy of an eighteenth-century tumbler is just as popular two hundred years later. Available in crystal and in amber, sapphire, amethyst and emerald.
Height 4".

WILLIAMSBURG
BONE CHINA

By Wedgwood

Colonial Sprays

Even though this pattern can be found on Wedgwood earthenware made in the eighteenth century, it retained its popularity and has been discovered among the patterns used on bone china in the 1812–22 period.

Bone china was developed in the English potteries during the last few years of the eighteenth century, and by the beginning of the next, it had become the standard ware of the fine English porcelain factories. So high was the quality of the English bone china that it continued to be the porcelain produced throughout the nineteenth century and—with only minor improvements—is still used today.

For a decade during the first quarter of the nineteenth century the Wedgwood company, managed by Josiah Wedgwood II, son of the great Josiah Wedgwood who, more than fifty years earlier, had founded the factory, produced this refined, translucent ware. It was decorated with many and varied patterns; some incorporating new motifs designed specifically for the ware and others taken from successful old patterns extending well back into the eighteenth century.

The Wedgwood firm has today produced for Colonial Williamsburg dinner services of the same fine bone china, including reproductions of early Wedgwood pieces in the collections of Colonial Williamsburg and in the Wedgwood company's own museum. To conform with twentieth-century table customs some pieces have become altered in size or form, and when no example from the period could be found to copy, as in the coffeepot, compatible forms were designed.

The decoration of the Wedgwood bone china services produced for Colonial Williamsburg include patterns used on Wedgwood's original bone china employing both motifs designed for the ware and patterns dating back to the period of the first Josiah, as well as a familiar bone china pattern produced by neighboring factories during the same period.

Chinese Flowers

The interest in things Oriental can be seen in these, an early nineteenth-century Englishman's conception of "Chinese flowers." They are so described in Wedgwood's pattern book.

209

Bianca

Probably the most familiar early nineteenth-century bone china pattern is this basket of flowers, used by several potteries but primarily by Wedgwood's Staffordshire neighbor, New Hall. There the pattern was employed on both earthenware and hardpaste porcelain before it was produced on bone china. Two other recorded New Hall patterns have been employed by Wedgwood, in conjunction with the basket of flowers, to unify the designs.

Cuckoo

This colorful chinoiserie pattern is reproduced from the motifs found on a coffee cup and saucer in Colonial Williamsburg's collection. It also appears in Wedgwood's pattern book where it is referred to as "flowers and bird."

Chinese Tiger

This dog-of-foo design, or Chinese tiger as it was called in the early nineteenth-century, is found on pieces of a tea service in the Wedgwood museum and on a plate owned by Colonial Williamsburg. Examples in other museums appear in colors such as red, blue, and black.

COMPLETE TABLE SETTINGS AVAILABLE IN BONE CHINA

CHINESE TIGER   8″ Bowl   10″ Bowl

BIANCA   Dinner Plate

COLONIAL SPRAYS
Coffeepot

CUCKOO   Teapot   Sugar   Creamer

CHINESE FLOWERS   Teacup and Saucer
After-dinner Cup and Saucer

COLONIAL SPRAYS   Sauce Boat and Stand   Oval Platter

WILLIAMSBURG
QUEEN'S WARE by Wedgwood

In 1759 Josiah Wedgwood, a skilled and successful potter, founded a firm of potters in Burslem, England. Today Josiah Wedgwood and Sons is known the world over for the quality and distinction of its ceramic ware.

Queen's Ware was an invention of Josiah Wedgwood, who said in 1767, "The demand for this . . . Queen's Ware . . . still increases. It is really amazing how rapidly the use of it has spread almost over the whole globe, and how universally it is liked." Originally called cream ware by its inventor, it was soon to bear the name Queen's Ware at the command of Queen Charlotte of England, whose admiration for Wedgwood's work was further expressed when she made him "Potter to Her Majesty."

The tradition of excellence established by Josiah Wedgwood is carried on by his descendants, who work today with the same high standards of design, skill, and integrity he set two hundred years ago.

Potpourri

Named for Queen Charlotte, Wedgwood's Queen's Shape dinnerware has been made continuously since 1765. In this delightful commemorative, it is imaginatively decorated in a rich fruit and flower pattern taken from an antique fabric. For information about the fabric, which has been reproduced, please see page 130.

POTTERY by *Williamsburg Pottery*

Inspired by fragments excavated in Williamsburg and at Jamestown, and by antiques in the Williamsburg collection, these attractive items are hand made by local craftsmen. Using traditional incised (sgraffito) and slip-colored techniques, these earthenwares and salt-glazed stonewares are comparable to those used in the Williamsburg area in colonial times.

Stoneware, a hard pottery impervious to liquids and acids, takes on a textured glaze (very like an orange peel) when common salt is thrown into the white-hot kiln. The salt glaze technique was invented by German potters in the fifteenth century, and adopted by eighteenth-century English potters. The techniques are used today in hand-crafting Williamsburg salt-glaze pottery. Approximately 25 hand operations are required to make every piece.

Saltglaze Mugs

These gray saltglaze mugs with cobalt blue decoration were inspired by fragments from the Williamsburg archaeological collection.

M 11 LARGE MUG. Height 5½"; capacity 36 ounces.

M 11s MUG. Height 4½"; capacity 16 ounces.

M 10 MEDIUM MUG. Height 5"; capacity 12 ounces.

M 12 CHILD'S MUG. Height 3¾"; capacity 8 ounces.

M 8 *Medium Jug and* M 9 *Large Jug*

Copied from antique gray stoneware jugs made in Germany for the English market. Similar ware with salt glaze and cobalt blue decoration is made in Germany today.

M 8 MEDIUM JUG—Height 6"; capacity 18 ounces.

M 9 LARGE JUG—Height 8"; capacity 36 ounces.

M 1 *Beer Mug*

The design of this yellow and brown mug dates back to the early settlement at Jamestown, Virginia. Height 5"; capacity 16 ounces.

M 25 *Pie Plate*

As useful now as it was two hundred years ago, this marbleized slipware plate makes an unusual pie plate or serving dish, or a fine ash tray. Its rich browns and yellows were copied from fragments unearthed in Williamsburg. Diameter 10¼".

Also available but not shown are two size adaptations:

*M 26 MEDIUM PLATE—Diameter 7½".

*M 27 SMALL PLATE—Diameter 5½".

M 7 *Slipware Pitcher*

The pleasing, rounded lines of this small pitcher were copied from early eighteenth-century fragments found on the site of the Semple House. The pitcher is yellow with streaks of brown. Height 6"; capacity 24 ounces.

*DB 5 *Bowl*

This piece of dotware displays an early form of slipware decoration. The dots are dark brown against a yellow background. Height 3".

*DP 2 PITCHER—A dotware companion to the DB5 Bowl. Height 3½".

*M 19 *and* M 20 *Pepper and Salt Shakers*

A Staffordshire saltglaze shaker now used in the Wythe House dining room was copied for these charming adaptations. The original, made about 1760, was decorated with enamel; the adaptations have a scratch blue design. Height 5".

M 3 *Medium Bowl*

A set of these yellow and brown bowls is delightful for serving individual casseroles and soups. The sgraffito or scratchware decoration is charming. Available in three sizes. Ovenproof.

M 3 MEDIUM BOWL. Diameter 6½".

M 2 SMALL BOWL (not shown). Diameter 4¾".

M 4 LARGE BOWL (not shown). Diameter 7¾".

M 13 *Jamestown Candlestick*

This unusual candlestick, copied after an original found in Jamestown, can add a decorative touch to any modern home. Available in yellow glaze with brown decoration. Height 6".

M 18 *Dotware Candlestick*

This charming small chamberstick was re-created from fragments excavated at the site of Anthony Hay's cabinetmaking shop. It is yellow with brown dots. Height 2½"; diameter 4".

M 5 *Large Trencher*

This large yellow-and-brown serving dish is copied from an antique now in the Raleigh Tavern. Ovenproof, it's an excellent choice for entertaining or large family meals. Its comb decoration is typical of eighteenth-century slipware. Length 16¾". Also available (not shown) are two size adaptations; all are ovenproof.

*M 6 SMALL TRENCHER. Length 8¼".

*M 14 MINIATURE TRENCHER. Length 4".

*Adaptation

M 33 *Preserve Jar*

A sturdy antique jar now in the Raleigh Tavern was copied to make this attractive stoneware container. Use it as a vase for leaves or flowers, or fill it with your own preserves or pickles.
Height 5⅜".

M 30 *Jug*

A Devonshire jug inspired this small slipware pitcher, done in yellow glaze with brown sgraffito decoration. Like the original it is inscribed "E.M. 1792."
Height 5".

M 21 *Pitcher*

An English antique, circa 1760, inspired this charming small pitcher with its scratch blue decoration. In this kind of ware the simple design is scratched into the soft clay and cobalt blue is painted in the scratches.
Height 3½".

M 28 *Cheese Jar*

An eighteenth-century antique was the inspiration for this stoneware jar which may be used to contain cheese, spreads, or dips. It is saltglaze with cobalt blue decorations.
Height 2⅞".

M 37 *Burslem Mug*

This sturdy brown stoneware mug holds a hearty pint of ale or beer. Copied from eighteenth-century fragments excavated on the site of the Printing Office.
Height 5¼"; capacity 16 ounces.

M 31 *Bird Bottle*

This novel birdhouse is a copy of an eighteenth-century bird bottle excavated in the garden of the James Geddy house. Hand-turned on a potter's wheel and fired to a rich brown glaze, it adds an authentic colonial touch to your garden. Hang it under the eaves of a building or from a tree, adding a stick for a perch.
Length 9".

C 8 *Fern Tray and* C 9 *Honeysuckle Tray*

These attractive serving dishes have been copied from antique sweetmeat trays made in Staffordshire, England, about 1760. Like the originals, these reproductions are footed.
C 8 FERN TRAY. Length 6".
C 9 HONEYSUCKLE TRAY. Length 6½".

M 34, M 35, *and* M 36 *Pottery Bowls*

These rustic slipware bowls decorated in warm tones of brown and yellow are typical of a style popular in the eighteenth century. Today they become excellent ash trays or unusual serving dishes for nuts, candy or hors d'oeuvres.
M 34 OBLONG BOWL. Diameter 6" x 5".
M 35 ROUND BOWL. Diameter 7¼".
M 36 ROUND BOWL. Diameter 7".

M 15 *Star Mold*

Bake individual desserts in it or use it to mold fancy gelatin salads. Every home should have several. This small star mold in white salt glaze is an ovenproof copy of an antique mold.
Height 1½; diameter 3½".

M 16 *and* M 17 *Fish Molds*

These appealing fish make excellent ash trays, pin trays, or individual hors d'oeuvres plates. The M 16 Mold is a copy of an antique; the M 17 Mold is a slightly larger adaptation. Both are ovenproof, made of white saltglaze.
M 16 FISH MOLD. Length 5⅞".
*M 17 FISH MOLD. Length 8⅛".

*Adaptation

Williamsburg Decor for Dining

Dinnerware

BIANCA

			1 Piece	6 Pieces
BA	1	*Dinner Plate	$ 20.45	$119.00
BA	3	*Dessert or Salad Plate	12.95	73.35
BA	5	*Bread & Butter Plate	8.85	49.20
BA	11	*Teacup & Saucer	20.45	119.00
BA	12	After Dinner Cup & Saucer	17.35	100.50
BA	16	Oval Platter, 14″	69.50	
BA	19	Vegetable Dish	40.35	
BA	21	Sauce Boat & Stand	64.35	
BA	24	Coffeepot	52.35	
BA	25	Teapot	46.35	
BA	26	Sugar	33.95	
BA	27	Creamer	22.95	
BA	34	Bowl, 8″	51.35	
BA	35	Bowl, 10″	66.50	
		*Place Set (5 pieces)	60.75	
		Starter Set (4 place sets)	240.00	

CHINESE FLOWERS

			1 Piece	6 Pieces
FL	1	*Dinner Plate	$ 18.95	$110.00
FL	3	*Dessert or Salad Plate	12.45	70.35
FL	5	*Bread & Butter Plate	8.35	46.20
FL	11	*Teacup & Saucer	18.95	110.00
FL	12	After Dinner Cup & Saucer	16.35	94.50
FL	16	Oval Platter, 14″	63.50	
FL	19	Vegetable Dish	37.85	
FL	21	Sauce Boat & Stand	59.35	
FL	24	Coffeepot	48.35	
FL	25	Teapot	43.35	
FL	26	Sugar	30.95	
FL	27	Creamer	21.95	
FL	34	Bowl, 8″	41.35	
FL	35	Bowl, 10″	61.50	
		*Place Set (5 pieces)	56.75	
		Starter Set (4 place sets)	224.00	

CHINESE TIGER

			1 Piece	6 Pieces
TG	1	*Dinner Plate	$ 18.95	$110.00
TG	3	*Dessert or Salad Plate	12.45	70.35
TG	5	*Bread & Butter Plate	8.35	46.20
TG	11	*Teacup & Saucer	18.95	110.00
TG	12	After Dinner Cup & Saucer	16.35	94.50
TG	16	Oval Platter, 14″	63.50	
TG	19	Vegetable Dish	37.85	
TG	21	Sauce Boat & Stand	59.35	
TG	24	Coffeepot	48.35	
TG	25	Teapot	43.35	
TG	26	Sugar	30.95	
TG	27	Creamer	21.95	
TG	34	Bowl, 8″	41.35	
TG	35	Bowl, 10″	61.50	
		*Place Set (5 pieces)	56.75	
		Starter Set (4 place sets)	224.00	

COLONIAL SPRAYS

			1 Piece	6 Pieces
SP	1	*Dinner Plate	$ 18.95	$110.00
SP	3	*Dessert or Salad Plate	12.45	70.35
SP	5	*Bread & Butter Plate	8.35	46.20
SP	11	*Teacup & Saucer	18.95	110.00
SP	12	After Dinner Cup & Saucer	16.35	94.50
SP	16	Oval Platter, 14″	63.50	
SP	19	Vegetable Dish	37.85	
SP	21	Sauce Boat & Stand	59.35	
SP	24	Coffeepot	48.35	
SP	25	Teapot	43.35	
SP	26	Sugar	30.95	
SP	27	Creamer	21.95	
SP	34	Bowl, 8″	41.35	
SP	35	Bowl, 10″	61.50	
		*Place Set (5 pieces)	56.75	
		Starter Set (4 place sets)	224.00	

All prices include shipping charges within the Continental United States and are subject to change without notice.

CUCKOO

		1 Piece	6 Pieces
KU 1	*Dinner Plate	$ 18.95	$110.00
KU 3	*Dessert or Salad Plate	12.45	70.35
KU 5	*Bread & Butter Plate	8.35	46.20
KU 11	*Teacup & Saucer	18.95	110.00
KU 12	After Dinner Cup & Saucer	16.35	94.50
KU 16	Oval Platter, 14″	63.50	
KU 19	Vegetable Dish	37.85	
KU 21	Sauce Boat & Stand	59.35	
KU 24	Coffeepot	48.35	
KU 25	Teapot	43.35	
KU 26	Sugar	30.95	
KU 27	Creamer	21.95	
KU 34	Bowl, 8″	41.35	
KU 35	Bowl, 10″	61.50	
	*Place Set (5 pieces)	56.75	
	Starter Set (4 place sets)	224.00	

POTPOURRI

		1 Piece	6 Pieces	8 Pieces
F 1	*Dinner Plate	$7.30	$40.50	$53.75
F 3	*Dessert or Salad Plate	5.10	28.10	37.35
F 5	*Bread and Butter Plate	3.85	20.45	27.20
F 7	Rim Soup Plate	6.30	34.50	45.75
F 8	Fruit Saucer	4.60	24.95	33.20
F 9	Oatmeal Saucer	4.85	26.60	35.35
F 11	*Teacup and Saucer	8.55	48.00	63.75
F 12	After Dinner Cup & Saucer	7.80	43.10	57.35
F 13	Cream Soup and Saucer	12.70	72.25	95.95

		Each
F 15	Oval Platter, 12″	$21.20
F 16	Oval Platter, 14″	25.35
F 18	Round Platter, 12″	22.35
F 19	Vegetable Dish	13.70
F 21	Sauce Boat and Stand	26.20
F 24	Coffeepot, 32 oz.	24.20
F 25	Teapot, 28 oz.	23.80
F 26	Sugar Box	14.45
F 27	Cream Pitcher	10.05
F 28	Square Cake Plate	11.80
	*Place Setting (5 pieces)	23.60
	Starter Set (4 place settings)	91.35

Matching linen place mats and napkins are $7.80 for a set of two mats and two napkins.

Pottery

		Each
C 8	Fern Leaf Tray	$ 3.10
C 9	Honeysuckle Leaf Tray	4.60
DP 2	Pitcher	3.75
DB 5	Bowl	3.60
	Set of DP 2 and DB 5	6.60
M 1	Beer Mug	
	Each	3.75
	Set of six	18.85
M 2	Small Bowl	3.75
M 3	Medium Bowl	4.75
M 4	Large Bowl	7.05
M 5	Large Trencher	16.75
M 6	Small Trencher	3.75
M 7	Slipware Pitcher	6.85
M 8	Medium Jug	6.35
M 9	Large Jug	8.35
M 10	Mug	
	Each	3.75
	Set of six	19.00
M 11	Mug	
	Each	5.85
	Set of six	31.30
M 11S	Mug	
	Each	3.85
	Set of six	19.55
M 12	Child's Mug	
	Each	3.75
	Set of six	18.85
M 13	Jamestown Candlestick	4.75
M 14	Miniature Trencher	2.60
M 15	Star Mold	2.35
M 16	Fish Mold	2.25
M 17	Fish Mold	3.60
M 18	Dotware Candlestick	
	Each	3.10
	Pair	5.75
M 19	Pepper Shaker	3.10
M 20	Salt Shaker	3.10
	Set of M 19 and M 20	5.50
M 21	Pitcher	5.10
M 25	Pie Plate	5.95
M 26	Medium Plate	3.25
M 27	Small Plate	2.60
M 28	Cheese Jar	2.10
M 30	Jug	5.25
M 31	Bird Bottle	6.55
M 33	Preserve Jar	6.35
M 34	Oblong Bowl	3.60
M 35	Round Bowl	3.75
M 36	Round Bowl	3.75
M 37	Burslem Mug	
	Each	3.75
	Set of Six	19.35

Sterling Silver

FLATWARE

Queen Anne Pattern

RT 1	Dinner Knife	$ 23.10
RT 2	Medium Knife	18.85
*RT 3	Small Dinner Knife	20.35
*RT 4	Dessert Spoon	19.35
RT 5	Tablespoon	31.95
RT 6	Tablespoon (notched)	42.45
*RT 7	Butter Spreader	13.60
RT 8	Coffee Spoon	8.35
*RT 9	Dinner Fork	22.85
*RT 10	Medium Fork	18.10
RT 11	Oyster Fork	11.60
*RT 12	Teaspoon	14.10
RT 13	Iced-Tea Spoon	18.35
RT 14	Roast Carving Set....2-piece	101.20
	....3-piece	145.00
RT 51	Ladle	19.35
RT 54	Salt Spoon	5.75
RT 60	Cold Meat Fork	33.95
RT 61	Steak Knife	20.85
	Set of 6, boxed	123.00
RT 62	Steak Carving Set	58.60
RT 63	Gravy Ladle	33.95
RT 64	Fish Knife	19.85
RT 65	Salad Fork	18.10
RT 68	Baby Spoon	10.60
RT 69	Baby Fork	10.60
RT 70	Sugar Shell	15.85
*Six-Piece Place Setting		106.25

Williamsburg Shell Pattern

*GS 1	Dinner Knife	$ 23.05
GS 2	Luncheon Knife	20.80
*GS 4	Service Spoon	18.30
GS 5	Tablespoon	33.05
*GS 7	Bread and Butter Knife	14.05
GS 8	Coffee Spoon	8.80
*GS 9	Dinner Fork	23.05
*GS 10	Luncheon Fork	17.55
GS 11	Cocktail Fork	11.55
*GS 12	Teaspoon	14.80
GS 13	Iced-Tea Spoon	18.30
GS 14	Roast Carving Set, 2-piece	111.25
GS 54	Salt Spoon	5.75
GS 60	Cold Meat Fork	34.55
GS 61	Steak Knife	20.80
GS 62	Steak Carving Set, 2-piece	66.10
GS 63	Gravy Ladle	34.30
GS 64	Fish or Butter Knife	20.80
GS 65	Salad Fork	17.55
GS 68	Baby Spoon	10.50
GS 69	Baby Fork	10.50
GS 70	Sugar Shell	17.55
*Six-Piece Place Setting		109.00

Baby Set Boxed	58.00
Decanter Label Set Boxed	46.50

HOLLOW WARE

RT 15	Sugar Bowl	$ 58.35
RT 16	Sugar Bowl Cover	32.15
RT 18	Cream Pitcher	133.50
RT 19	Teapot	517.00
RT 20	Small Compote	87.75
RT 21	Large Compote	127.75
RT 22	Gravy Boat	161.35
RT 23	Finger Bowl	34.65
RT 24	Candlestick	78.65
RT 25	Mustard Pot	126.00
RT 26	Syrup Pitcher	176.25
RT 27	Tray	29.40
RT 28	Bowl	63.25
RT 29	Coffeepot	693.00
RT 30	Muffineer	261.45
RT 31	Trencher Salt	23.15
RT 32	Individual Coffeepot	173.75
RT 33	Cream Pitcher Small	111.00
RT 34	Sugar Bowl Small	38.15
RT 35	Sugar Bowl Cover Small	29.40
RT 36	Pepper Shaker	87.25
RT 66	Skewer	31.85
RT 67	Brandy Warmer	52.75
RT 71	Cup	38.50

Plated Silverware

J 1	Bowl	$ 22.50
J 2	Candlestick	
	Each	27.85
	Pair	54.00
J 3	Sugar Bowl	19.15
J 4	Sugar Bowl Cover	12.65
J 5	Creamer	38.00
J 6	Compote	32.35
J 8	Coffeepot	150.25
J 9	Standing Cup	32.75

Pewter

CW 2	Cup	$ 11.55
	Set of CW 2, CW 76 and CW 89	19.00
CW 3	Bowl	19.50
CW 5	Bowl	20.35
CW 6	Bowl	36.85
CW 7	Bowl	66.35
CW 9	Bowl	31.10
CW 10	Bowl	11.55
CW 12	Tray	20.15
CW 14	Dressing Spoon	22.70
CW 15	Porringer	11.55
CW 16	Porringer	9.05
CW 30	Candlestick	
	Each	28.25
	Pair	55.00
CW 32	Candlestick	
	Each	56.20
	Pair	110.00
CW 43	Pewter Sundial	4.75
CW 47	Taperstick	
	Each	9.00
	Pair	17.00
CW 49	Cup	
	Each	6.75
	Set of 6	37.50

Pewter, *continued*

CW 49M	Cup		
		Each	$ 4.25
		Set of 6	22.50
CW 51	Berry Spoon		6.50
CW 52	Ladle		4.85
CW 53	Teaspoon		4.10
CW 54	Strawberry Dish		26.30
CW 55	Tankard		20.45
CW 56	Soup Spoon		5.00
CW 58	Soup Plate		21.90
CW 59	Plate		22.45
CW 60	Porringer		27.95
CW 64	Pap Boat		6.35
CW 76	Plate		6.30
CW 78	Helmet Inkstand		29.35
CW 80	Teapot		76.75
CW 81	Cream Pitcher		18.10
CW 82	Sugar Bowl		18.10
		Set CW 81 and CW 82	35.00
		Set CW 80, CW 81, and CW 82	110.00
CW 83	Large Cream Pitcher		20.05
CW 84	Large Sugar Bowl		20.05
		Set CW 83 and CW 84	38.50
		Set CW 80, CW 83, and CW 84	113.50
CW 85	Sugar Scoop		4.10
CW 87	Chamberstick		20.05
CW 88	Beaker		21.95
CW 88M	Cordial Cup		
		Each	5.75
		Set of 6	31.50
CW 89	Coffee Spoon		3.05
CW 90	Salt Spoon		2.60
CW 91	Cream Pitcher		17.05
CW 92	Sugar Bowl		15.80
		Set CW 91 and CW 92	31.25
CW 93	Humidor		28.10
CW 94	Humidor		43.70
CW 95	Pitcher		84.25
CW 96	Salt Shaker		20.05
CW 97	Pepper Shaker		20.05
		Set CW 96 and CW 97	38.50
CW 98	Open Salt		7.30
		Set CW 97, CW 98, and CW 90	28.00
CW 99	Caster		28.35

Glassware

			Each	Half Dozen
CW 1G	Baluster Goblet		$13.30	$77.00
CW 1S	Baluster Sherbet		13.30	77.00
CW 1W	Baluster Wine		13.30	77.00
CW 2G	Teardrop Goblet		15.80	92.00
CW 2P	Pilsener Glass		16.10	92.20
CW 2S	Teardrop Sherbet		15.80	92.00
CW 2V	Teardrop Vase		27.70	
CW 2VL	Teardrop Vase		32.35	
CW 2W	Teardrop Wine		15.80	92.00
CW 3G	Airtwist Goblet		17.30	101.00
CW 3S	Airtwist Sherbet		17.30	101.00
CW 3W	Airtwist Wine		17.30	101.00
CW 5M	Old-Fashioned		7.80	43.00
CW 5S	Cordial		5.25	28.20
CW 5T	Iced Tea		9.95	56.50
CW 5W	Water		8.80	50.00
CW 6	Square Decanter		32.85	
CW 7	Finger Bowl		10.80	62.00
CW 8	Hurricane Shade			
		Each	13.70	
		Pair	25.50	
	CW 8 with CW 16-39 Taperstick		22.75	
	CW 8 with CW-47 Taperstick		21.25	
CW 9	Hurricane Shade		31.50	
		Pair	60.00	
	Set CW 9 with CW 16-20 Candlestick		44.50	
	Set CW 9 with CW 16-35 Candlestick		49.50	
CW 10	Hurricane Shade		38.25	
		Pair	72.50	
	Set CW 10 with CW 16-33 Candlestick		71.25	
CW 11	Teardrop Candlesticks	Each	56.50	
		Pair	110.00	
CW 12	Wine Bottle		12.50	
CW 13	Tall Decanter		30.00	
CW 15	Plain Flip Glass		15.70	
CW 31L	Double Old-Fashioned		8.30	47.20
CW 31S	Old-Fashioned		7.30	41.00
CW 36L	Pitcher		13.30	
CW 36S	Pitcher		10.30	
CW 38P	Plain Water Jug		27.35	
CW 40	Greenhow Bottle		16.10	
CW 42S	Decanter		44.00	
CW 43	Highball		10.80	62.00
CW 45	Baluster Candlestick	Each	44.00	
		Pair	85.00	
CW 46	Wine Glass		12.80	74.00
CW 47	Airtwist Wine Glass		15.30	89.00

A Williamsburg
Potpourri of Gifts

HISTORIC Colonial Williamsburg provides an array of attractive gifts and unusual souvenirs that will delight you, your family and your friends. Some are copies of objects once in daily use; some are reminiscent of the folk arts of the period; some evoke the atmosphere of the past in articles of our own day. Included in the offerings are toys and activity kits with the theme of colonial times. These unique gifts for all ages are at once charming, evocative and educational.

Homely objects of the eighteenth century, like the trivets used as stands for hot dishes prepared in separate kitchens, have been copied in iron and brass—using elaborate and fanciful monograms, royal arms, and cyphers as themes. While they still protect a table from a steaming casserole, they are highly attractive, and usable as pure decoration for wall or table.

Mid-eighteenth century children have left us many examples of their sampler work with the obligatory alphabet and numbers together with artless scenes and the name and age of the busy stitcher. Sampler kits are available as gifts illustrating familiar Williamsburg scenes.

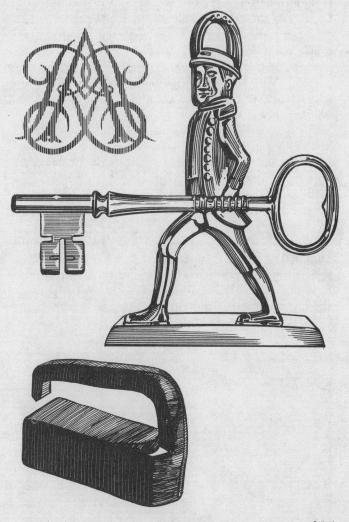

There is also a replica of little Mary Starker's elaborate sampler of 1760 for a real challenge. At a more sophisticated level, crewel kits reproduce early American designs like the ones used on antique bed coverings in the Peyton Randolph House. These designs can then be framed or applied to pillows and chair seats. Slightly younger children will appreciate the do-it-yourself reconstruction kits of famed Williamsburg landmarks and the colonial doll sets.

For the executive desk there are brass harness-ornament paper clips; a pewter sundial paper weight copied from an antique; and ash trays in Williamsburg designs, including a pair with contemporary portrait-engravings of King William and Queen Mary. The colonists, of course, smoked pipes, and fanciful tampers are reproduced from seventeenth- and eighteenth-century "tobacco stoppers."

For the bar and sideboard, sterling silver decanter labels are reproductions of antiques; a corkscrew in brass and steel is also an authentic copy (the basic corkscrew has changed little over the centuries). Williamsburg's four famous taverns are commemorated in bright linen cocktail napkins.

Today's housewife would probably burn up the laundry if she ironed with the gift-replica of a colonial pressing iron in the Williamsburg Archeological Museum. Therefore, it is much better to use this weighty object as a door stop. Or, two of them provide handsome book ends for a desk.

The gift-giver will also find towels hand woven in traditional designs and weave; soap balls in nostalgic fragrances; and candles of beeswax and bayberry, made by hand in Williamsburg; and a potpourri of herbs, flowers, and spices that is ready to do duty in linen drawers and blanket chests.

For a personal touch, colonial objects like a decorated keyhole escutcheon have been reproduced as an unusual pin, "the Lion and the Unicorn," while the historic symbols of authority, the Capitol mace and the Williamsburg mace, are miniatured as lapel or scarf pins in gold and silver wash. A cup pin inspired by a 1649 model holds water to keep small flowers fresh.

Williamsburg Gifts have been designed with the discriminating person in mind. Each one has been specially selected and carefully crafted to illustrate an authentic facet of Colonial Williamsburg. They can, indeed, provide the just-right thoughtful gift for special occasions.

POTPOURRI OF GIFTS

Fife and drums, and pins and things . . . and books to read. As important as any other *Williamsburg* reproduction and adaptation, these small items—little gifts to friends or yourself—spell the meaning of Williamsburg. They add a touch of our colonial past in a small but significant way.

Trivets

CW 10-11 *William and Mary Trivet*
The monogram is that of William and Mary, who reigned jointly as sovereigns of Great Britain from 1689 until Mary's death in 1694. Available in brass or iron. 6″ x 8″.

CW 10-17 *King's Arms Trivet*
The design is taken from the coat of arms on the sign of the famous King's Arms Tavern in Williamsburg. Available in brass or iron. 5½″ x 6″.

CW 10-9 *King George Trivet*
Ornamented with the monogram of George II, King of England from 1727 to 1760, this trivet is available in brass or iron. 4″ x 5″.

CW 10-10 *Queen Anne Trivet*
This trivet is composed of the initials "AR," representing the Latin "Anna Regina." It is the monogram of Queen Anne, who reigned in England from 1702 until her death in 1714. Available in brass or iron. 9″ x 10½″.

CW 10-14 *Colonial Williamsburg Trivet*
The initials "CW" decorate this interpretation of a cypher form that would have been used by wealthy colonials to mark their important possessions. Available in brass, iron, verdigris, or white bronze. Diameter 6″.

Pins

RT 50 *Lapel Pin*
A sterling silver pin that even holds water to keep small flowers fresh. The original from which this was taken is a large gold and silver cup, dated 1649, in the Williamsburg collection. 1½″ x 2¼″.

S 48 *Williamsburg Mace Pin*
The mace of the city of Williamsburg in miniature is available in silver or gold wash. The original bears a London silversmith's mark, dated 1749. Quite delightful because of its long slender appearance. Length 3¾″.

S 120G *and* S 120S *Capitol Mace Pin*
Copied from the Colonial Williamsburg mace, this pin is available in gold wash (S 120G) or silver wash (S 120S). Length 3¼″.

RT 55 *Spoon Pin*
This sterling silver pin is a miniature copy of the rat-tailed spoon design popular in the eighteenth century. Length 3″.

CW 24-71 *Lion and Unicorn Pin*
Copied from a keyhole escutcheon excavated at the Governor's Palace, this unusual pin is a handsome addition to a simple outfit. Polished brass. 1¾″ x 2¼″.

RT 53 *King's Arms Pin*
This is a sterling silver copy of the coat of arms on the sign of the King's Arms Tavern. The arms are those of George I, George II, and George III. 2″ x 2″.

217

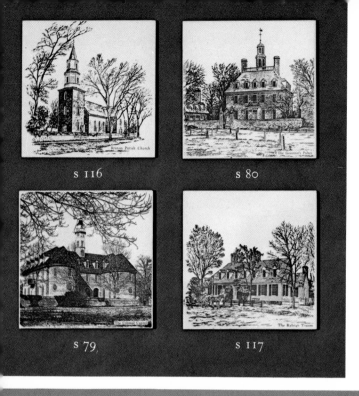

s 116   s 80

s 79   s 117

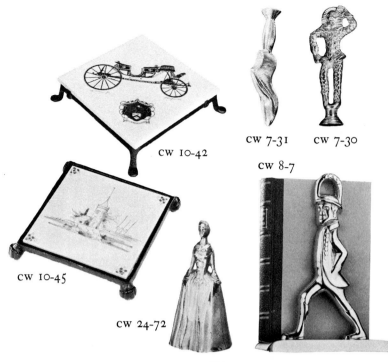

cw 7-31   cw 7-30

cw 8-7

cw 10-42

cw 10-45

cw 24-72

s 139-1   s 139-2   s 139-3   s 139-4

**s 79, s 80 and s 116, s 117
Scenic Tiles**

Enjoy a reminder of Williamsburg with these attractive sepia tiles. Use them to protect your table from hot dishes, or as wall ornaments. Four of Colonial Williamsburg's most historic buildings are illustrated.
6″ x 6″.
s 79 Capitol
s 80 Governor's Palace
s 116 Bruton Parish Church
s 117 Raleigh Tavern

**s 139-1 to s 139-4 *Williamsburg
Military Tiles***

Four eighteenth-century military units are commemorated on these charming tiles. The illustrations are done in the style of eighteenth-century cartoons, and have the same subjects and colors as the Military Prints shown on pages 154 and 155.
6″ x 6″.
s 139-1 Virginia Militia
s 139-2 44th Regiment
s 139-3 48th Regiment
s 139-4 British Marines

cw 10-42 *Trivet Stand with Tile*

This black iron trivet stand will hold any of the tiles shown on this page. When ordering, please specify tile desired.

cw 10-45 *Delft Tile Holder*

This iron trivet was adapted from the square base of an antique brass candlestick, and designed specifically to hold one of the Williamsburg delft tiles (page 174). Also available in white bronze.

cw 7-31 *Slipper Pipe Tamper

A brass pipe tamper made in the shape of a lady's slipper. It is a replica of an antique. Such tampers were first devised by seventeenth-century craftsmen.
Length 2¾″.

cw 24-72 *Williamsburg Hostess Bell*

Colonial Williamsburg's hostesses, dressed in the fashion of 1760–65, inspired this delightful bell. Available in polished brass or white bronze.
Height 5″.

cw 8-7 and cw 18-65 *Striding Man*

Use this jaunty gentleman alone as a doorstop, or try a pair of them as bookends. Heavy brass, in two sizes.
cw 8-7 Height 8½″.
cw 18-65 Height 11¾″.

cw 7-30 *Harlequin Pipe Tamper

Copied from an early eighteenth-century "tobacco stopper," this fanciful pipe tamper is made of brass. For non-pipe smokers, the Harlequin and Slipper tampers make unusual curios for table tops or shelves.
Length 2¾″.

218

s 107 and s 108 *William and Mary Ash Trays*

The portraits of King William and Queen Mary that decorate these Wedgwood ash trays were taken from eighteenth-century engravings attributed to Gaspar de Hollander, a publisher in Antwerp. A pair of these ash trays is an unusually fine gift. Diameter 6¼".
s 107 King William Ash Tray
s 108 Queen Mary Ash Tray

cw 3-27 *Paper Mulberry Leaf Tray*

The design of this small tray is taken from a leaf of the gnarled paper mulberry trees that line Blair Street in Williamsburg. Brass. Length 5½".

cw 6-44 *Key*

A copy in brass of one of the keys to the Governor's Palace. Makes an excellent paper-weight.
Length 8".

cw 7-21 *Holly Leaf Paper Clip*

This unusual desk accessory was inspired by the American holly leaf which grows so luxuriantly in Williamsburg. It's a pretty way to keep papers in order. Polished brass. Length 4½".

cw 16-37 *Traveling Candleholders*

To be assured of light, the eighteenth-century traveler frequently carried his candlesticks with him. Modeled after an original made about 1770, the candleholder is compact when not in use. When opened, it becomes two graceful small candleholders.
Diameter 3¾"; height 2½".

s 119 *Soap Balls*

Fragrantly scented soap shaped into balls as they were in the eighteenth century. Fill a large glass apothecary jar or brandy snifter with them for a bright spot of color in the bathroom, or leave them open in the linen closet for subtly scented sheets. Box of three: one each bayberry (green), lavender (lavender), lemon (yellow).

s 119

Williamsburg Candles

Bayberry Candles. The spicy aroma of these decorative candles is reminiscent of colonial festivities. Soft green in color, the candles are made by hand in Williamsburg.
R 4 Small Candles. 9¼"
R 5 Large Candles. Fit cw 16-33 Spiked Candlestick (page 165). 8½"

R 4

Beeswax Candles. The excellent burning quality of beeswax candles made them very fashionable in the eighteenth century. These candles are made in Williamsburg.
R 7 Small Candles. 9¼"
R 8 Large Candles. Fit cw 16-33 Spiked Candlestick (page 165). 8½"

s 189 *Christiana Campbell's Tavern Towel*

This oversized linen tea towel taken from the advertising banner in front of Christiana Campbell's Tavern is both decorative and useful. 19¾" x 29½".

cw 24-49 *Bell Metal Porringer*

This substantial porringer is a reproduction of the antique made about 1780, now in the kitchen of Wetherburn's Tavern.
Diameter 5⅜".

cw 16-08 *Brass Hook*

Copied from an English antique of about 1785, this brass hook has many uses from a tieback for draperies to a chimney hook.
Over-all length 4⅜".

s 189

cw 16-08

cw 24-49

cw 24-13 *Shoehorn*

This man-size brass shoehorn was copied from an antique made in England about 1750. Length 8¼".

cw 16-37

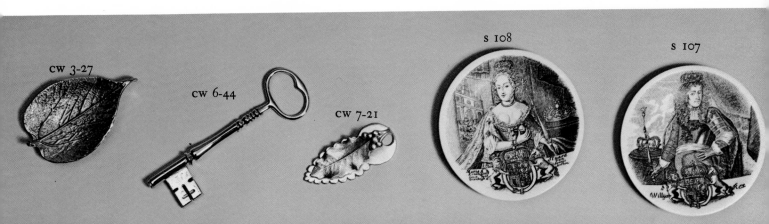

cw 3-27

cw 6-44

cw 7-21

s 108

s 107

s 85

Record Albums

WS 100

WS 103

WS 102

WS 104

WS 105

s 29

s 70

s 16

s 154

K 135

K 136

s 157

s 147

s 33

s 147

s 103

S 85 Four Documents of Freedom

Facsimiles on antiqued parchment paper of four historic American documents are available for study and for framing. They are the Virginia Resolution for Independence, Virginia Declaration of Rights, Declaration of Independence, and federal Bill of Rights. 13¾" x 15⅝".

WS 100 A Williamsburg Candlelight Concert

The Palace Orchestra, directed by Cary McMurran, presents a program of outstanding works known to have been performed in eighteenth-century Williamsburg. A collector's item for those who appreciate the music of the period and/or have enjoyed a memorable evening at a Candlelight Concert at the Governor's Palace.
Stereo (compatible with monaural needle).

WS 101 Fifes & Drums

Colonial Williamsburg's unique Band of Musick offers popular eighteenth-century tunes performed on instruments of the period, and the Fife & Drum Corps plays the stirring martial music of 200 years ago.
Stereo (compatible with monaural needle).

WS 102 O Come Sweet Music

This recording gives an enticing "taste" of the wide variety of music known during the many decades when Britain ruled these colonies. More important, it revives the spirit and enthusiasm for part singing that existed two centuries ago.
Stereo (compatible with monaural needle).

WS 103 An Evening of Music at Carter's Grove Plantation

Ann Rowe, Mezzo-soprano,
J. S. Darling, Harpsichord,
Elizabeth Chapman, Violin, and
Frances Hooper, Violoncello.

This record, made at Carter's Grove, a plantation just below Williamsburg on the James River, presents an evening of music as it might have occurred two hundred years ago.

Miss Rowe acts as Colonial Williamsburg's singer in residence, Mrs. Chapman and Mrs. Hooper regularly play in the Governor's Palace ensemble, and Mr. Darling is the organist of Bruton Parish Church.

WS 104 The Music Teacher

Colonial Virginians enjoyed music and many were accomplished performers. Versatile music teachers provided instruction especially to middle and upper class families. In addition to the harpsichord, guitars, recorders, violins, violas da gamba, and other instruments were well known—as were composers Schickhardt, Pepusch, Teleman, and Loeillet. This recording made at Williamsburg features the staff of the music teacher's shop—a regular presentation for visitors.

Williamsburg Pencil Sketch Notes

Scenes of Williamsburg and the surrounding historic area decorate this selection of note papers by Charles Overly. Envelopes are included with each package of notes.

S 16 Sketch Notes

Twelve different sketches of Williamsburg's buildings, gardens, and interiors capture the spirit of the restored town. 4" x 4¾".

S 29 Sketch Notes

Twelve sketches of eight Williamsburg scenes are delightful reminders of a visit to the colonial capital. 3½" x 4½".

S 70 Recipe Notes

Your messages to friends will be doubly welcome with this nostalgic notepaper. Williamsburg kitchens and taverns are illustrated, and each scene is accompanied by an authentic eighteenth-century recipe. A box includes ten notes. 5½" x 8¼".

S 103 Jamestown, Williamsburg, Yorktown Notes

Twelve folded notes show views of important scenes in the "historic triangle," from the Jamestown Fort and famed Williamsburg Buildings to Yorktown's Moore House. 3¾" x 7¼".

*Williamsburg Music Sheets

Each of these packets of songs contains six facsimile reproductions of eighteenth-century music taken from George Bickham's *Musical Entertainer*, published in London in 1738. The melodies may be performed on modern musical instruments, and the gracefully illustrated sheets may be framed for hanging in library or music room. 10½" x 16½".
Songs of Politics and Potation
Songs of Gentility

*Reproduction

S 147 Tavern Sign Notes

Four-fold note paper decorated with signs of the four taverns of Williamsburg and a view of Duke of Gloucester Street. All in soft pastels. Twelve notes and envelopes to the box. 6" x 4½".

S 154 Color Wash Notes

A box of ten informal correspondence notes and envelopes with views of Williamsburg as sketched by Charles Overly. Each drawing has a soft color wash of either blue or yellow. 4⅝" x 6⅛".

S 187 Embroidery Notes

An English embroidery, made about 1710, was the prototype for these delightful notes. There are six views (two of each) in a box of twelve notes and envelopes. 4¼" x 6".

K 135 and K 136 Post Paper

This fine quality stationery was copied from antique letter paper in the archives of Colonial Williamsburg. Its charming package is tied with red ribbon and sealed with wax.
K 136 Note Paper.
30 sheets, 20 envelopes;
5" x 8".
K 135 Letter Paper.
24 sheets and envelopes;
8" x 12".

S 33 Sketch Portfolio

These four pencil sketches were carefully reproduced from fine drawings by Charles Overly. Views of Bruton Parish Church, Wren Building, Capitol and Governor's Palace are included.
11½" x 15" including margins.

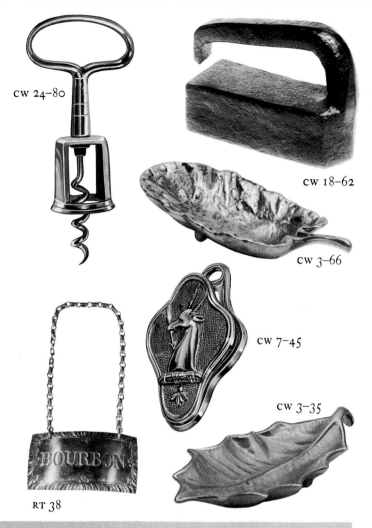

*CW 24-80 *Corkscrew*

Made of brass and steel, this useful tool is an authentic copy of an eighteenth-century English corkscrew. Length 5″.

*CW 18-62 *Pressing Iron*

A replica of an original on exhibit in the Williamsburg Archaeological Museum, this iron is useful as a bookend or doorstop. Length 5″.

Williamsburg Leaf Trays

These leaf trays are based on trees and plants which were known and grown in eighteenth-century Williamsburg. The trays make exceptionally handsome and practical ash trays.

CW 3-66 English Primrose Leaf Tray. Brass; length 4½″.

CW 3-35 American Holly Leaf Tray. Brass; length 4″.

*RT 38 *Decanter Labels*

These sterling silver labels with antique lettering are reproductions of those used in the eighteenth century. Available individually for Rye, Scotch, Bourbon, Port, Sherry, Brandy, Rum, Gin and Vodka or as boxed set of six (page 200). Label 1¾″; chain 6″.

*CW 7-45 *Randolph Paper Clip*

The plate of this intriguing piece is an exact copy in brass of an old harness ornament bearing the Randolph crest. The base and spring have been added to make it an ideal paper clip or paperweight. 4½″ x 3″.

R 3 *Hearth Broom*

This version of a colonial broom is useful and charming on the hearth. It is made of undressed broom straw. Length 26″.

s 66½ *Potpourri Packets,*
s 66 *Potpourri Bottle*
s 66-2 *Potpourri Sachet*

The mixture of dried herbs, flowers, and spices in these colorful packages gives a delightful fragrance to linen closet, blanket chest, or chest of drawers. The envelopes are illustrated from a group of eighteenth-century mezzotints in the Williamsburg collection, showing the four seasons of the year.

s 66 Bottle; 4½ ounces.

s 66½ Packet; 6½″ x 5″.

s 66-2 Sachet; 5″ x 5″.

*Reproduction

NP 38

NP 32   NP 33

NP 31   NP 30

NP 35   NP 34

NEEDLEWORK and LINEN

CREWEL KITS

Now that needlework is popular once again, these authentic early American crewel designs are an especially welcome addition for the ladies who enjoy creative needlework. The designs are taken from the antique bed coverings in the Peyton Randolph House, and printed on 100% linen. Each kit contains the stamped linen, wool embroidery yarn, and instructions.

NP 38 *Bell Pull.* A narrow, colorful strip to hang beside a door, this was once useful for summoning servants; it now makes an attractive wall hanging. 100% Belgian linen twill. Hardware not included. Completed size 4½" x 54".

NP 30, NP 31 *and* NP 32, NP 33 *Crewel Flower Pictures.* The finished work on creamy white linen, framed and hung on the wall, will brighten any room. Where two pictures are needed, a pair makes a real impression. Frames not included.
NP 32 *and* NP 33. 19" x 16".
NP 30 *and* NP 31. 12" x 10".

NP 34 *and* NP 35 *Pillow Kits.* Multicolored, with gold predominating on creamy white 100% Belgian linen twill. Each kit includes four narrow side strips with a vine-like pattern. Completed size 13½" x 13½".

NP 36 *and* NP 37 *Chair Seats* (not shown). 100% Belgian linen twill. Each 30" x 30".
NP 36 Same design as NP 34 Pillow.
NP 37 Same design as NP 35 Pillow.

SAMPLER KITS

These six colorful samplers are easy to work, yet look delightfully complex when completed, framed and hung on the wall. Each features a noted building of colonial Williamsburg. Each kit contains a stamped sampler on 100% Belgian linen, embroidery thread and instructions. Frames not included. (Pictured on left, below.) Cut size 14" x 16".

*s 142 *Sampler Kit*

The original of this sampler was worked in 1760 by 11 year old Mary Starker. This reproduction duplicates the bright colors and stylized design. It takes its name, "The Chase," from the bottom of the sampler, where a dog is shown chasing a stag. Mary Starker's name, place of birth "Newbury, New England" and a pious "Goodness and Mercy Ever follow [t]hose who shape there Conduct by Gods Holy Laws" have been deleted so that each person may stitch her own name into the sampler.

The kit contains the sampler, stamped on 100% Belgian linen, embroidery thread and instructions. 16½" x 24½" cut size.

Frame not included.

s 132

Governor's
Palace

*Reproduction

s 149
The Capitol

s 155
Courthouse
of 1770

s 156
Bruton Parish
Church

s 172
Raleigh Tavern

s 173
Magazine and
Guardhouse

s 142

223

NP 50   FLAME STITCH   NP 53
NP 51   NP 54
NP 52   NP 55

Needlepoint

NP 1 NEEDLEPOINT. The background wool is a rich gold with pattern colors of soft greens, roses and blues. Suitable for a stool or pillow cover. Design 21½" x 13½". Canvas 35" x 23".

NP 2 NEEDLEPOINT. Rich tones of red, yellow, blue and green against a two-tone brown background. Appropriate for a chair seat or pillow cover. Design 17" x 18½". Canvas 28" x 30".

Flamestitch

Flamestitch, which derives its name from the zigzag pattern characteristic of the design, is worked in a vertical canvas stitch traditionally known as bargello or florentine embroidery. This design has been adapted from an eighteenth-century American pocketbook in the Colonial Williamsburg collection.

NP 50, NP 51 and NP 52 are muted colors, dominately blue and gold.

NP 50 NEEDLEPOINT. Canvas 20" x 20". Finished size 16" x 16". Sufficient yarn for 256 square inches of design.

NP 51 NEEDLEPOINT. Suitable for slip seat, large pillow or bench. Canvas 27" x 24". Finished size 22" x 20". Sufficient yarn for 440 square inches of design.

NP 52 NEEDLEPOINT. This is large enough to upholster a chair or large bench. Canvas 32" x 40". Finished size 27" x 30". Sufficient yarn for 810 square inches of design.

NP 53, NP 54 and NP 55 are bright colors, dominately green, black, gold and blue.

NP 53 NEEDLEPOINT. Canvas 18" x 18". Finished size 14" x 14". Sufficient yarn for 196 square inches of design.

NP 54 NEEDLEPOINT. Suitable for slip seat, large pillow or bench. Canvas 27" x 24". Finished size 22" x 20". Sufficient yarn for 440 square inches of design.

NP 55 NEEDLEPOINT. Appropriate for upholstering a chair or large bench. Canvas 32" x 40". Finished size 27" x 30". Sufficient yarn for 810 square inches of design.

Hand Towels

S 137 HAND TOWELS. Hand woven in the traditional "M's and O's" weave, these towels are 50% linen and 50% cotton. White, with a choice of red, blue, brown or yellow decoration. 14½" x 20½".

S 105 HERB TOWELS. Six herbs and the John Blair kitchen and herb garden are printed on linen. Set of three in red, yellow and blue, one of each color. 15⅝" x 28¼".

Williamsburg Handkerchiefs

S 99 WILLIAMSBURG HANDKERCHIEF. Printed with signs and symbols of Williamsburg. Linen. Available in green, blue, brown or maize.

S 100 GOVERNOR'S PALACE HANDKERCHIEF. Stylized drawings of the Palace and other colonial buildings. Linen. Colors same as above.

Placemats

S 170 CHARLES II PLACE MATS. This striking design was taken from a wallpaper pattern of 1660. Printed in bold blue, green, charcoal or gold on fine natural linen. Mats 14" x 17"; napkins 17" square. Four mats, four napkins per set.

Napkins

S 148 TAVERN SIGN COCKTAIL NAPKINS. Four of Williamsburg's famous taverns are represented: Chowning's, the Raleigh, Christiana Campbell's and the King's Arms. Sets of four or eight, in red and green, or olive and tan. 6⅝" square.

TOYS AND GAMES

s133 *Doll*

The perfect gift for your favorite doll collector. This handmade stuffed doll is dressed in the style of Colonial Williamsburg's hostesses. Face is hand-painted. Height 11½".

s174 *"Jennie" Doll Kit*

Make this for your favorite little girl, or help her to do it herself. Kit includes printed doll on pure Irish linen, easy-to-follow instructions. Cut out, stitched up, then stuffed with cotton, Jennie stands about 16" tall.

s171 *Colonial Dolls*

Children delight in producing and directing their own versions of "The Story of a Patriot" . . . especially if they've seen this outstanding film at the Williamsburg Information Center. Set includes eight 9" cardboard figures of characters from the movie with paper costumes and accessories to fit each.

s159 *Candle Molding Kit*

Hours of productive fun for all ages. Makes eight 10" candles just as they were made in colonial Virginia. Kit includes a reusable tin candle mold, wicking and beeswax, with full instructions.

s193 *Williamsburg Paintable Kit*

Six different black and white sketches of popular Williamsburg subjects, complete with watercolors, brush, and color suggestions, will provide hours of fun for the amateur artist. 17⅜" x 11¾".

s190 and s191 *Williamsburg Jigsaw Puzzles*

Enjoy the challenge of these interesting and colorful Williamsburg jigsaw puzzles by Eaton. More than 500 pieces in each puzzle.
s190 The Palace Wine Cellar. 18⅛" x 24⅛".
s191 Chimneys and Blossoms. 20¼" x 20¼".

s109 *The Great Game of Visiting Williamsburg*

For ages 7 to 12. This exciting game takes children on a tour of historic Williamsburg, and teaches history as they play.

s133

s174

s159

s171

s190

s191

s193

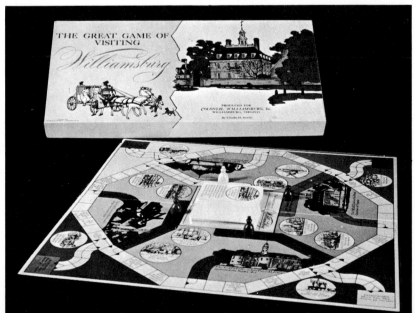

s109

s150 *Fife*

Banded with brass ferrules, it comes complete with instructions and the notes for two songs of the Revolutionary period: "Yankee Doodle" and "The World Turned Upside Down." Length 16¾".

Playing Cards

One of these decks has an exterior view of the Capitol in Williamsburg; the other a view of the Governor's Palace.

s 50 DOUBLE DECK
s 111 TRIPLE DECK (specify design)
s 157 SINGLE DECK (specify design)

s40 *Bridge Pack*

Scenes of Williamsburg decorate this set of three score pads and twelve tallies.

s185 *Party Invitations*

Twelve party notes with illustrations of eighteenth-century card players on the cover make delightful invitations for any social get-together.

s186 *Bridge Pack*

Illustrations on this set of two score pads and eight tallies are the same as on the s185 Party Invitations.

s188 *Williamsburg Christmas Cards*

The well-known Virginia artist, Kenneth Harris, painted the original watercolor pictures from which these cards were taken. They may be imprinted or used as notes. Eight different subjects assorted. Sixteen cards with envelopes. 6¼" x 4½".

s127A *Abby Aldrich Rockefeller Folk Art Collection Greeting Cards*

Paintings and other objects in the Folk Art Collection are reproduced in color to make these beguiling notes. Twelve assorted subjects with envelopes. 4¼" x 5⅞".

s 158

s 150

s196 *Williamsburg Model Kit*

This kit provides everything young architects will need to make their own reconstruction of the George Wythe House, home of a signer of the Declaration of Independence, and headquarters for Washington during the American Revolution. Die-cut for easy assembly, this H. O. scale kit includes the main house, ten outbuildings, pictorial instructions, and historical notes.

s127A

s188

s 50

s 185

s 111

s 40

s 157

s 186

Colonial Williamsburg PUBLICATIONS: A Selection

The pages of history literally unfold as you browse through the Williamsburg books published by Colonial Williamsburg. As an integral part of its educational program, Colonial Williamsburg has developed an expanding publications program that includes books of scholarship, popular histories, volumes styled after the fashion of the eighteenth century, works on contemporary Williamsburg, and books for children. All Colonial Williamsburg publications, and a wide selection of Williamsburg books of other publishers, may be obtained at Craft House.

General Publications

THE WILLIAMSBURG COLLECTION OF ANTIQUE FURNISHINGS. A pictorial survey of selected items from Colonial Williamsburg's vast collection. With an introduction by Carlisle H. Humelsine on the purposes, growth, and prospective uses of the collection. 216 full-color photographs. 128 pages. Paperbound and hardbound.

CHRISTMAS IN WILLIAMSBURG by Taylor Biggs Lewis, Jr. and Joanne B. Young. An enchanting glimpse of holiday customs two centuries old as the colonial capital lights its candles, decorates its doors, and cooks its Christmas specialties. Illustrated in full color. 64 pages. Paperbound and hardbound.

COLONIAL WILLIAMSBURG: ITS BUILDINGS AND GARDENS by A. L. Kocher and Howard Dearstyne. More than 200 photographs highlight descriptions of restored buildings, furnishings, celebrated gardens, history, and planning of an eighteenth-century Virginia city. Revised edition. 112 pages. Hardbound.

COLONIAL WILLIAMSBURG OFFICIAL GUIDEBOOK AND MAP. Here is Colonial Williamsburg, street by street, house by house, with the intimate story of each building and shop in terms of the people who lived and worked in eighteenth-century Williamsburg. Illustrated. Color map. 108 pages. Paperbound.

THE FLOWER WORLD OF WILLIAMSBURG by Joan Parry Dutton. Traces the development of eighteenth-century gardens and styles of flower arranging. Illustrated in full color. Revised edition. 128 pages. Paperbound and hardbound.

THE GARDENS OF WILLIAMSBURG. An examination, with 90 full-color photographs, of Williamsburg's formal gardens and open greens. 48 pages. Paperbound and hardbound.

A HARPSICHORD OR SPINNET MISCELLANY by Robert Bremner. A facsimile reproduction of the original edition of about 1765, edited, with introduction, by J. S. Darling. 32 pages. Paperbound and hardbound.

LEGACY FROM THE PAST. A portfolio of the original eighteenth-century and early nineteenth-century buildings located in the Historic Area of Williamsburg illustrated in 130 full-color photographs. 80 pages. Paperbound and hardbound.

PLANTS OF COLONIAL DAYS by Raymond L. Taylor. A guide to 160 flowers, shrubs, and trees in the gardens of Colonial Williamsburg. Illustrated. 112 pages. Paperbound.

A LITTLE KEYBOARD BOOK edited by J. S. Darling. A collection of eight eighteenth-century keyboard tunes arranged for intermediate students of the piano and harpsichord. 24 pages. Paperbound.

SONGS FROM A COLONIAL TAVERN by Tayler Vrooman. A selection of eighteenth-century popular songs, set for medium voice and piano keyboard (with guitar chords), as sung by Tayler Vrooman on festive occasions at Colonial Williamsburg. Illustrated. 48 pages. Paperbound.

SONGS FROM THE WILLIAMSBURG THEATRE by John W. Molnar. Fifty pieces performed on the stage in the colonial capital arranged for voice and keyboard. With historical commentaries on early performances and performers as well as on the authors, composers, and plots of the vehicles in which the songs were given. 292 pages. Hardbound.

THE WILLIAMSBURG ART OF COOKERY by Helen Bullock. Time-tested recipes of our colonial forebears. Includes a table of favorite garden herbs. Eighteenth-century typography, ninth printing. Illustrated. 306 pages. Hardbound and leatherbound.

THE WILLIAMSBURG COOKBOOK. A collection of 170 traditional and contemporary recipes initially compiled and adapted for today's home kitchen by Letha Booth, with commentary by Joan Parry Dutton. 12 full-color illustrations by Taylor Biggs Lewis, Jr. 40 line drawings by Vernon E. Wooten. 172 pages. Paperbound and hardbound.

WILLIAMSBURG IN VIRGINIA by Rutherfoord Goodwin. "A brief and true Report concerning Williamsburg in Virginia: Being an Account of the most important Occurrences in that Place from its first Beginning to the present Time." Eighteenth-century typography. Illustrated. 428 pages. Hardbound and leatherbound.

A WINDOW ON WILLIAMSBURG by Taylor Biggs Lewis, Jr., John J. Walklet, Jr., and Thomas K. Ford. An intimate glimpse of restored Williamsburg, its gardens and greens, its buildings, crafts and people. Revised edition. 131 full-color photographs. 80 pages. Paperbound and hardbound.

Eyewitness to History Series

THE JOURNAL AND LETTERS OF PHILIP VICKERS FITHIAN edited by Hunter Dickinson Farish and illustrated by Fritz Kredel. The journal and letters of a twenty-three-year-old tutor of the children of Councilor Robert Carter at "Nomini Hall" that brings to life in vivid colors the social customs of the day. 304 pages. Hardbound.

THE JOURNAL OF JOHN FONTAINE edited by Edward Porter Alexander. The carefully kept and now fully annotated diary of a young Hugenot who spent several years in Virginia. He was one of the "Knights of the Golden Horseshoe," who trekked across the Blue Ridge Mountains with Governor Spotswood in 1716. Illustrated. 224 pages. Hardbound.

THE JOURNAL OF MAJOR GEORGE WASHINGTON edited, with introduction and notes by James R. Short and Thaddeus W. Tate, Jr. A stirring journal of young Major George Washington on his mission to warn the French against encroaching on British territory. Facsimile edition. Illustrated. 56 pages. Hardbound.

Williamsburg Archaeological Series

The following publications are by Ivor Noël Hume, director of the Department of Archaeology at Colonial Williamsburg. The archaeological findings and excavations of Williamsburg have provided the background for this fascinating series. Each account is 48 pages and paperbound.

No. 1—GLASS IN COLONIAL WILLIAMSBURG'S ARCHAEOLOGICAL COLLECTIONS.

No. 2—POTTERY AND PORCELAIN IN COLONIAL WILLIAMSBURG'S ARCHAEOLOGICAL COLLECTIONS.

No. 3—ARCHAEOLOGY AND WETHERBURN'S TAVERN.

No. 4—THE WELLS OF WILLIAMSBURG: COLONIAL TIME CAPSULES.

No. 5—JAMES GEDDY AND SONS: COLONIAL CRAFTSMEN.

No. 6—WILLIAMSBURG CABINETMAKERS: THE ARCHAEOLOGICAL EVIDENCE.

Williamsburg Architectural Studies

THE EIGHTEENTH-CENTURY HOUSES OF WILLIAMSBURG by Marcus Whiffen. A comprehensive study describing the men who built the houses, their tools and materials, their books, the factors that affected the general design of the houses and, in detail, their design and structure. Illustrated. 225 pages. Hardbound.

THE PUBLIC BUILDINGS OF WILLIAMSBURG by Marcus Whiffen. A thorough architectural study of some of the most significant buildings in colonial America. Illustrated. 286 pages. Hardbound.

TIDEWATER TOWNS: *City Planning in Colonial Virginia and Maryland* by John W. Reps. A detailed study of town planning in the tidewater area, from the earliest settlements at Roanoke Island and Jamestown through the colonial period and ending with Latrobe's plan for the new federal capital in the District of Columbia. 206 maps and plans. 360 pages. Hardbound.

Williamsburg in America Series

ALEXANDER SPOTSWOOD: PORTRAIT OF A GOVERNOR by Walter Havighurst. Governor of the royal colony of Virginia from 1710 to 1722, Alexander Spotswood, ambitious and resolute, left his mark on the colony and on Williamsburg, its capital. 144 pages. Hardbound.

BLOOD OF FREEDOM by Earl Schenck Miers. The story of the British colonists in North America who endured suffering and privation in Jamestown, who rose to magnificent heights in their search for right and justice at Williamsburg, and who gained final triumph at Yorktown. Illustrated by Richard J. Stinely. 192 pages. Hardbound.

DISORDERED MINDS: THE FIRST CENTURY OF THE EASTERN STATE HOSPITAL IN WILLIAMSBURG, VIRGINIA, 1766-1866, by Norman Dain. A history of the origins, leadership, therapeutic practices, and troubles of the first public mental hospital in the British American colonies from its founding through the Civil War. Illustrated. 208 pages. Hardbound.

GEORGE MASON, RELUCTANT STATESMAN by Robert A. Rutland. A brief biography of George Mason, author of the Virginia Declaration of Rights and principal architect of the first Virginia Constitution. Illustrated. 128 pages. Hardbound.

THE GOLDEN AGE OF PIRACY by Hugh F. Rankin. A lively, factual account of piracy in the seventeenth century. Illustrated with contemporary prints. 160 pages. Hardbound.

SEAT OF EMPIRE by Carl Bridenbaugh. Tells why Williamsburg ranked as the political and social peer of other colonial capitals and produced its galaxy of leaders. Illustrated. 96 pages. Hardbound.

VIRGINIANS AT HOME by Edmund S. Morgan. Presents with an easy informality the day-to-day life of eighteenth-century Virginians. Illustrated. 112 pages. Hardbound.

A WILLIAMSBURG GALAXY by Burke Davis. Lively, brief biographies of Thomas Jefferson, Patrick Henry, James Blair, George Washington and sixteen other great men who influenced the early history of our country, and who were residents of the colonial capital, Williamsburg. Illustrated with photographs of portraits. 232 pages. Hardbound.

Books for Children

AMERICA'S FIRST ARMY by Burke Davis. Illustrations by Richard J. Stinely and photographs by John Crane. The exciting story of America's first soldiers who defeated troops of England, the greatest military power of that day, in the American Revolution. Ages 6–12. 48 pages. A 7-inch 33⅓ rpm LP record of present-day Williamsburg militia muster is included. Paperbound (with mailing envelope) and hardbound.

THE BELOVED FRIEND by Marguerite Vance and illustrated by Leonard Weisgard. The story of young George Washington and his beloved friend Sally Cary Fairfax, the kind, vivacious young neighbor who helped him take his place in a gracious plantation life he never had time to know. Ages 10–14. 120 pages. Hardbound.

BRAVE HORSE by Manly Wade Wellman and illustrated by Peter Burchard. The story of the gallant Janus, who was disabled and retired from the English track, yet who lived to challenge Williams Byrd's Valiant, the finest racehorse in the colony of Virginia, and to become the foundation sire of the American quarter horse. Ages 10–14. 118 pages. Hardbound.

THE FRENCH ARE COMING by Wilma Pitchford Hays and illustrated by Leonard Weisgard. The arrival of the long-promised French aid made the difference in the outcome of the confrontation at Yorktown between the British and American troops. But to Rene Dupre, a ten-year-old resident of Yorktown, their arrival meant that his pride in the land of his ancestors was restored. Ages 10–14. 102 pages. Hardbound.

A GARLAND OF GAMES & OTHER DIVERSIONS by Barbara Cooney. Known throughout the book world for her delightful imaginative paintings, Barbara Cooney has written and illustrated (full color) an appealing ABC book of merry rhymes and pictures of eighteenth-century Williamsburg children at play. Ages 4–8. 32 pages. Paperbound and hardbound.

MARY'S STAR by Wilma Pitchford Hays and illustrated by Lawrence Beall Smith. A tale of three orphans in Virginia near the close of the Revolutionary War. Ages 10–14. 108 pages. Hardbound.

PIRATE CHASE by Earl Schenck Miers and illustrated by Peter Burchard. Captured and forced to become an unwilling member of the pirate crew, 15-year-old Timothy Baillie learned from his own experience the ruthlessness of the pirate Blackbeard. Ages 10–14. 129 pages. Hardbound.

PROUD PRISONER by Walter Havighurst and illustrated by Leonard Vosburgh. The story of Lieutenant Governor Henry Hamilton, British commander at Detroit during the early days of the Revolution, who was captured at Vincennes by George Rogers Clark and brought in irons to Williamsburg gaol. Ages 10–14. 130 pages. Hardbound.

THE SCARLET BADGE by Wilma Pitchford Hays and illustrated by Peter Burchard. The "scarlet badge" was worn by those who remained loyal to King George III at the outbreak of the Revolution. This is the story of a Loyalist family at the crossroads of their lives on the eve of the birth of a new nation. Ages 11–14. 109 pages. Hardbound.

SECOND SON by Nancy Faulkner and illustrated by Vernon Wooten. By a highly respected author of historical books, this is the story of young Christopher Gordon of the Virginia colony, who is apprenticed to a merchant in London. Ages 10–14. 163 pages. Hardbound.

TO THE WALLS OF CARTAGENA by Allan Dwight and illustrated by Leonard Vosburgh. A story of spies and scoundrels, of buccaneers and booty, and of the courage and loyalty of 16-year-old, Greg Shelby, set in 1739 against the background of the War of Jenkins' Ear. Ages 10–14. 176 pages. Hardbound.

TOMAHAWK BORDER by William O. Steele and illustrated by Vernon Wooten. In 1714, the southwestern frontier of Virginia was patrolled by rangers to protect the settlers and the peaceful Indians. Among the rangers was young Delk Rogers, who worked to gain the respect of the other rangers and earned acceptance as a man. Ages 10–14. 128 pages. Hardbound.

WAYAH OF THE REAL PEOPLE by William O. Steele and illustrated by Isa Barnett. Wayah, the Wolf, Cherokee boy of Chota, goes to Williamsburg to attend the Brafferton School for Indians at the College of William and Mary. For a year he endures sickness, hostility, and heartache before returning to his village to help bring understanding between Indians and whites. Ages 10–14. 136 pages. Hardbound.

Williamsburg Potpourri of Gifts

Needlework and Linen

NP 1	Needlepoint	(Not Available)
NP 2	Needlepoint	(Not Available)
NP 30	Flower Picture	$ 3.35
NP 31	Flower Picture	3.35
NP 32	Flower Picture	7.80
NP 33	Flower Picture	7.80
NP 34	Pillow	10.80
NP 35	Pillow	10.80
NP 36	Chair Seat	9.80
NP 37	Chair Seat	9.80
NP 38	Bell Pull	10.80
NP 50	Flamestitch Needlepoint	18.95
NP 51	Flamestitch Needlepoint	28.95
NP 52	Flamestitch Needlepoint	49.95
NP 53	Flamestitch Needlepoint	15.95
NP 54	Flamestitch Needlepoint	28.95
NP 55	Flamestitch Needlepoint	49.95
S 99	Williamsburg Handkerchief	
	Each	1.50
	Set of four	5.25
S 100	Governor's Palace Handkerchief	
	Each	1.50
	Set of four	5.25
S 105	Box of three Herb towels	5.10
S 132	Governor's Palace Sampler Kit	2.85
S 137	Hand-woven Towel	
	Each	3.00
	Set of Three	7.95
S 142	Chase Sampler	8.80
S 148	Tavern Sign Cocktail Napkins	
	Set of Four	2.70
	Set of Eight	4.85
S 149	Capitol Sampler	2.85
S 155	Court House Sampler	2.85
S 156	Bruton Parish Sampler	2.85
S 170	Charles II Place Mats	9.75
S 172	Raleigh Tavern Sampler	2.85
S 173	Magazine Sampler	2.85

Miscellaneous

CW 3-27	Mulberry Leaf Tray	$ 6.65
CW 3-35	Holly Leaf Tray (Pair)	7.65
CW 3-66	Primrose Leaf Tray	6.15
CW 6-44	Key	8.30
CW 7-21	Holly Paper Clip	7.15

CW 7-30	Harlequin Pipe Tamper	$ 2.85
CW 7-31	Slipper Pipe Tamper	2.85
CW 7-45	Randolph Paper Clip	7.70
CW 8-7	Striding Man	
	Each	18.50
	Pair	35.00
CW 10-9	King George Trivet	
	Brass	6.35
	Iron	2.85
CW 10-10	Queen Anne Trivet	
	Brass	17.50
	Iron	7.00
CW 10-11	William and Mary Trivet	
	Brass	11.85
	Iron	4.85
CW 10-14	Colonial Williamsburg Trivet	
	Brass	9.35
	Iron	4.35
	Verdigris	5.35
	White Bronze	10.35
CW 10-17	King's Arms Trivet	
	Brass	10.35
	Iron	4.35
CW 10-42	Trivet for 6" Tiles	2.95
CW 10-45	Iron Trivet with delft tile	8.50
CW 16-08	Brass Hook—*Available* 1974	
CW 16-37	Traveling Candleholders —*Available* 1974	
CW 18-62	Pressing Iron	6.00
CW 18-65	Striding Man	
	Each	31.25
	Pair	60.00
CW 24-13	Shoe Horn	11.15
CW 24-49	Porringer—*Available* 1974	
CW 24-71	Lion and Unicorn Pin	6.85
CW 24-72	Hostess Bell	
	Brass	9.35
	White Bronze	12.35
CW 24-80	Corkscrew	7.75
K 135	Letter Paper	4.45
K 136	Note Paper	2.55
R 3	Hearth Broom	3.70
R 4	Bayberry Candles	
	Pair	1.80
R 5	Bayberry Candles	
	Pair	4.00
R 7	Beeswax Candles	
	Pair	1.80
R 8	Beeswax Candles	
	Pair	4.00
R 10	Beeswax tapers (six to box)	1.90
RT 38	Decanter Label	8.00

All prices include shipping charges within the Continental United States and are subject to change without notice.

Miscellaneous, *continued*

RT 50	Lapel Pin	$20.95
RT 53	King's Arms Pin	8.20
RT 55	Salt Spoon Pin	7.35
S 9	White Candles, Pair	1.80
S 16	Pencil Sketch Notes	1.50
S 29	Pencil Sketch Notes	1.50
S 33	Overly Sketch Portfolio	2.30
S 40	Bridge Pack	1.75
S 48	Silver Mace Pin	1.40
S 49	Gold Mace Pin	1.40
S 50	Double Deck Playing Cards	2.20
S 66	Potpourri	5.00
S 66½	Four Seasons Potpourri	
	Each	1.75
	Set of four	6.50
S 66-2	Potpourri	2.60
S 70	Recipe Notes	1.50
S 79	Capitol Tile	2.80
S 80	Palace Tile	2.80
S 85	Four Documents of Freedom	1.10
S 103	Jamestown, Williamsburg, Yorktown	
	Notes	1.50
S 107	King William Ashtray	4.85
S 108	Queen Mary Ashtray	4.85
	Set of S 107 and S 108	9.50
S 109	The Great Game of Visiting	
	Williamsburg	4.95
S 111	Triple Deck Playing Cards	3.25
S 116	Bruton Parish Church Tile	2.80
S 117	Raleigh Tavern Tile	2.80
	Set of S 79, S 80, S 116 and S 117	10.00
S 119	Soap Balls	2.20
S 120 G	Capitol Mace Pin Gold	3.15
S 120 S	Capitol Mace Pin Silver	2.65
S 127A	Abby Aldrich Rockefeller Folk Art	
	Collection Greeting Cards	2.25
S 133	Doll	6.00
S 139-1	Virginia Regiment Tile	2.95
S 139-2	44th Regiment Tile	2.95
S 139-3	48th Regiment Tile	2.95
S 139-4	Royal Marines Tile	2.95
	Set of four military tiles	10.25
S 147	Tavern Sign Notes	1.75
S 150	Fife	4.25
S 154	Color Wash Notes	1.50
S 157	Single Deck Playing Cards	1.15
S 159	Candle-Molding Kit	7.65
S 171	Colonial Dolls	3.10
S 174	Jennie Doll	3.10
S 185	Party Invitations	1.25
S 186	Bridge Pack	1.50
S 187	Embroidery Notes	1.75
S 188	Christmas Cards	2.25
S 189	Christiana Campbell's Tavern Towel	2.30
S 190	The Palace Wine Cellar Jigsaw Puzzle	4.95
S 191	Chimneys and Blossoms Jigsaw Puzzle	4.95
S 196	Williamsburg Model Kit	5.80
WS 100	Palace Candlelight Concert	4.45
WS 101	Fifes and Drums and The Band of	
	Musick	4.45
WS 102	O Come Sweet Music	4.45
WS 103	An Evening of Music at Carter's	
	Grove Plantation	4.45
WS 104	The Music Teacher	4.45
	Songs of Gentility	1.75
	Songs of Politics and Potation	1.75

Publications

Alexander Spotswood: Portrait of A Governor	$ 4.20
America's First Army—Paperbound	2.75
Hardbound	3.75
Antiques At Williamsburg	2.20
Archaeology And Wetherburn's Tavern	1.25
The Beloved Friend	4.20
Blood Of Freedom	5.20
Brave Horse	4.20
Christmas in Williamsburg—Paperbound	2.20
Hardbound	5.20
Colonial Williamsburg: It's Buildings and Gardens	5.20
Colonial Williamsburg Official Guidebook And Map	.75
Disordered Minds: The First Century of the Eastern State Hospital In Williamsburg, Virginia	6.20
The Eighteenth-Century Houses of Williamsburg	12.25
The French Are Coming	4.20
The Gardens of Williamsburg—Paperbound	1.75
Hardbound	4.20
A Garland Of Games and Other Diversions—Paperbound	2.20
Hardbound	4.20
George Mason, Reluctant Statesman	3.75
Glass In Colonial Williamsburg's Archaeological Collections	1.25
The Golden Age of Piracy	5.20
A Harpsichord or Spinnet Miscellany—Paperbound	2.75
Hardbound	6.20
James Geddy And Sons: Colonial Craftsmen	1.25
The Journal And Letters of Philip Vickers Fithian	4.20
The Journal of John Fontaine	5.20
The Journal Of Major George Washington	2.75
Legacy From The Past—Paperbound	2.20
Hardbound	5.20
A Little Keyboard Book	1.25
Mary's Star	4.20
Pirate Chase	4.20
Plants Of Colonial Days	2.20
Pottery And Porcelain In Colonial Williamsburg's Archaeological Collections	1.25
Proud Prisoner	4.20
The Public Buildings Of Williamsburg	12.75
The Scarlet Badge	4.20
Seat of Empire	4.20
Second Son	4.20
Songs From A Colonial Tavern	3.00
Songs From The Williamsburg Theatre	15.25
Tidewater Towns: City Planning in Colonial Virginia And Maryland	15.25
Tomahawk Border	4.20
To The Walls Of Cartagena	4.20
Virginians At Home	3.75
Wayah Of The Real People	4.20
The Wells Of Williamsburg: Colonial Time Capsules	1.25
The Williamsburg Art of Cookery	3.75
Williamsburg Cabinetmakers: The Archaeological Evidence	1.25
The Williamsburg Collection of Antique Furnishings—Paperbound	4.20
Hardbound	7.20
The Williamsburg Cookbook—Paperbound	3.20
Hardbound	6.20
A Williamsburg Galaxy	5.20
Williamsburg In Virginia—Hardbound	6.20
Leatherbound	10.25
A Window On Williamsburg—Paperbound	2.75
Hardbound	6.20

Articles in this catalogue have been approved by *Colonial Williamsburg*

Licensed Manufacturers

Bedspreads
Bates Fabrics, Inc.
1431 Broadway
New York, New York 10018

Brass and Iron Accessories
Virginia Metalcrafters, Incorporated
Waynesboro, Virginia 22980

Clocks
Chelsea Clock Company
284 Everett Avenue
Chelsea, Massachusetts 02150

Delft
Foreign Advisory Service Corp.
Princess Anne, Maryland 21853

Messrs. Oud Delft of Nijmegen,
Holland

Dinnerware and Ceramics
Josiah Wedgwood & Sons, Inc.
24 East 54th Street
New York, New York 10022

Fabrics
F. Schumacher & Company
58 West 40th Street
New York, New York 10018

Figurines and Character Jugs
Doulton & Company, Incorporated
400 Paterson Plank Road
Carlstadt, New Jersey 07072

Fireplace Equipment
The Harvin Company
Waynesboro, Virginia 22980

Furniture
Kittinger Company, Incorporated
1893 Elmwood Avenue
Buffalo, New York 14207

Glass
Foreign Advisory Service Corp.
Princess Anne, Maryland 21853

Royal Leerdam, Leerdam, Holland

Lamp Accessories
Knob Creek of Morganton
Morganton, North Carolina 28655

Leather
Lackawanna Leather Company
Hackettstown, New Jersey 07840

Lighting Fixtures
Virginia Metalcrafters, Incorporated
Waynesboro, Virginia 22980

Locks
Folger Adam Company
P. O. Box 688
Joliet, Illinois 60434

Mirrors
Friedman Brothers Decorative Arts,
Incorporated
305 East 47th Street
New York, New York 10017

Needle Point & Needlework
Paragon Art and Linen Co., Inc.
385 Fifth Avenue
New York, New York 10016

Paint
Martin-Senour Paints
2500 South Senour Avenue
Chicago, Illinois 60608

Pewter and Silver
The Stieff Company
Wyman Park Driveway
Baltimore, Maryland 21211

Pottery
Williamsburg Pottery Factory, Inc.
Rt. 3, Box 261
Williamsburg, Virginia 23185

Prints
The Dietz Press, Incorporated
109 East Cary Street
Richmond, Virginia 23219

Stationery
Eaton Paper Corporation
Pittsfield, Massachusetts 01203

Wallpaper
Katzenbach & Warren, Incorporated
155 East 56th Street
New York, New York 10022

Wooden Accessories
Victorius, Incorporated
Waynesboro, Virginia 22980

Other Manufacturers

Correspondence Notes
Charles Overly Studios
Old Littleton Road
Harvard, Massachusetts 01451

Dried Flowers
18th Century Bouquet, Incorporated
53 State Road
Princeton, New Jersey 08540

Soap
Carolina Soap and Candlemakers
P.O. Box 20
Oshkosh, Wisconsin 54901

Directions for Ordering

An order blank and a postage-saver envelope are enclosed for your convenience. Please furnish your name and address (including Zip Code Number), as well as catalogue number and description of articles ordered.

All prices quoted include shipping charges by usual methods. Special delivery or air mail charges will be extra.

Craft House sells at retail only.

Special prices for sets or pairs (as quoted) are for shipment to one address.

Safe delivery of shipments is guaranteed. In case of damage, please notify Craft House without delay.

If you do not have a Craft House Charge Account Number enclose a check (payable to Craft House) for the total amount of purchase. If you wish to open a Charge Account an application will be sent upon request.

To order by telephone, call Area Code 804, 229-1000 between 9:00 A.M. and 5:00 P.M. Monday through Saturday.

Craft House will gladly forward gifts directly to your friends. Enclose your card with the order, furnishing name and address (including Zip Code Number) of the recipient.

PRICES SUBJECT TO CHANGE WITHOUT NOTICE

All income derived from Craft House is used to maintain and develop Colonial Williamsburg and to carry forward its educational program.

INDEX

Colonial Williamsburg
ROBERT W. SPURGEON
RICHARD J. STINELY

Editorial Consultant
SARAH TOMERLIN LEE

Photography Stylist
FRANCES HEARD

Special Photography
HEDRICH-BLESSING
STEPHENS BIONDI DE CICCO

Edited, Designed and Printed by
The Lakeside Press
R. R. DONNELLEY & SONS COMPANY

AUTHENTIC COLONIAL

WILLIAMSBURG · RESTORATION

COLORS®

MARTIN SENOUR PAINTS®

THE MARTIN-SENOUR® COMPANY PRESENTS

Williamsburg®

PAINT

This new offering of Williamsburg researched colors is a rich cultural and esthetic bounty for all who seek to reproduce in their own homes some small part of their American heritage. Martin-Senour and its dealers throughout the country feel honored to have been chosen by Williamsburg Restoration, Inc., to present these colors, reformulated for you, in modern quality paints.

WILLIAMSBURG HALLMARK

Your seal of authenticity is the WILLIAMSBURG Hallmark. No other paints have been matched to the specimens in Williamsburg and approved by Williamsburg Restoration, Incorporated. Look for the WILLIAMSBURG Hallmark. It alone identifies genuine WILLIAMSBURG Paints made exclusively by Martin-Senour.

MARTIN-SENOUR QUALITY

WILLIAMSBURG Colors are the finest paints available today. They are manufactured to meet the highest standards of quality and performance. Ready-mixed, easy to apply, they have excellent hiding power and dry to a beautiful, durable finish. WILLIAMSBURG Colors stay bright and new-looking longer because of pigments with superior permanence.

Williamsburg is a cross-section of our American culture taken at the dynamic time in our history when this country was just emerging as an independent Republic. It is here and at this time that many founders of our country were first proclaiming the inalienable rights of man and hammering out the revolutionary principle of a government that was destined to become the world model of modern democracy.

The charm of Williamsburg is that it is not the dusty museum of a dead past. It is a living breathing community, vividly re-created, where millions of Americans can walk today in the same footsteps, experience the same sights, sounds and smells, feel the same textures as that small handful of persons who, two hundred years ago, were shaping the form of our nation.

In Williamsburg the blacksmith can be seen plying his craft in his own shop. So, too, can the bootmaker, baker, chandler and silversmith. Each is using the

(CONTINUED ON INSIDE FLAP)

INTERIOR PAINT COLORS

		MEDIUM	MEDIUM LIGHT	LIGHT
MARKET SQUARE GREEN	W1031	W1032	W1033	W1034
PALACE BALLROOM BLUE	W1035	W1036	W1037	W1038
KING'S ARMS ROSE PINK	W1027	W1028	*W1029	*W1030
JOHN GREENHOW GREEN (COLONIAL GREEN)	W1023	W1024	W1025	*W1026
WYTHE HOUSE GOLD	W1055	W1056	W1057	*W1058
CHOWNING'S TAVERN ROSE TAN	W1019	W1020	W1021	W1022
RALEIGH TAVERN TAN	W1051	W1052	*W1053	*W1054
PELHAM GRAY	W1039	W1040	W1041	W1042
RALEIGH TAVERN PEACH	W1047	W1048	*W1049	*W1050
APOLLO ROOM BLUE	W1011	W1012	W1013	W1014
APOTHECARY SHOP BLUE	W1015	W1016	W1017	W1018
RALEIGH TAVERN GREEN	W1043	W1044	W1045	W1046

COLOR SAMPLES ABOVE ARE AVAILABLE IN FLAT, SATIN OR LATEX

*AVAILABLE IN GALLONS ON

(CONTINUED FROM FRONT COVER)

tools and wearing the clothes he wore in Revolutionary days when Williamsburg was the capital of his Majesty's Colony of Virginia and the training ground for American patriots.

The very taverns frequented by George Washington, Patrick Henry and Thomas Jefferson are restored and open for business today. They are still serving the same hearty fare of our forefathers. Snug homes and shops of workers and craftsmen nestle among the larger townhouses of proud planters. Even the Governor's Palace is on view.

Visitors to Williamsburg are charmed by its colors. Lusty rustic hues mingle with subtler tones and tints of old world elegance. Paint is everywhere. Fine woods were scarce. Except for furniture imported from England, many Williamsburg woods are simply crafted and often painted. The stark, plain lines of cabinets, chests, benches and chairs are gentled with soft color. The brick reds, muted blues, greens and warm golds on this palette are all good furniture-painting colors.

There are many whitewashed† walls in Williamsburg. They are seen in homes, shops, taverns and even in some formal homes. But painted woodwork distributes friendly color around the rooms.

Apothecary Shop Blue is one of the most appealing of these woodwork-colors-with-white—as any visitor to that charming little shop will testify.

Perhaps the most notable of all Williamsburg woodwork colors is the subtle Charcoal Brown that can be seen on woodwork, wainscoating and dados in Campbell's Tavern where George Washington and his friends frequently dined. The crisp contrast of this brownish, greenish, charcoal with the rough textured whitewashed walls is surprisingly modern in effect.

Often doors are painted in a color different from the woodwork as in the Palmer House, where doors are brown and woodwork is dark green.

In formal rooms the elaborately moulded and fluted woodwork is often painted white against softly colored walls. Palace Ballroom Blue is one of these subtly elegant wall colors as is King's Arms Rose Pink, Daphne Room Beige and the John Greenhow and Bassett Hall greens.

The contemporary look of these two hundred year old colors is a source of amazement to all designers and stylists who see them. The very current "Hot Browns" are to be seen here in the deepest tans, yellow/browns and brick colors. The off-beat neutrals are those colors most needed for the modern "naturalistic" look. They are the warm grays, buffs, tans and browns that blend with wood, stone, brick, raw fibers and rough textures. This new Williamsburg palette is rich in golds and yellowy greens—presently most favored of all home furnishing colors—and even the "mods" should respond to the lusty Raleigh Tavern Chinese Red, the peppery Powell Waller Red and the glowing Powell Waller Gold.

The color and texture of WILLIAMSBURG Whitewash makes it an excellent choice of white to go with rough-hewn wood beams, natural brick, natural stone, raw fibers and other rough textured materials. It lends surface interest to smooth walls.

When restoring or remodeling old buildings, prime walls with Martin-Senour P.V.A. Quik-Sealer No. 2646 to bridge over hairline cracks. Finish with a coat of WILLIAMSBURG Simulated Whitewash.

†WILLIAMSBURG Whitewash is a modern paint formulated to imitate the rough grainy texture and rustic off-white color of Early American homemade whitewash, without the chipping, peeling and shredding that accompanied that primitive paint.

Meaning of the word "tenement" has changed since Colonial days when it simply meant "rental property." Such extra living quarters were in demand, particularly during sessions of the House of Burgesses when delegates assembled in Williamsburg for many months at a time. Ludwell Tenement was one of these houses-for-rent.

The kitchen in Old Williamsburg usually was a separate building. This kept the fire hazard of open-hearth cooking away from the dwelling.

Along with other outbuildings, the kitchen sometimes was painted a color different from the house. Levingston Kitchen Green and Palmer House Kitchen Brown are two such colors.

In 1926 Mr. John D. Rockefeller, Jr. became interested in the preservation and restoration of Williamsburg. This work has continued and today the Historic Area of Colonial Williamsburg embraces 130 acres. Within this area, there are nearly one hundred original Eighteenth Century homes and shops. Ninety acres of colorful gardens and greens have been re-created using only plants known to Eighteenth Century colonists.

Paint was widely used in Colonial Williamsburg and here the visitor can see the homes and shops restored to their original colors—many of which are reproduced on this color card.

HISTORIAN DETECTIVES

When a group of historian-detectives began the work of rebuilding, duplicating the original paint colors was one of their major problems. The old houses had been repainted many times. Often a careful scraping and minute examination of the particles was necessary before the character of the original paint was revealed. Other times the old paint could be discovered amazingly fresh and bright behind cornices and in dark closets, or beneath two centuries of paint and wallpaper. In other cases, it might be made up from a "recipe" mentioned in a directive to painters or from a list of materials in old letters ordering such exotic ingredients as copperas, fish oil, lamp black, Spanish brown, verdigris, and indigo.

TREND SETTING INTERIORS

As these diligent researchers revealed the original colors they found those enjoyed by the great statesman Thomas Jefferson as well as the humble milliner Margaret Hunter. Perhaps they didn't realize that also they were setting new contemporary standards of color for interior decoration. The selection of soft, rich WILLIAMSBURG interior colors reflected one aspect of Colonial society that the Twentieth Century eagerly embraced. WILLIAMSBURG colors are now firmly established in the American decorating tradition.

This card shows for the first time thirty-eight more authenticated Williamsburg interior colors, now available in modern quality paint formulations.

EXTERIORS TOO!

The variety of exterior colors to be seen in Williamsburg never fails to surprise the visitor. Some houses show as many as five different colors on the exteriors. The color combinations are fresh and new. Some even almost contemporary. New exterior color discoveries are being made every year.

INTERIOR ALKYD FLAT
USES: For wall and ceiling surfaces of plaster, wallboard, cement block and brick, as well as metal.
SUGGESTED APPLICATION RATE: Apply uniformly at the rate of 300-400 sq. ft. per gal. depending on surface texture and porosity.
DRYING TIME: To touch: 4-6 hrs.; dry overnight before recoating.
APPLICATION: Brush or roller.
SURFACE PREPARATION—NEW WORK: Surfaces must be clean, dry and free from contaminants. Fill cracks and holes with patching plaster or spackle. Seal drywall with No. 347 PVA. Cure new plaster 6 wks.; prime with No. 347 PVA or No. 348 Primer/Sealer. For deep tones use an additional coat of No. 2668 Seal-Coat tinted with 1 qt. finish color.
Prime metal and galvanized metal with appropriate primer; dry thoroughly. Prime masonry surfaces with No. 2672 Block Filler.
REPAINT WORK: When using pastel shades on surfaces in good condition, one coat will generally suffice. When using deep tone colors, follow directions for new work.

INTERIOR LATEX FLAT
USES: For wood, drywall, masonry, plaster, wallboard, brick and metal.
SUGGESTED APPLICATION RATE: Apply uniformly at the rate of 300-400 sq. ft. per gal. depending on surface texture and porosity.
DRYING TIME: To touch: 2-4 hrs.; dry overnight before recoating.
APPLICATION: Brush or roller.
SURFACE PREPARATION—NEW WORK: Surfaces must be clean, dry and free from contaminants. Fill cracks and holes with patching plaster or spackle. Sand smooth and spot prime with finish color.
Drywall: Apply 2 coats. Cure new plaster 6 wks.; apply 2 coats.
Prime new wood with No. 32 or No. 2660 Enamel Undercoat. Dry 16-24 hrs., then sand lightly.
Prime metal and galvanized metal with appropriate primer; dry thoroughly.
Prime masonry surfaces with No. 2672 Block Filler.
REPAINT WORK: Spot prime bare areas with finish color. Dry overnight before applying overall finish coat.

INTERIOR SATIN GLOSS
USES: For plaster, wallboard, cement block and brick, as well as wood and metal trim.
SUGGESTED APPLICATION RATE: Apply uniformly at the rate of 400 sq. ft. per gal.
DRYING TIME: To touch: 4-6 hrs.; dry overnight before recoating.
APPLICATION: Brush or roller.
SURFACE PREPARATION—NEW WORK: Surfaces must be clean, dry and free from contaminants. Fill cracks and holes with patching plaster or spackle. Seal drywall with No. 347 PVA. Cure new plaster 6 wks.; prime with No. 347 PVA or No. 348 Primer/Sealer. For deep tones use an additional coat of No. 2668 Seal-Coat tinted with 1 qt. finish color.
Prime wood trim with No. 32 or No. 2260 Enamel Undercoat. Dry 16-24 hrs.; then sand lightly. Prime metal and galvanized metal with appropriate primer; dry thoroughly. Prime masonry surfaces with No. 2672 Block Filler.
REPAINT WORK: When using pastel shades on surfaces in good condition, one coat will generally suffice. When using deep tone colors, follow directions for new work.

SIMULATED WHITEWASH
USES: For interior walls and ceilings of plaster, wallboard, wood trim and previously painted surfaces.
SUGGESTED APPLICATION RATE: Apply at the rate of 300-350 sq. ft. per gal. depending on texture of surface.
DRYING TIME: To touch: 4-6 hrs. When necessary to recoat, dry overnight.
APPLICATION: Use Tampico bristle brush using diagonal, horizontal and vertical brush strokes finishing as you go to produce the desired whitewashed effect.
SURFACE PREPARATION: Prime drywall with No. 347 PVA. Cure new plaster 6 wks. before priming with No. 347 PVA or No. 348 Primer/Sealer. Follow appropriate dry times. Same instructions apply to repaint work.
Prime new masonry surfaces with No. 2672 Block Filler. To recoat: if previous finish is satin or gloss enamel wire brush for good adhesion. Spot prime porous areas with No. 347 PVA.
Prime wood trim with No. 32 or No. 2660 Enamel Undercoat; dry 16-24 hrs.

EXTERIOR GLOSS HOUSE PAINT
USES: For wood, siding, shingles, shakes, cement block and metal.
SUGGESTED APPLICATION RATE: Apply uniformly at the rate of 300-400 sq. ft. per gal. depending on surface texture and porosity.
DRYING TIME: To touch: overnight. Dry 3-4 days before recoating.
APPLICATION: Brush or roller.
SURFACE PREPARATION—NEW WORK: Surfaces must be clean, dry and free of loose and peeling paint. See label directions for removal of mildew.
New Wood—Shellac knots and sap streaks. Putty nail holes and cracks after priming with No. 262 H.P. Undercoat.
Prime metal and galvanized metal with appropriate primer: dry thoroughly.
Prime masonry surfaces with No. 2672 Block Filler.
REPAINT WORK: Consult label directions.
BEFORE APPLYING ANY OF THE WILLIAMSBURG® PAINT FINISHES ALWAYS CONSULT LABEL DIRECTIONS FOR MORE CONCISE INSTRUCTIONS.

Williamsburg ®
and (CW4XX)® are trademarks of
The Colonial Williamsburg
Foundation, Reg. U.S. Pat. Off.

G14-162

MARTIN SENOUR PAINTS®   •   2500 SOUTH SENOUR AVENUE   •   CHICAGO 60608

Williamsburg Paint Colors

Paint

(See Paint Chart)

Shipping Charge: $1.50 per gallon; $.75 per quart

EXTERIOR PAINT

			Gallon	Quart
W	950	Trim & Tinting White Base for Trim	$10.20	$3.15
W	951	Outside White Finish	10.95	3.30
W	1060	Archibald Blair Gold	12.45	3.80
W	1061	Archibald Blair Green	11.35	3.55
W	1062	Barraud House Green	12.45	3.80
W	1063	Blair House Green	10.35	3.30
W	1064	Bracken House Biscuit	11.35	3.55
W	1065	Bracken House Blue Slate	11.80	3.65
W	1066	Bracken House Brown	10.35	3.30
W	1067	Brush-Everard Gold	11.80	3.65
W	1068	Bryan House Chocolate	10.35	3.30
W	1069	Carter-Saunders Tobacco	11.35	3.55
W	1070	Chowning's Tavern Brown	10.35	3.30
W	1071	Draper House Green	10.35	3.30
W	1072	Governor's Palace Tan	11.80	3.65
W	1073	Griffin House Ivory	11.35	3.55
W	1074	Holt's Storehouse Gray	11.80	3.65
W	1075	James Geddy Green	12.45	3.85
W	1076	King's Arms Tavern Gray	11.80	3.65
W	1077	Levingston Kitchen Green	10.35	3.30
W	1078	Ludwell Tenement Gold	12.45	3.85
W	1079	Ludwell Tenement Sage	11.80	3.65
W	1080	Moir Shop Fawn	11.80	3.65
W	1081	Nicholson Shop Red	10.35	3.30
W	1082	Nicholson Shop Taupe	12.45	3.85
W	1083	Palace Arms Red	10.35	3.30
W	1084	Palmer House Green	11.35	3.55
W	1085	Palmer House Kitchen Brown	11.35	3.55
W	1086	Peyton Randolph Gray	11.80	3.65
W	1087	Pitt-Dixon Caramel	11.35	3.55
W	1088	Pitt Dixon Green	11.35	3.55
W	1089	Powell-Waller House Green	11.35	3.55
W	1090	Purdie House Gray Slate	12.45	3.85
W	1091	Raleigh Tavern Sorrel	12.45	3.85
W	1092	Taliaferro-Cole Black Green	10.35	3.30

INTERIOR PAINT

			Finish	Gallon	Quart
W	900	Powell-Waller Gold	Alkyd flat	$10.95	$ 3.40
W	930	Powell-Waller Gold	satin gloss	11.95	3.80
W	901	Campbell's Tavern Charcoal Brown	alkyd flat	10.95	3.40
W	931	Campbell's Tavern Charcoal Brown	satin gloss	11.95	3.80
W	902	Wigmaker's Shop Green	alkyd flat	10.95	3.40
W	932	Wigmaker's Shop Green	satin gloss	11.95	3.80
W	903	Carter-Moir Green	alkyd flat	12.10	3.65
W	933	Carter-Moir Green	satin gloss	11.95	3.80
W	904	Capitol Light Brown	alkyd flat	10.95	3.40
W	934	Capitol Light Brown	satin gloss	11.95	3.80
W	905	Powell-Waller Red	alkyd flat	12.10	3.65
W	935	Powell-Waller Red	satin gloss	11.95	3.80
W	906	Carter-Moir Brick	alkyd flat	12.10	3.65
W	936	Carter-Moir Brick	satin gloss	11.95	3.80
W	907	Griffin House Brick	alkyd flat	12.10	3.65
W	937	Griffin House Brick	satin gloss	11.95	3.80
W	940	Chowning's Tavern Rich Tan	satin gloss	11.95	3.80
W	941	Raleigh Tavern Chinese Red	satin gloss	13.75	4.10
W	942	Palmer House Brown	satin gloss	11.95	3.80
W	943	Hartwell Perry Green	satin gloss	11.95	3.80
W	970	Williamsburg Simulated White Wash	alkyd flat	10.95	3.40
W	980	White	latex flat	9.55	3.00
W	1011		alkyd flat	10.55	3.35
W	1012	Apollo Room Blue	latex flat	10.15	3.15
W	1013		satin gloss	12.20	3.80
W	1014				
W	1015		alkyd flat	10.55	3.35
W	1016	Apothecary Shop Blue	latex flat	10.15	3.15
W	1017		satin gloss	12.20	3.80
W	1918				
W	1019		alkyd flat	10.55	3.35
W	1020	Chowning's Tavern Rose Tan	latex flat	10.15	3.15
W	1021		satin gloss	12.20	3.80
W	1022				
W	1023		alkyd flat	10.55	3.35
W	1024	John Greenhow Green (Colonial Green)	latex flat	10.15	3.15
W	1025		satin gloss	12.20	3.80
*W	1026				
W	1027		alkyd flat	10.55	3.35
W	1028	King's Arm Rose Pink	latex flat	10.15	3.15
*W	1029		satin gloss	12.20	3.80
*W	1030				

All prices are subject to change without notice

Interior Paint, *continued*

W No.	Color	Finish	Gallon	Quart
W 1031 W 1032 W 1033 W 1034	Market Square Green.	alkyd flat latex flat satin gloss	$10.55 10.15 12.20	$3.35 3.15 3.80
W 1035 W 1036 W 1037 W 1038	Palace Ballroom Blue.	alkyd flat latex flat satin gloss	10.55 10.15 12.20	3.35 3.15 3.80
W 1039 W 1040 W 1041 W 1042	Pelham Gray........	alkyd flat latex flat satin gloss	10.55 10.15 12.20	3.35 3.15 3.80
W 1043 W 1044 W 1045 W 1046	Raleigh Tavern Green.	alkyd flat latex flat satin gloss	10.55 10.15 12.20	3.35 3.15 3.80
W 1047 W 1048 *W 1049 *W 1050	Raleigh Tavern Peach.	alkyd flat latex flat satin gloss	10.55 10.15 12.20	3.35 3.15 3.80
W 1051 W 1052 *W 1053 *W 1054	Raleigh Tavern Tan..	alkyd flat latex flat satin gloss	10.55 10.15 12.20	3.35 3.15 3.80
W 1055 W 1056 W 1057 *W 1058	Wythe House Gold...	alkyd flat latex flat satin gloss	10.55 10.15 12.20	3.35 3.15 3.80
W 1150	Alexander Craig Green............	alkyd flat latex flat satin gloss	12.35 13.50 14.20	3.80 4.10 4.20
W 1151	Bassett Hall Antique Gold.............	alkyd flat latex flat satin gloss	10.55 11.95 11.95	3.35 3.80 3.80
W 1152	Bassett Hall Green...	alkyd flat latex flat satin gloss	10.55 10.30 11.95	3.35 3.25 3.80
W 1153	Blair House Buff.....	alkyd flat latex flat satin gloss	12.35 13.50 14.20	3.80 4.10 4.20
W 1154	Blue Bell Tavern Buff.	alkyd flat latex flat satin gloss	10.55 10.30 11.95	3.35 3.25 3.80
W 1155	Brafferton Blue......	alkyd flat latex flat satin gloss	12.35 11.95 14.20	3.80 3.80 4.20
W 1156	Brick House Light Peach............	alkyd flat latex flat satin gloss	10.55 10.30 11.95	3.35 3.25 3.80
W 1157	Brown House Beige..	alkyd flat latex flat satin gloss	10.55 10.30 11.95	3.35 3.25 3.80
W 1158	Brush-Everard Blue..	alkyd flat latex flat satin gloss	12.35 13.50 14.20	3.80 4.10 4.20
W 1159	Brush-Everard Gray..	alkyd flat latex flat satin gloss	10.55 10.30 11.95	3.35 3.25 3.80
W 1160	Coachhouse Green...	alkyd flat latex flat satin gloss	12.35 13.50 14.20	3.80 4.10 4.20

W No.	Color	Finish	Gallon	Quart
W 1161	Daphne Room Beige..	alkyd flat latex flat satin gloss	$10.55 10.30 11.95	$3.35 3.25 3.80
W 1162	Governor's Palace Buff..............	alkyd flat latex flat satin gloss	12.35 13.50 14.20	3.80 4.10 4.20
W 1163	James Geddy Gray...	alkyd flat latex flat satin gloss	10.55 10.30 11.95	3.35 3.25 3.80
W 1164	James Geddy Tan....	alkyd flat latex flat satin gloss	12.35 13.50 14.20	3.80 4.10 4.20
W 1165	Palace Dining Room Gray.............	alkyd flat latex flat satin gloss	10.55 10.50 11.95	3.35 3.25 3.80
W 1166	Palace Guardhouse Green............	alkyd flat latex flat satin gloss	12.35 11.95 14.20	3.80 3.80 4.20
W 1167	Peyton Randolph Gray.............	alkyd flat latex flat satin gloss	12.35 13.50 14.20	3.80 4.10 4.20
W 1168	Prentis Store Gray Green............	alkyd flat latex flat satin gloss	12.35 11.95 14.20	3.80 3.80 4.20
W 1169	Purdie House Gray...	alkyd flat latex flat satin gloss	12.35 11.95 14.20	3.80 3.80 4.20
W 1170	Red Lion Inn Green..	alkyd flat latex flat satin gloss	12.35 13.50 14.20	3.80 4.10 4.20
W 1171	Red Lion Inn Gray...	alkyd flat latex flat satin gloss	10.55 10.30 11.95	3.35 3.25 3.80
W 1172	Wetherburn's Tavern Bisque...........	alkyd flat latex flat satin gloss	10.55 10.30 11.95	
W 1173	James Southall Blue..	alkyd flat latex flat satin gloss	10.55 10.30 11.95	3.35 3.25 3.80
W 1174	Wetherburn's Pale Blue.............	alkyd flat latex flat satin gloss	10.55 10.30 11.95	3.35 3.25 3.80

Leather

A booklet of leather samples showing full color range is available for a deposit of $6.00 plus $.50 mailing charge.

One full hide (approximately 48 sq. ft.)
Glazed Antique finish.......................... $264.00
Masterpiece finish............................ 268.80

One half hide (approximately 24 sq. ft.)
Glazed Antique finish.......................... 136.80
Masterpiece finish............................ 139.20

TO: *Craft House*

Williamsburg, Virginia 23185

Date_____

If you are using your
Craft House Charge Account,
Please give your
account number.

_____

Please Print
{ Your Name_____
Street_____
City & State_____ Zip_____

FOLLOWING ITEMS TO BE SHIPPED TO ABOVE ADDRESS:

Quantity	Catalog No.	Article	Unit Price	Total Price

USE SPACE BELOW FOR GIFT ITEMS TO BE SHIPPED DIRECTLY TO RECIPIENT

Please Print
{ Name_____
Street_____
City & State_____ Zip_____

Gift Card Message

_____

_____

_____

Quantity	Catalog No.	Article	Unit Price	Total Price
		Purchased for or by Virginia resident add 4% sales tax.		

If you do not have a Craft House Charge Account Number
enclose check (payable to Craft House) for total amount of purchase

Total ➡

IMPORTANT: Charge Accounts may be established with Craft House.
Application forms sent upon request.
To order by telephone, call Williamsburg, Va., 804 CA 9-1000
    between 9:00 A. M. and 5:00 P. M. Monday through
    Saturday.
All articles postpaid within United States.
Safe delivery guaranteed.

Distinctive Craft House cartons used except where other
    packing is necessary to insure safe delivery.
Special prices for sets or pairs (as quoted) are for shipment
    to one address.

PRICES SUBJECT TO CHANGE WITHOUT NOTICE.

This flap is gummed. Fold to form envelope, seal and mail. Check may be safely enclosed.